ADVENTURE STORIES

First published 1979 by
Sundial Books Limited
59 Grosvenor Street
London W1

© 1979 Hennerwood Publications Limited

ISBN 0 906320 02 X
Second Impression *1980*
Printed in the United States of America

ADVENTURE STORIES

EDITED BY
HAYDEN McALLISTER

Sundial

contents

ANNAPURNA

Dougal Haston

In 1970, a mountaineering expedition led by Chris Bonnington made an attempt to climb to the 26,545 foot peak of Annapurna. It was a formidable task, for Annapurna's South Face is constantly swept by avalanches . . . Dougal Haston takes up their story . . .

There isn't really such a thing as a rest day at 24,000 feet. The morning saw the usual rime-filled tent and frozen sleeping-bag. I tried to spin out making the porridge. We had been left a bar of chocolate and some nuts. These were added to the mixture to try and make something tasty. To our jaded palates it almost assumed the proportions of a treat. The sun didn't come around to Camp VI until around 9 a.m. A vague warmth began to creep into the tent but with it came the melting rime. Soon the inside was dripping. But we didn't really care too much. Talk was at a minimum as we had already discussed most of our hopes and plans. We knew that the morrow would be an important day. As the sun grew hotter and the inside started to dry our eyelids began to close. I lay in a half-sleep state feeling incredibly relaxed in the warmth. It must have been some kind of reaction from the long, cold, tense, cramped nights. Those few hours in the sun were more pleasant than all the nights I had previously spent at this spot. The afternoon clouds soon rolled up but we continued to lie and doze. There was nothing else to do except wait for the tug of Chris coming up the fixed rope. Late in the afternoon he fixed the last tired jumar stroke over the edge. Tiredness was all over his face. We had our tent and some food but he had been unable to carry his personal gear as well. A bitter disappointment for him. But Ian Clough was due to come up to V that day so they could at least make the second summit bid. A weary farewell left us to a change in menu—a mixed grill, with some nuts and chocolate left for the next day. Given good weather the summit seemed a possible two days away. Even the lack of stars in the sky couldn't curb our happiness at the chance to launch out fully again. Sleep was good.

I was once again up at five making the reviving drinks. Throats were raw from gasping in the thin cold air. During the night my whole mouth would dry up and I had to suck on a precious fruit-gum to get the saliva working again. Consequently we had to get the first drink down before we could begin to think of talking other than in monosyllabic grunts. This particular morning there was nothing much to discuss. It was the day for establishing Camp VII. Once again it was cold with snapping spindrift-laden wind. The sun was two hours away from the gully when we started the upward jumar. I had thought previous mornings cold but this was the one that was way out ahead. Every few minutes saw us stopping to warm one extremity or another. For the first time my nose began to freeze and even with my face covered with a duvet hood plus balaclava I still had to stop and bury it in my gloved hands in order to regain some vestige of warmth. Don had his boots off and on but was still suffering. It took a long time to reach the end of our fixed ropes. By this time the weather had closed in completely. My immediate prospect was a three hundred foot run-out to the top of the gully. At first thought this didn't seem

It was a nightmare climbing situation.

too bad as we had soloed it two days previously. But things were slightly different on this day. I had only gone fifty feet when I could barely see any more. Goggles were ripped off in a rage but then I found my eyelids freezing solid. I tried to clean my goggles and put them on again but they were totally useless by this time. There was no way of cleaning my eyelids. Dachstein mitts were completely covered in snow and to take them off would have meant instant frostbite. Powder avalanches were sloughing down the gully and the swirling wind was blasting spindrift both up and from the sides. It was a nightmare climbing situation—yet the strange thing about it was that I never contemplated turning back. There was only one thought and that was to reach the end of the gully and pitch the tent for Camp VII. I had never thought I could get into as testing a situation as doing a hundred-and-fifty-foot run-out on hard ice in a storm on the Eiger with only an ice-peg and no axe or hammer but this seemed even more harrowing. It was twice as long and difficulties very similar. My eyes were so glued up and painful that I couldn't think of looking for a place to put a runner-peg. There was no contact with Don. The wind had drowned out shouted sounds after five feet. I fumbled onwards and only once did a brief thought break the terrible concentration. A flash of the possibilities of a fall. This was quickly cut dead. One doesn't even contemplate going for six hundred feet.

After I don't know how long the end was in sight. Ten feet to go when the rope went tight. I just had to ram in my axe and tie off the end as I was sure Don would interpret the pull as a signal to come up and I didn't want him to start jumaring with my body as anchor. I just sat there numb and empty as I felt the movement begin on the rope. It was a total dream state and it could have been minutes or hours before Don arrived. It was in fact a long time. His appearance on the stance broke the dream state, face completely crusted with ice. Even then we didn't say anything about retreat. I fixed a peg, tied off the rope then we both turned and began to move upwards looking for a flattish spot to dig out for the tent. Don took over and we front-pointed into the clouds.

Soon we reached some rocks and this was where Don had reckoned to place the camp. He started digging but each time the snow was taken off the surface, the entrenching-tool struck hard ice. Nothing doing there so he wandered upwards but the slope still continued steeply.

As I stood waiting I suddenly realized that the whole of the outside of my left hand had gone numb. I quickly stuck it under my armpit. Slowly it dawned on us that things were serious. Retreat and defeat were right there with us. Still our minds would hardly let the thoughts begin to flow. We were so keyed up for the upward push. Down we had to go. Even that was a struggle. Our tracks were completely wiped out and in the whiteout and wild storm it was hard to know which way to turn to rereach the top of the gully. As we stumbled in the estimated direction there was an amazing ten-second break in the clouds and there it was about three hundred feet beneath us. Once there we still didn't want to give in and I tried to beat out a platform where the gully led out onto the icefield. Still no go. Every stroke met hard ice. Then it was suddenly inevitable and Don turned round, climbed down to the top of the fixed rope and started to abseil. Every foot we descended life seemed to get easier. Even though the storm was still at full blast it seemed relatively sheltered in the gully compared with the holocaust on the upper plateau. Retrospective analysis is interesting. We had been bewildered, lost, weary but still capable of making rational decisions.

Back at VI we found Chris and Ian. Shelter had been reached but the thought of four in the tent was something else again. Everyone was totally covered in ice. The spindrift had infiltrated the rucksacks and sleeping-bags were frozen and ready to become sodden. Somehow we packed in out of the storm. Ian was bent double in the far corner. Don and Chris facing each other with legs bent and intertwined. I was in an icy pool at the door. This meant I had to do most of the chores but it was relief to be occupied because sleeping was going to be difficult. Once I had to stagger out and clear the snow from the back of the tent. One good thing was that four bodies at least gave the tent extra ballast and there seemed little likelihood of it blowing away on this night. Discussion and tea-making was the solution to the night. It had been a defeat but already we were contemplating bouncing back for more. Chris and Ian reckoned they weren't going well enough to try for the summit. Their decision was to drop right down to Camp IV, leave us with the food they had brought up and then leave Mick Burke and Tom Frost who were already at V to support us while they in turn supported them. Don and I were to sit out the bad weather and then have another try at establishing VII.

The morning light flashed on our rime-coated bodies dozing in strange contorted positions. Chris and Ian eventually extricated themselves and left us alone once again with the wind and the swirling snow. There was no improvement in the weather. Sleep was about the only urge left in our bodies but the tent had to be cleared if we were going to do any surviving at all. Hours later we had all the surplus snow thrown out and the rime scraped from the bags. Our underclothes were still dry and with the stove burning constantly we fell into deep stupors. Thus passed the day. From the radio it turned out that nearly all activity had stopped on the mountain. There had been heavy snowfalls at all the camps. It looked like being a sit-out period. Most of the other really bad weather had passed reasonably quickly but this spell looked as if it had set in for a few days. Conversation came in spasms. Slight depression was beginning to set in again. If the snow got too heavy on the lower level there would be no carries. No carries meant no food and even at our present low consumption level we only had enough for two more days at the very most. When we did move it looked as if we would have to try and establish Camp VII then come down again for supplies before we could actually occupy it. The summit was once again beginning to fade into the vague future. We were alone with our sombre thoughts and the wind. Without the extra weight, being blown away again became a distinct possibility. The usual night passed. There was a gap where the entrance zip didn't quite close and each gust or jet of spindrift would seek out any exposed part of flesh. I slept with everything on, even overboots, and had the sleeping-bag tied right up with only a small breathing space. During the night the moisture from breathing would freeze round this hole and moustache and beard hairs would stick to it.

The new day was no better than the old. We passed it in the usual way. The only good news was that Mick and Tom had gone down to the dump at the end of the Ice Ridge to meet Chris, Ian and Dave Lambert, who had brought up loads of food and would try to make a carry the next day to alleviate our food situation. After the radio call I looked out. There wasn't so much wind activity. Some stars were actually visible and the Fang came into sight for the first time in three days. At least it looked as if we could try to establish the camp on the morrow. We were off by seven. Don left a few minutes before me as I was trying to organize the movie camera. It seemed like a good idea to take some film of the gully and also the establishment of VII so I stuck one cartridge in the camera and a spare in my pocket. The weather was by no means perfect. Spindrift and cloud were still making their presence felt. But compared to the other days in the gully it seemed relatively mild. Eleven o'clock saw us once again on the plateau. An exciting moment. In the clear spells we could see the summit of Annapurna at close quarters for the first time. I picked up the RAFMA and we had a short discussion. Don said, 'I think we should press on and find a campsite as close to the final wall as possible.' I was in complete agreement but we were both obviously thinking of greater things.

Here's the way it looked. There was an icefield leading up to a sharp snow ridge which in turn led to a mixed face of around eight hundred feet. At the top of this face? Annapurna. Once again we just turned to movement without any more discussion. It didn't need telepathy to communicate our thoughts. The summit was a real possibility. The big question was the weather. There was no way we wanted to get into a situation similar to our previous attempt. True, we could probably erect the tent on the ridge but it would be a bivouac without food, stoves or sleeping-bags. Certainly survival would have been O.K. but the weakening factor would have been enormous. Don led, I carried the tent and rope. Front-pointing up the ice slope the ridge was there. I just set the tent down on a platform and on we went. Time was pressing and there seemed no point in taking belays. Each moved upwards in his own special world. The climbing on the face was reasonably difficult. Little steep ice pitches combined with scattered rock moves. The mind was still working well. I got out the camera and shot off the first cartridge. Through the lens it looked sensational. A lone figure carving his way upwards towards the twin summit ridge cliffs, occasionally being blotted out by clouds of spindrift. I kept having trouble with my right crampon. It came off three times on the summit wall. But I was thinking clearly and stopped each time in contorted positions and fixed the straps. Due to this Don was about a hundred feet ahead.

The wonderful thing was that there was no breathing trouble. I had imagined great lung-gasping at 26,000 feet but I was moving with no more difficulty than I'd experienced four thousand feet lower down. Likewise Don was having no such problems. He picked a beautiful line through towards the summit ridge. Then he disappeared over the edge and I was alone for a brief spell. The final fifty feet needed care. Big flat unsolid snowy rocks which had to be scraped clean. Over the ridge and suddenly it was calm. There was no wind on the north side. Long, relatively flat spaces led down into the cloud. Don was already fixing a rappel peg. We didn't speak. There was no elation. The mind was still too wound up to allow such feelings to enter. Besides the supreme concentration was needed to get down. The real problem was the actual summit. We were on a ridge. The snow peak to the left looked highest so Don plodded up the thirty feet or so to its top while I filmed the historic moment. Vague traces of what must have been army footprints showed beneath the snow. I, in turn, stood on the peak. The view was disappointing. Only the east summit was clear. I had looked forward to seeing Dhaulagiri on one side and right down to Base on the other but there was only a vast sea of grey cloud about a thousand feet beneath us. The greatest moment of both our climbing careers and there was only a kind of numbness. But we knew the elation would come when we unwound. Meanwhile there was still the face to climb down. Fortunately I had carried up a hundred and fifty feet of rope in my pack so the hardest section could be bypassed by abseiling. That was our summit monument. A fixed rope. It seemed appropriate as it was the last of fifteen thousand feet of such.

The climb down took all the concentration we had. Twice again my crampon came off. Once on the summit wall and once on the icefield leading down to the top of the gully. Going down the fixed ropes the tensions started to wear away. It was turning into a good late afternoon. Everything seemed beautiful. Inside and out. I got back to Camp VI to find Don just about to tune in on the radio. He handed it to me muttering, 'You've made all the bloody communications till now, so you may as well make this one!' A serious-sounding Chris came on, 'Chris calling Camp VI. Did you manage to get out today?' I answered, 'Aye, we've just climbed Annapurna.' Atmospherics were so bad that he asked me to repeat. I was just about to do so when bedlam broke loose on the set. Base Camp had been listening in and it had come across loud and clear. Then Chris got the message and all the other camps and you could almost feel the relief and happiness vibrating along the sound waves.

CAR WITH NO BRAKES

James Herriot

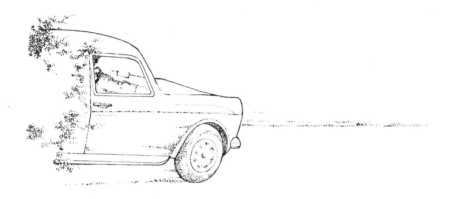

If only my car had had any brakes I would certainly have enjoyed looking down on Worton village from the high moor. The old stone houses straggling unevenly along the near bank of the river made a pleasant splash of grey on the green floor of the valley and the little gardens with their clipped lawns gave a touch of softness to the bare, rising sweep of the fellside on the other side of the Dale.

But the whole scene was clouded by the thought that I had to get down that road with its 1 in 4 gradient and those two villainous S bends. It was like a malevolent snake coiling almost headlong from where I sat. And, as I said, I had no brakes.

Of course the vehicle had originally been fitted with the means of bringing it to a halt, and during most of the year I had ridden in it a violent pressure on the pedal would have the desired effect even though it caused a certain amount of veering about on the road. But lately the response had been growing weaker and now it was nil.

During the gradual deterioration I had brought the matter up with Siegfried now and then and he had expressed sympathy and concern.

'That won't do at all, James. I'll have a word with Hammond about it. Leave it with me.'

And then a few days later when I made a further appeal.

'Oh Lord, yes. I've been meaning to fix it up with Hammond. Don't worry, James, I'll see to it.'

Finally I had to tell him that when I put my foot on the pedal there was nothing at all and the only way I had of stopping the car was to crash it into bottom gear.

'Oh bad luck, James. Must be a nuisance for you. But never mind, I'll arrange everything.'

Some time later I asked Mr Hammond down at the garage if he had heard anything from Siegfried, but he hadn't. The motor man did, however, hop into the car and drive it slowly down the street. He came to a jerking, shuddering halt about fifty yards away and then got out. He made no attempt to back up but walked thoughtfully towards me. Normally an imperturbable man, he had gone rather pale and he looked at me wonderingly.

'And you mean to tell me, lad, that you do all your rounds in that car?'

'Well, yes, I do.'

'You ought to have a medal, then. I dursn't drive across market place in that bloody thing.'

There wasn't much I could do. The car was Siegfried's property and I'd have to await his pleasure. Of course I had had experience of this sort of thing before in the shape of the movable passenger seat he had in his own vehicle when I first came to Darrowby. He never seemed to notice when I went over backwards every time I sat in it and I don't suppose he would ever have done anything about it but for an incident one market day when he noticed an old lady with a large basket of vegetables walking into Darrowby and courteously offered her a lift.

'Poor old girl's feet went straight up in the air and she just disappeared into the back. Had a hell of a job getting her out—thought we'd have to get a block and tackle. Cabbages and cauliflowers rolling all over the place.'

I looked again down the steep track. The sensible thing, of course, would be to go back into Darrowby and take the low road into Worton. No danger that way. But it meant a round trip of nearly ten miles and I could actually see the smallholding I wanted to visit just a thousand feet below. The calf with joint ill was in that shed with the green door—in fact there was old Mr Robinson coming out of the house now and pottering across the yard with a bucket. I could almost reach out and touch him.

I thought, not for the first time, that if you had to drive a car with no brakes one of the last places in England you'd want to be was the Yorkshire Dales. Even on the flat it was bad enough but I got used to it after a week or two and often forgot all about it. As when one day I was busy with a cow and the farmer jumped into my car to move it so that one of his men could get past with a tractor. I never said a word as the unsuspecting man backed round quickly and confidently and hit the wall of the barn with a sickening crash. With typical Yorkshire understatement, all he said was: 'Your brakes aren't ower savage, mister.'

Anyway, I had to make up my mind. Was it to be back to Darrowby or straight over the top? It had become a common situation and every day I had the experience of sitting wrestling with myself on the edge of a hill with my heart thumping as it was now. There must have been scores of these unwitnessed dramas played out in the green silence of the fells. At last, I started the engine and did what I always did—took the quick way down.

But this hill really was a beauty, a notorious road even in this country, and as I nosed gingerly on to it, the whole world seemed to drop away from me. With the gear lever in bottom and my hand jammed against it I headed, dry-mouthed, down the strip of tarmac which now looked to be almost vertical.

It is surprising what speed you can attain in bottom gear if you have nothing else to hold you back and as the first bend rushed up at me the little engine started a rising scream of protest. When I hit the curve, I hauled the wheel round desperately to the right, the tyres spun for a second in the stones and loose soil of the verge, then we were off again.

This was a longer stretch and even steeper and it was like being on the big dipper with the same feeling of lack of control over one's fate. Hurtling into the bend, the idea of turning at this speed was preposterous but it was that or straight over the edge. Terror-stricken, I closed my eyes and dragged the wheel to the left. This time, one side of the car lifted and I was sure we were over, then it rocked back on to the other side and for a horrible second or two kept this up till it finally decided to stay upright and I was once more on my way.

Again a yawning gradient. But as the car sped downwards, engine howling, I was aware of a curious numbness. I seemed to have reached the ultimate limits of fear and hardly noticed as we shot round the third bend. One more to go and at last the road was levelling out; my speed dropped rapidly and at the last bend I couldn't have been doing more than twenty. I had made it.

It wasn't till I was right on to the final straight that I saw the sheep. Hundreds of them, filling the road. A river of woolly backs lapping from wall to wall. They were only yards from me and I was still going downhill. Without hesitation I turned and drove straight into the wall.

There didn't seem to be much damage. A few stones slithered down as the engine stalled and fell silent.

Slowly I sank back in my seat, relaxing my clenched jaws, releasing, finger by finger, the fierce grip on the wheel. The sheep continued to flow past and I took a sideways glance at the man who was shepherding them. He was a stranger to me and I prayed he didn't recognize me either because at that moment the role of unknown madman seemed to be the ideal one. Best not to say anything; appearing round a corner and driving deliberately into a wall is no basis for a rewarding conversation.

The sheep were still passing by and I could hear the man calling to his dogs. 'Get by, Jess. Come by, Nell.' But I kept up a steady stare at the layered stones in front of me, even though he passed within a few feet.

I suppose some people would have asked me what the hell I was playing at, but not a Dales shepherd. He went quietly by without invading my privacy, but when I looked in the mirror after a few moments I could see him in the middle of the road staring back at me, his sheep temporarily forgotten.

My brakeless period has always been easy to recall. There is a piercing clarity about the memory which has kept it fresh over the years. I suppose it lasted only a few weeks but it could have gone on indefinitely if Siegfried himself hadn't become involved.

It was when we were going to a case together. For some reason he decided to take my car and settled in the driver's seat. I huddled apprehensively next to him as he set off at his usual brisk pace.

Hinchcliffe's farm lies about a mile on the main road outside Darrowby. It is a massive place with a wide straight drive leading down to the house. We weren't going there, but as Siegfried spurted to full speed I could see Mr Hinchcliffe in his big Buick ahead of us proceeding in a leisurely way along the middle of the road. As Siegfried pulled out to overtake, the farmer suddenly stuck out his hand and began to turn right towards his farm—directly across our path. Siegfried's foot went hard down on the brake pedal and his eyebrows shot right up as nothing happened. We were going straight for the side of the Buick and there was no room to go round on the left.

Siegfried didn't panic. At the last moment he turned right with the Buick and the two cars roared side by side down the drive, Mr Hinchcliffe staring at me with bulging eyes from close range. The

A few stones slithered down as the engine stalled and fell silent.

farmer stopped in the yard, but we continued round the back of the house because we had to.

Fortunately, it was one of those places where you could drive right round and we rattled through the stackyard and back to the front of the house behind Mr Hinchcliffe who had got out and was looking round the corner to see where we had gone. The farmer whipped round in astonishment and, open-mouthed watched us as we passed, but Siegfried, retaining his aplomb to the end, inclined his head and gave a little wave before we shot back up the drive.

Before we returned to the main road I had a look back at Mr Hinchcliffe. He was still watching us and there was a certain rigidity in his pose which reminded me of the shepherd.

Once on the road, Siegfried steered carefully into a layby and stopped. For a few moments he stared straight ahead without speaking and I realized he was having a little difficulty in getting his patient look properly adjusted; but when he finally turned to me his face was transfigured, almost saintly.

I dug my nails into my palms as he smiled at me with kind eyes.

'Really, James,' he said, 'I can't understand why you keep things to yourself. Heaven knows how long your car has been in this condition, yet never a word from you.' He raised a forefinger and his patient look was replaced by one of sorrowing gravity. 'Don't you realize we might have been killed back there? You really ought to have told me.'

TWO VC'S FOR SUBMARINE THRASHER

Sidney Hart

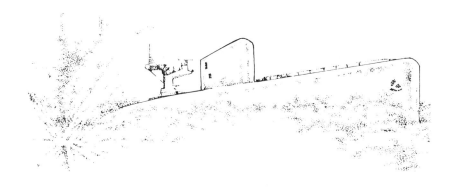

Addressing me, Fox asked: 'What was your last submarine?' *'Truant,'* I answered. He solemnly passed over his rum measure and said, 'Have a sip of my tot—honoured!' From then on sips were offered freely, coming from all angles, so that the omens promised a skinful. Coupled with my own 'whack' these freewill offerings were taking effect, and from then forward we were a band of brothers, all for one and one for all.

A few trips ashore with Fox, Rembrance and Berwick tightened the bonds, and in the meantime *Thrasher* was getting ready to sail. Friday night was to witness our departure. It was impossible not to wonder what the next patrol would be like, as a shaking-up time.

On that Friday when all the fresh stores were being brought aboard and stowed, someone said at dinner-time in the mess, 'I'll bet a pound we don't sail today.'

'Why not?' asked another rating.

'Because it's Friday the thirteenth,' came the ominous retort.

Superstition was by now very predominant amongst submarine crews, but I knew well enough, after seeing all the new stores brought aboard, that we'd sail exactly as appointed. Some other observer there spied the cups on the mess-shelf. 'Thirteen cups; I don't like this,' he said. But happy-go-lucky Rampton found a quick solution to that immediate problem. He picked up one of the cups and smashed it to bits on the deck. If only all our troubles could have been so easily dealt with!

It was 6 p.m. on Friday the thirteenth, and *Thrasher* was pretty nearly ready for sailing. The for'ard hatch and the engine-room hatch were being bolted from the outside. All the crew were on board. Even then the more superstitious members thought our sailing orders might be altered at the last minute. 'Harbour Stations!' put a stop to that dream. Age-old superstitions might be all right in the piping times of peace, but modern war puts a different complexion on things. The same motor movements as I had seen and heard aboard my other submarines characterized the departure of *Thrasher* from harbour; in a trice she was heading for the wide, open spaces.

'Half ahead both engines. Fall out, Harbour Stations. Diving Stations in half an hour.' The familiar routine gave a promise of action that was welcome to all of us, I think. It was quite a long run out to where we could perform our necessary trim-dive, one of the most necessary of all the submarine service's Thirty-nine Articles.

Whilst waiting for that testing plunge I went into the control room, lit a cigarette and looked up through the hatch. My eyes watched the overhead sky, changing quickly from vivid blue to darkling grey, as night was coming. Mediterranean twilight is shorter than that of the more northern latitudes. Even the air rushing down the conning tower on its way to feed the hungry engines was changing—as the sky—only from a genial luke-warmth to an icy cold blast. 'Till the sands of the desert grow cold,' I thought, having noticed that phenomenon of something near to frost-bite in the recently baking desert sands.

With my cigarette half-smoked, the bridge voice-pipe, for all the world sounding like an old-fashioned gramophone, rasped out: 'Diving Stations!' At my appointed station in the after-end, in company with Conroy, I watched the depth-gauge as *Thrasher* did her first dive, behaving very much as *Truant* had done. There was exactly the same hanging back at 10 feet, the same seeming reluctance to leave God's free air behind, and then down, down, down. Experts had us in hand; our trim was perfect. Nothing to worry about so far! 'Surface!' She was coming up . . . 70 feet . . . 50 feet . . . 30 feet . . . when Conroy said: 'Hang on when she breaks surface. She always comes up with a list.' Twenty feet . . . 10 feet . . . there was a sickening lurch and the ship took a sickening list to port. There followed the crash of crockery going west in fragments, the hollow rumble of overturning buckets. I grabbed a bunk-chain and hung on like a monkey, Conroy followed my example, and we hung on until *Thrasher* was well on the surface. A Friday sailing! 'She always surfaces like this!' explained Conroy in a matter of fact way. An eel can get used to skinning, so I reckoned I'd grow accustomed to her ladyship's antics.

For weal or woe I was once again off to an allotted patrol area, this time in a different ship, and a mighty temperamental one at that! As full of whims as a highly-strung woman, maybe. I said to Conroy: 'She'd make a damn sight better bucking bronco than a submarine!' The buzz now came through that our allotted patrol area was to be the Aegean Sea. For myself, having done several patrols in that classical stretch of water, I rather liked the prospect, although I was able to anticipate quite a packet of trouble from enemy aircraft, working from the occupied Greek islands, where the Italians and Germans were reputed to be in force.

The Stokers' Mess considered me as something of an authority on various patrol areas, as I had been in nearly all of them. Questions about the Aegean came freely, and when I told them (was my tongue in my cheek?) that it was one of the easiest of the lot, everybody seemed happy. Next morning, just before break of dawn saw us diving down. I was taking a breather in the control room, and I made the acquaintance of Lieutenant Mackenzie, RN. I was studying the chart spread out on the table under the switched-on light, when a pleasant voice behind me said: 'Excuse me, please.' I stepped to one side to make way for a sandy-haired, agreeable looking officer in his middle twenties. When he stooped over the chart, I asked the helmsman if this stranger was the Navigating Officer.

'Navigating Officer!' he echoed, eyeing me with considerable disgust; 'Why, that's the Skipper, Lieutenant Mackenzie.' I ought to have known, I suppose, but you don't get the hang of a new ship all in a minute. I explained that I'd only been aboard for a dog-watch or so. Two empty weeks of cruising around the Greek islands followed, never a ship was sighted, and I said, jokingly, 'Now, if that had been *Truant* we'd have put a couple of them down the hatch long before this.' To a sailor his last ship is always the best! My bit of brag fetched an instant reply from Nippy Rembrance: 'That's our trouble,' he said, 'you *Truant* blokes have sunk every darned ship that floats around these seas!' We'd evidently earned quite a name for ourselves!

Some few days later, one morning around 11 o'clock, *Thrasher* was at 32 feet, hanging off one of the Grecian islands. We had spotted a supply ship and five escort vessels. There was also one aircraft flying methodically around, taking a general look-see at the situation. A promising sight enough for an enthusiastic submariner. In the darkened stokers' mess, oblivious to what was taking place beyond, whether in the control room or on the sea above, the only signs of life noticeable in the damp, thick atmosphere were loud snores and the occasional mutterings of a restless sleeper. Then a snapped, 'Diving Stations!' brought a magic

'Diving stations!'

change and immediate life into that hushed compartment. Men rolled and tumbled out of their bunks as if electrified; lights were switched on, boots pulled on, and two odd boots didn't really matter, even if they belonged to someone else, so long as they were boots, and readiness for instant action was reported. Those who were unlucky about their boots ran to their diving stations in stockinged feet.

Conroy and I were all who remained in that mess, our diving station being there where our duty was to look after the steering-gear, the hydroplane gear, and a blower. I looked at the depth-gauge. It showed 32 feet. Periscope depth. From the manoeuvring of the hydroplanes and steering-gear we knew that an attack was in progress. Conroy was just sticking his head through the open bulkhead door when, instead of information to satisfy our natural curiosity, we got a rush of air-pressure on our ears, as first one and then three other torpedoes left their tubes. Simultaneously there sounded, directly over our heads, a harsh BRA . . . M! BRA . . . M! There were two terrific explosions. A shower of cork chippings scaled off the beams; broken electric light bulbs showered down. It looked as if we'd been hit, and not lightly at that.

Through the boat echoed the clamour of 'Shut off shallow-water depth-gauges!' We were going deep—on the gauge, the needle went round like a dizzy teetotum: 100 feet . . . 150 feet . . . 200 feet. It stayed at 200 feet. Conroy's voice seemed to be an infinite distance away when he called, 'What were those?' I hope my voice wasn't as shaky as it seemed to me to be, when I replied, 'Bombs, and damned close ones at that. We're going to get some real depth-charging in a minute, you can bet your life. That plane has left a smoke-flare or some sort of marker on the water.' Several minutes later down came the first pattern of depth-charges. We clearly heard them swishing through the water and then the ensuing; brump . . . brump . . . brump, as they exploded.

Thrasher's pressure hull was splattered with the shrapnel from these engines of doom, whilst inside, strained and anxious, we glanced upwards, expecting to see the whole fabric split wide open. The first attack ended, and experience taught us that the escorts would be swinging round on their heels and listening for any suspicious movement from our ship. Both motors were stopped dead, naturally, but as the escorts came in again, the beat of their propellers plainly audible, the telegraphs rang to 'Half ahead' as we tried to creep away from the danger-zone—and it was a danger-zone.

There came that hollow, mocking, 'brump . . . brump . . . brump' denoting yet another pattern of depth-charges. Once more came the nerve-racking silence as the motors were stopped. The swish of disturbed water against the hull was ominous. But there's no need to enlarge on the emotions at play in our prison. We were scared, yes, but it didn't freeze us into inaction. Hard training allowed us to function as if the conditions were purely normal. We knew the enemy escort shops would be listening intently on their echo-sounding gear, ears strained to the utmost in the effort to detect any suspicious sound from below. They couldn't be listening more tensely than we were. That 200-foot cushion of water above us might be our safeguard, it might also be our grave.

'Half ahead, both motors!' came the signal.

Obviously the enemy were coming in for the kill. Science had obviously betrayed us. *Thrasher*'s screws seemed to be only just turning, would they rotate fast enough to get us away from the position where the escorts were about to drop those destructive depth-charges? Strained faces and bulging eyes, amongst our crew, indicated the tension, but, the bonds of discipline held stoutly, and the will-power that discipline had ingrained in us kept us outwardly calm during the ordeal.

The escort ships roared as they approached our position. When the inevitable, 'Clang—clash—clang . . .' came it was for all the world like a frantic giant striking on an outsize anvil, except that the din was magnified a thousand times. We were the unfortunate 'so-and-so's' inside that anvil! *Thrasher* plunged up as if a volcano had erupted beneath her, she bucked savagely and plunged down again: our state of suspense is better left to the imagination since words fail to do it justice. The third attack concluded, leaving the submarine trembling like a whipped dog.

After several more attacks, each one seeming farther away than the one before, we realized that *Thrasher* had eluded the hunters. Word came from the control room that the supply ship had almost certainly been sunk. 'Fall out diving stations!'

The little mess in *Thrasher*'s stern was crowded in a remarkably short time. Very little sleep was possible since all hands were discussing the recent action. Berwick said: 'I'll bet you never had charges as close as those in *Truant*, Syd.'

I answered jokingly: 'Hell, we used those for appetizers before breakfast in the old ship!'

It was well after dark when *Thrasher* surfaced, as usual with her alarming list, but once fully on top she quickly settled on an even keel. And then came a discovery, the memory of which still brings me out in a lather of sweat. Anything might happen to a submarine, whether in time of war or in peace, and it is generally the unusual that comes her way. Let my readers judge for themselves as to the sterling work done by Lieutenant Roberts and Petty Officer Gould. At 11 p.m.—twelve hours after starting our attack on the enemy convoy—*Thrasher* was charging her batteries, rolling easily in the slight sea that was then running, when from the for'ard messes it was reported that something was rolling about in the forepart casing. On making an investigation, Lieutenant Roberts discovered two unexploded bombs between the casing and the pressure-hull. At the time of this discovery I was on watch in the engine-room. Turning round from the fuel-tanks I spotted Leading Stoker Rembrance making urgent signs to me. Going to his side, I heard him bawl in my ear above the roar of the engines, 'Heard the latest? There's two unexploded bombs in the casing!'

It was necessary to put on an act, I being the tried old-timer. 'That's all right, Nippy, leave them there,' I said, feeling a lot less cheerful than I pretended to be. Live bombs in such a position might mean anything. About the least they could mean was that our number, if not actually up, was being put in the frame. There is no need to exaggerate the situation, but on the best showing it was, as Mr Chucks would have said, 'Precarious and not at all permanent!' The ship's people rose to the emergency with true Service coolness and practical action. That is to say, Lieutenant Roberts and Petty Officer Gould crawled through the small access door into *Thrasher*'s casing—a distance of several yards—to the place where the bombs were, quite well aware that, should the submarine be spotted, she would be compelled to crash-dive in a hurry, and drown them like rats in a trap. More two o'clock in the morning courage!

Inside the ship there was an eerie silence, as if all hands were waiting for the usual depth-charge attack, to which we had grown more or less accustomed. But this occasion told a very different story. Above our heads two daring men were working in a confined space, a space slimy and slippery with stagnant sea-water, handling two slithery, live bombs dragging them inch by inch out of that narrow casing, where there was little enough room for manoeuvring the deadly things. I doubt if anyone, even the most expert bomb disposal squads, ever handled bombs under such dangerous conditions. It seemed like eternity before the welcome news wafted through the ship that Roberts and Gould had the two missiles out of the casing, and were ready to drop them overboard. They had worked as coolly as if on a formal parade.

The order to 'Stop both motors: Slow astern both motors!' came like the sudden snapping of a cord to break the breathless tension. The bombs were lowered gently over *Thrasher*'s bows with all the respect and reverence shown by a funeral party and they were committed to the deep with a prayer of thankfulness, not of pity. Is it any wonder that both these heroes received the Victoria Cross in reward for their bravery? Never were those bits of bronze more rightly awarded. It is not for me to attempt to do justice to an act that undoubtedly saved the lives of all hands had those bombs exploded when we were submerged. Personally, I felt it a very high honour indeed to be deemed worthy to sail with such men.

Off watch that night in the after-mess, the single topic of conversation revolved round the bombs and the men who'd handled them. Stoker York expressed the company's relief when he said: 'I'd just love to shake hands with the person (he used a different word) who made those "qualified" bombs!' Leading Stoker Rembrance made his entrance through the watertight door into the mess, looked squarely at me as I lay on my bunk reading, and then shook me by the shoulder.

'What about the *Thrasher* now?' he asked. That was a challenge to my claims for my last ship, of course.

'Not half bad,' I replied. 'Almost up to *Truant* form.'

The look he gave me revealed more annoyance than humour, so I gave a little chuckle to show I was joking. I then teased him a little more by saying; 'I bet the *Truant*'s knocking those Japs about in the Far East.' Feigning an angry voice, my messmate snapped back; 'Won't you ever forget the—*Truant*?' and as he stepped out of the mess, laughed, and pitched a book at me. I hoped I'd not shot too much of a line about my last ship! It wouldn't have run true to submariner form.

TREASURE IN LORD KITCHENER'S TOMB

Hans Roden

Leutnant-zur-see Max Weissfelt pored over the plan of the minefields spread out on the map-table in the German sub-marine *U75* (commissioned 26.3.16, mined and sunk in the North Sea 14.12.17). He drew twenty-two small red crosses in the square and added: 59° 07′ N., 03° 25′ W., Brough of Birsay—Marwick Head.

For days *U75* had been on its way to the north of the British Isles, the first German U-boat to mine the west coast of the Orkneys, a route much used by British warships.

The date was 29 May 1916, and it had taken from 6.00 to 8.35 a.m. to lay and anchor the twenty-two mines, which were so placed that they were twenty-two feet beneath the surface at high water. Unobserved by the enemy, *U75* turned round and set course for the German coast.

If the crew had known what was to happen a week later on this lonely stretch of coast they would have been particularly proud of the success of their mission. On 6 June 1916, at 6.30 in the morning the English cruiser *Hampshire* (11,000 tons, launched 1905), escorted by two destroyers, left Scapa Flow by the western exit and sailed for Archangel in a northerly direction along the coast.

Because of north-easterly (veering to north-westerly) gales the *Hampshire* was forced to keep her speed down to 15 knots, as the two escort ships were finding it difficult to keep up in the heavy seas. After only an hour they made signals, 'Can no longer follow', and were ordered by the *Hampshire* to turn back and make for the coast. *Hampshire* carried a crew of 650 and there was one special 'passenger'[1] who stood on the bridge beside the captain wearing a khaki officer's greatcoat with the collar fastened up to his throat.

The cold grey eyes under the wide gold-braided peak of his cap scanned the boiling sea, watching the spray fly up to the bridge. Nobody could guess the thoughts of this taciturn man, and none dared speak to him, falling back respectfully. Field-Marshal Horatio Herbert Kitchener, Earl Kitchener of Khartoum, may have been looking back over his life, so full of battles and danger, and crowned with so many victories, or perhaps he was remembering his campaigns against the Mahdists in 1898, or his appointment as Minister of War in 1914, or making plans for the new and difficult task which lay ahead: to put new hope and courage into the Russian allies at this critical phase of the war, and to bring them financial aid. In extra strong, heavy boxes in the steel-plated hold of the cruiser lay £10 million in gold, a loan from England to Russia.

---

[1] Lord Kitchener with the following members of his staff, General Ellershaw, Sir Frederick Donaldson and his secretary Robertson, O'Brien from the Foreign Office, the interpreter Lieutenant McPherson with a clerk, Detective-Inspector McLoughlin, Sergei, the Field-Marshal's batman, and two other servants, had embarked the day before.

The seas grew heavier, the slate-grey of the Atlantic waves dashed against the bow of the *Hampshire*, broke over the deck, and soaked the men at the guns and on the bridge. Every now and again through the sea-mist they caught a glimpse of the coast of the Orkneys, some two sea miles away.

It was 7.30 a.m. when a jet of water shot up near the *Hampshire* and a dull roar shook the cruiser. A second explosion followed. Smoke poured through the decks, and the electricity was put out of action. The alarm was sounded on the bosuns' pipes, and from the radio room the SOS messages began to go out—in vain, for wireless contact was broken. The boats tipped over as they were being lowered, and were dashed to pieces. Twelve men[1] had clung to a raft battling with failing strength against the mighty seas. The *Hampshire*, torn apart by the explosion of the mines, listed heavily to starboard and sank in fifteen minutes—with 638 men, the captain, officers, sailors, and Field-Marshal Lord Kitchener and his staff.[2]

There is no possible doubt that £10 million in gold went down with the ship. This was later confirmed by reliable British authorities, and there are eye-witnesses still alive who helped to load the mysterious heavy chests, and can supply fuller details. The catastrophe had been seen from the shore, but no boats could be launched because of the high seas.

When the coastguard vessels and destroyers met at the spot between the Brough of Birsay and Marwick Head where the ship had gone down they found nothing but a few floating bits of wreckage.

---

[1] William Bennett, John Robert Bowman, Horace Llewellyn Buerdsele, William Cashman, Walter Charles Farnden, William Charles Philipps, Alfred Ernest Read, Charles Walter Rogerson, Richard Simpson, Frederick Lot Sims, Samuel Edward Sweeney, Wilfred Wesson.

[2] Announcing the loss of the Orkneys, by a mine or torpedo, of the Russian-bound *Hampshire* with Lord Kitchener on board, the Admiralty held out little hope that there could be any survivors.

Seventeen years had passed when in the spring of 1933 the salvage ship *K.S.R.*[1], fitted out with the most modern technical equipment and flying a British flag, anchored over the spot where the *Hampshire* had sunk with a hole in her starboard side.

Three deep-sea diving aces were on board: the Australian Costello from Sydney, Sam Mansfield from Norfolk, Virginia, and Charles Courtney, from 125th Street, New York, who was also a safe expert. In addition to these specialists there were some auxiliary divers under the command of the German Captain Brandt.

Max Weissfelt, former Leutnant-zur-See, who had been found only after a long search, was there too, for his knowledge was considered essential. During the voyage of the *U75* in 1916 off the Orkneys he had made his official entries in a notebook which was still in his jacket pocket in 1918, when the War ended and he doffed his uniform. He put the book away carefully in a box in the loft of his Stettin home—for ever, as he thought—and it was still there on the day that his name cropped up as being someone who would know exactly where the *Hampshire* had gone down, and he was duly visited by a representative of the divers.

From then on everything went without a hitch. Weissfelt found his old notebook with the minefields off the Orkneys marked, and here the cruiser had sunk. He joined the enterprise, and went aboard the *K.S.R.*, but this year he and the Englishman Henry Row succeeded only in locating the wreck, for bad weather prevented any further diving.

The following year, as soon as the winter storms had ended, salvage operations began in secret. For days the men sat idly in a little inn in Stromness waiting for favourable weather, until they noticed that people were beginning to take an interest in them. Then they suddenly vanished and took a roundabout way back to their ship.

The *K.S.R.* lay at anchor off the Orkneys one sunny morning.

---

[1] The Greek industrialist Sir Basil Zaharoff (1849–1936) is said to have helped to finance these salvage operations.

Skeletons in naval uniform greeted the divers.

The sea-bed is some 250 feet deep here, and very special technical equipment was needed to make diving and salvage work possible, but the ship had brought everything necessary from Königsberg, including three of the newest German armoured deep-sea diving suits.

Costello went first, letting himself down by the cable of the marker buoy that he had attached to the wreck the previous year. The ship had hardly shifted. The stern was silted over, and had sunk a few fathoms deeper, but the fine white sea sand was piled high over the gun turrets and the superstructure of the bridge. The diver was able to locate two holes in the hull of the steel giant, with the jagged edges driven inward, so he was sure that the ship had sunk as the result of an 'outside influence', and not through a boiler-explosion or some 'infernal machine'.

The wreck had to be cleared of mud and slime, sand and seaweed before the first group of divers could get to work. The suction pumps throbbed monotonously day and night, and the outline of the cruiser became gradually more distinct. Costello, Mansfield, and Courtney glided down into the depths, and in the green twilight of the water they could see clearly the gigantic wreck lying on the sea-bed.

When they clambered up on to the first gun turret they started back, for the scene that greeted them was too horrifying. The gunners lay near their guns, skeletons in naval uniform, earphones still on their skulls, just as they had gone to their battle-stations when the heavy explosions rocked the ship and the bosuns' pipes sounded the 'Alarm' through the ship.

It did not take long to establish that it would be impossible to force a way into the wreck of the *Hampshire* without using explosives. Explosives! The ship was full of live ammunition on a wartime scale. It would be a dangerous plan—indeed, madness— for either the whole ship would go up, and that would be the end of the gold, or the charge would be too small to achieve the desired effect. Moreover, the sea was getting rough again. Underwater currents were becoming noticeable even on the sea-bed, but the divers were anxious not to delay the work any longer, and when the sea grew calmer towards evening they went down again.

With underwater flame-cutters the men attacked the ship's hull, working by the ghostly light of the flood-lamps until far into the night, their ship floating far above their heads. Just as they thought they had reached the armoured hold of the ship, containing the money, their hopes were dashed. The arc-lights suddenly went out, the greenish-blue flames of the cutters were extinguished, and the men were buffeted about by strong jets of water. They just managed to jerk the signal line: 'Danger—pull us up!' Battered and bleeding, the three divers were lifted on board the *K.S.R.*, wondering what could have happened.

The rising sea had tangled the lines and tubes connecting the divers below with the salvage ship, and when the men on board could not make contact with the divers (who were obviously in trouble) they quickly decided to haul them up. They now had to decide on the next step, for there could be no question of working with the flame-cutters in such weather, and conditions did not change for several days. There was nothing for it but blasting, or giving up the work altogether just when they were so near—only a few yards from the steel treasure chamber!

They waited that night, and Costello and Mansfield went down with the charges and fixed them with time-fuses to the ship, then they were hauled up and the ship raced away from the danger spot, for each second was precious. If the explosion was too great it would tear the whole ship to pieces, and with it the *K.S.R.*

Everything went well. At the exact minute a column of water shot up and the *K.S.R.* steamed slowly back to her previous position, where the sea was strewn with wreckage.

Suddenly Mansfield, standing by the rails, went chalk-white, a horrified expression on his face. Shouting loudly, and waving his arms towards where the charges had exploded, he pointed to a long dark shape gliding towards the salvage ship.

'Torpedo! Torpedo! Full speed astern!' Mansfield shrieked to the bridge. Captain Brandt at once realized the danger.

Seconds passed; the ship's telegraph clanged, and the wheel was wrenched hard over. The deadly missile slipped past less than ten yards away, its wake giving a dramatic greeting from the wreck of the sunken cruiser.

The men stood at the stern and watched death slipping away—death that had been so near. Their faces were grey with shock and the realization of the danger they had just escaped. The ship's tubes had been loaded all those years, and the explosion had shaken the wreck, releasing the torpedo into the sea.

The men worked for more than a fortnight on the sea-bed, until at last they managed to force their way into the depths of the wreck through an opening in the desk. It was dark in the labyrinth of narrow, winding corridors, and they had to use a guide rope as they groped forward. In the next seventeen days they went down twenty-six times to the wreck of the *Hampshire*. They found the captain's cabin, and stood before two tall safes, but Courtney, the safe expert, realized at once that these could not be what they were seeking, for it would have been impossible to get as much as £10 million in gold into them.

They set to work, but it was hours before the locks gave and the doors opened. Cascading towards the divers came gold coins, documents, diaries, and the ship's log. Everything was packed into the little sailcloth bags the men had brought with them, and hauled up on the assistant diver's cable to the salvage ship on the surface.

While Courtney was opening the second safe and clearing it out Costello was preparing to break a way into the adjoining cabin. When the divers opened the air-tight steel door and looked into the chamber they saw eleven heavy safes of the most modern design standing against the walls, each as tall as a man. They were suddenly filled with terror as two figures in uniform glided through the water-filled room . . . came towards them . . . pale human faces . . . British naval officers, with the rings of gold braid on their sleeves showing their rank.

They floated past, gruesome phantoms, shot out by the pressure of water created by the opening of the steel door: two officers of the *Hampshire* whom death had surprised as they sat here at their desks making entries and calculations when the explosion shook the ship and the water rushed in and imprisoned them.

Swiftly Courtney darted towards them, snatching with the clamp of his diving suit at one of the corpses as it passed him. He got hold of its right hand, which came off as the body swam away. There was a signet ring on the second finger, and this Courtney took off for later identification of the dead man.

The divers tore at the signal line and had themselves brought to the surface. They clambered on deck, and when their suits were taken off they were shaking from head to toe with the horror of what they had just seen. Grabbing hold of the brandy flasks, they drank, and drank, and drank . . .

The work continued after a twenty-four-hour pause. The ship's papers were recovered from the captain's cabin in the *Hampshire*, as well as the sealed orders and the ship's log-book. The men brought up altogether £15,000 in gold from the safes, and then steamed to Stromness for a few days' rest. Then back to the old place, and to work; but in the few days everything had changed. Sand and sea-weed had closed up the openings, and a heavy sea was running. It would be plain suicide to dive under these conditions, but as every day's wait cost money—500 dollars to be precise—which was a loss to the whole crew, something dramatic was needed to put an end to the work.

On the morning of 24 April 1933, Costello, Mansfield, Courtney, and Weissfelt went down with an assistant diver. When they opened the strongroom door and bent over the chests filled to the brim with golden sovereigns the current buffeted them and tossed them about. Sack after sack was hauled up aboard the salvage ship. Suddenly, with incredible force, a rising stream of water shut the bulkhead door behind Courtney. The lights went out, and his hand was trapped. From the frightful surge of pain he realized that his wrist was broken. Blood was flowing all over his body inside the diving-suit, and he was getting no air at all. He heard Costello and Weissfelt shouting, then lost consciousness.

After some perilous minutes when everything seemed hopeless the five men were hauled up. Courtney, whose wrist was in fact broken, was brought up by his companions and collapsed a second time. Weissfelt had a broken spine and other severe injuries, and Mansfield lay with his eyes closed. His breathing was shallow, and internal damage made each breath agony. Costello, the slim Australian, had been laid on the deck with a badly crushed chest, and the German assistant-diver Kruger was dead.

Salvage operations were suspended; the badly injured men were taken ashore to a hospital, and that seemed to put an end to attempts to recover the treasure. Mansfield, the Virginian, died, and in accordance with his wishes his ashes were scattered over the site of the *Hampshire*. Costello (who died in 1947) and Courtney went home after a long period in hospital. Max Weissfelt was buried in a Berlin cemetery. After all, the former German naval officer had met his death at sea; the entries in his notebook had ultimately brought him to disaster.

In 1934 the Admiralty vetoed any further salvage work on the *Hampshire*, the wreck of the cruiser being indisputably the property of His Britannic Majesty.

A memorial to Earl Kitchener of Khartoum stands in St Paul's but he does not lie there. His body was never found; it still rests in the wreck of the *Hampshire*, where the Atlantic seas wash over her tragic gold.

RALLY DRIVE

Innes Ireland

The Mercedes Benz 280SE was manned by co-drivers Innes Ireland, Michael Taylor and Andrew Hedges.

They were just one team of entrants in the *Daily Express* **London to Sydney Marathon of 1968. A race full of incident and adventure . . .**

The ferry boat crossing of the Bosporus was but a few miles away, and we all sensed that this water crossing marked the end of the continent we knew, and the start of the eastern world which was a stranger. It was almost as if the adventure were just beginning.

Wednesday morning, 27 November, was as dirty and filthy a morning as I can remember. It was still raining and bitterly cold with a gusty wind. We got into the car and left Istanbul about 6 a.m. heading for the ferry boat.

We had worked out that we would be among the last of the cars to catch the first ferry, so we hustled along as best we could without getting lost and it was a bit of a scrummage getting aboard. On board the boat there was an elderly looking horse, looking rather sorry for itself with an enormous burden strapped to a carrier on its back. The old horse's owner looked almost as decrepit and tatty, but his leathery, sun-tanned face, deeply lined from the weather, had a kindly look. We decided there and then on the best way to lighten the load on our car, and piled all the gifts that we had received onto this delightful old man, among them a large box of Turkish Delight that was given to us by the Mercedes agent in Istanbul. The poor old horse wasn't too thrilled by our kindly gesture, but we thought it didn't have nearly as far to go as we did. To show his gratitude, the old man scuttled off into the depths of the ferry boat and reappeared some time later with a bag of oranges which he gave to us.

The mounting tension of the rally which we felt was obviously shared by most of the other crews, for the minute the gangway was down there was a great jostling match to get ashore—Hyde Park Corner in the rush hour had nothing on this. The old man and the horse thought discretion the better part of valour, and they hung back to allow the mad pack to get on with their carving-up session.

The drive to the next control was only 550 miles and the driving was shared by Mikey and Andy. It was followed by the very difficult section to Erzincan, which was a true rally stage and run very much against the clock. It was to be 176 miles and the time allowed only 2 hours and 45 minutes. It was expected that every crew would lose time here, but it was the first of two special stages incorporated in the event in order to give a position classification by the time we all got to Bombay.

I was delighted to find that I had been voted into the hot seat for both the special stages, for I would have been a nervous wreck had I had to sit beside someone else driving like a lunatic. It was because of this strenuous drive that lay ahead that I was allowed to have a good long rest until we reached Sivas.

We wanted to get there just as quickly as possible, for Dunlop had a service point where we could change all our wheels for others fitted with Weathermasters. Several weeks prior to the start, we had given Dunlop a set of six wheels, and tyres were fitted before they were air freighted out to Sivas. Since priority would be given to works cars we wanted to get to the mechanics before the hordes descended and they would be required to attend to others.

The weather was simply foul and the roads thronged with vast numbers of enormous trucks, most of them articulated. The Mercedes agents were obviously pretty active in this part of the world, for the great majority of them sported the Daimler Benz three pointed star. But the standard of driving was atrocious, and the road was littered with wrecked lorries and cars. Trying to overtake those that hadn't yet had their accident for the day was a major problem, as they didn't seem to have any particular preference for which side of the road they should occupy. We found that our flashing light on the roof was the most effective weapon of defence—or attack—and we had this on for most of the trip. And how we cursed the windscreen wipers and wished we hadn't exchanged them for the original Mercedes ones, for they juddered across the screen in a thoroughly useless fashion.

Immediately on disembarking from the ferry the tempo of the event had speeded up considerably. Perhaps this was due to a large number of cars leaving a point all together, but whatever the reason, the whole thing developed into a kind of Ankara Grand Prix. Dodging and overtaking the lorries required a great deal of concentration from the drivers if one was to survive this section of the trip. One car that didn't survive was Peter Sargent's Chrysler Valiant with Peter Lumsden aboard. It was side-swiped by an oncoming lorry and the damage sustained was bad enough to render the car hors de combat. After the impact, the lorry lurched violently back to its own side of the road then back out into the middle almost collecting six other rally cars that were following Sargent in line astern.

Climbing up the Bolu Pass we went into low cloud which made life difficult for there were still many heavy lorries and those going in our direction were grinding slowly uphill and overtaking became a problem. The top of the pass was 2,500 feet but 30 miles farther on we climbed to almost 4,500 feet and the low cloud disappeared.

We were swinging our way gaily uphill at one stage when Mikey came to a fastish but blind right-hander to find a lorry going in the same direction as ourselves, but completely on the wrong side of the road. As we had a speed differential of something like 60 mph Mikey just kept going and overtook this fellow on the inside, hoping that he wouldn't suddenly decide to come back to his correct side of the road. Guesswork played a major part in the early stages of our journey through Turkey.

With incidents of this sort happening by the mile, Mikey later expressed a considerable degree of self-flattery in that his two passengers were sound asleep. I would have hated to shatter this illusion by saying that sleep was induced by the same sort of fear that made me fall asleep in aeroplanes just before I was going to make a parachute descent!

As we neared Sivas, gaily painted donkey carts were an added hazard for they were driven with the same disregard of the highway code—frankly I doubt if they have one in Turkey—as the trucks. We decided that all truck drivers were in fact donkey cart drivers who had been promoted and still hadn't appreciated the fact that their 'donkeys' weighed 10 tons and travelled at 60 mph. Their appreciation of closing speeds of oncoming traffic was non-existent.

About 30 miles short of Sivas we came through a particularly scruffy little village. It consisted mainly of one narrow street with houses and shops on either side, but it was congested by far more people than its size indicated. They seemed very reluctant to get out of the way and we were reduced to a crawl as we forced a clearance for the car to get through.

And then we had our first taste of unmade roads. With the wet weather it was very slippery and muddy but Mikey warmed to his task. He was fairly throwing the car along the road, to such an extent that Andy asked, 'What the hell is all the hurry for?' Mikey then informed us that he was trying to keep up our estimated time of arrival at Sivas, 2.30 p.m., at which gem of information Andy and I assured him that we wouldn't think badly or hold it against him in any way should we be a minute or two late!

Although it was quite a riot, as Mikey tweaked his way along this road with Andy and I chuntering at him continuously, this was where the rally stopped being a quiet canter along the kind of roads we have always been used to—and where it became infinitely more serious.

The remoteness of the country, too, dawned upon us when we saw a bus disgorge two of its occupants at the side of the road, miles and miles from anywhere. One went in one direction and the other fellow, bowed almost double by an enormous bag and several packages, trundled off into the boondocks. As far as we could see, in the direction he was heading, there was not a sign of any form of habitation, and we could see all the way to the foothills 10 miles distant.

Our main tank ran dry about 15 miles from Sivas and we stopped to empty one of the jerry cans into it. I suggested it would be a good idea if I drove the rest of the way to get a little practice with the car on the rough and slippery roads, for we realized that the tough difficult stage to Erzincan would be of a similar nature. My short practice session produced some fairly amusing, if unprintable, comments from my fellow travellers. When I went through a tight S-bend pretty quickly to cross a railway line in a series of power-on, opposite lock slides with mud and stones flying from the tyres, Mikey announced that it was a long time since he had been frightened in a motor car!

However, we duly arrived at Sivas, safe and sound, and immediately sought out the Dunlop service point which we knew had been set up in the town. It was located in a dim, dark, earthen-floored shed, devoid of windows and lit only by two electric bulbs, the light from them being of the brilliance of the proverbial Naafi candle.

I have had a long association with the Dunlop tyre people, for I always used their tyres in my motor racing days. Their service had always been impeccable, with highly proficient mechanics who would do one's bidding at the drop of a hat. In sharp contrast to their efficient mobile workshops and business-like air, the scene at Sivas was a complete shambles. To be fair to the chap in charge, the amenities at his disposal were crude to say the least and he had only three of his own mechanics to assist him. Added to this he had the frustration of the local customs authorities, who had refused to allow him to import all his wheels and tyres. And to confuse the issue even more, a little customs man made a note of the serial number of each individual tyre that was removed from a rim, and the number of the tyre that replaced it.

To our horror we discovered that the wheels we had given to Dunlops two months earlier to be fitted with their Weathermaster tyres and sent to Sivas were among those interned at the local airport customs shed. I very quickly grabbed a set of 15-inch tyres that I found among the stacked up wheels, collared a mechanic, and set him about the task of changing our tyres before the works cars started to arrive. To make matters even worse, most of the Dunlop equipment was lying in the customs shed along with our wheels and there wasn't a spare jack in the place; Andy Hedges had to go and borrow one from a nearby garage. I then discovered that there wasn't a pump or an air bottle, but by this time nothing would have surprised me. Once again, Andy came to the rescue, and in his best Turkish arm-waving accents managed to make some shopkeeper understand his requirements, although the best he could muster was a hand pump. Then we discovered there was no wheel balancing equipment!

Fortunately we had four hours in hand and had also been the first car to get to the Dunlop service point, for it took almost this amount of time to effect our wheel changes. I stood guard over the mechanic, who was by now sweating profusely with the cumbersome equipment he had to use, for I was afraid that he would be collared to go and work on one of the factory entered cars which had begun to fill the place to overflowing. Several of them were being worked on out in the streets, and it was with a feeling of complete relief that I drove out of the dingy shed with a new set of tyres and an hour to spare.

Mikey, the administrator, had been busy all this time trying to find an honest and reliable taxi driver. It wasn't that he was terrified of driving to Erzincan with me—actually he was, but managed to conceal it by dedicated industry!—but to give ourselves the least time deficit over the next stage, which, as I have said, was very much against the clock, we decided to have all our tremendously heavy load taken ahead of us to Erzincan. The local Mercedes agent, a delightful and most helpful fellow, came to the rescue and we piled all our gear into a mini bus with explicit instructions to the driver to go as fast as prudence would allow, to meet us at the Erzincan control point. As he disappeared in a cloud of dust each one of us heaved a sigh and wondered if we would ever see our kit again.

I was decidedly apprehensive of the task that lay ahead of me. The 176 miles of unmade, rough, rock-strewn and muddy road that wound its way up and over a dangerous mountain pass were completely unfamiliar to me, we had no pace notes and it would be dark when we set out. I knew that I would have to go as fast as I knew how and I, alone, was responsible for our safety. Never having done anything of this sort before, I eagerly sought as much information on the route as I could, but the results of my efforts were scanty indeed. Tommy Sopwith was in charge of the Sivas control and, over a cup of tea with him, I learned that the ground was pretty wet and muddy, and there was supposed to be a lorry blocking the road about 100 miles distant.

Mikey and Andy must have sensed my concern, for they were being unusually witty as we awaited our turn to leave. Mikey asked for his darkest pair of sun glasses to make the black night even blacker, saying they were in the pale-coloured case in the glove pocket, to which Andy retorted that they weren't the only pale coloured things in the car at that precise moment! He also dug out one of our medical cases, the immediate first aid one, and helped himself to a liberal gulp of the Courvoisier 'medicinal purposes' brandy. Mikey followed suit, but they firmly denied me a ration of Dutch courage!

The seat belts we had had fitted, at considerable trouble to their makers, had come in for all sorts of criticisms during the run so far and, being so troublesome to put on, they had lain in a twisted mass on the floor. Suddenly they went up in the popularity polls as we all struggled to adjust and fit them, and Mikey put on his old blue crash helmet for the first time in eight years.

I jockeyed the car into a position that would give us a clear run away from the mud-surrounded control, one that would give Mikey the shortest possible run to the car with our route book. A certain amount of confusion was added when Nick Brittan arrived later, in his works-prepared Ford with its right front wing considerably damaged and no windscreen, as a result of having come in violent contact with some poor donkey.

And so, in the darkness of Wednesday night, 27 November, Mike Taylor and I had our first initiation into the world of rally driving. Andy, who had done a few rallies, was probably much more apprehensive, for he knew what sort of thing to expect. As Mikey leapt into the back seat with our route book, I let in the clutch and we roared off into the night.

The first part of the road was hard dirt with loose stones, but was reasonably straight. I could keep up 90 mph or more most of the time, but there were dozens and dozens of blind humps which, had I had pace notes, I could have taken flat out and so saved a great deal of time. But as we had been misled on one of them by the line of telegraph poles which kept going straight and just over the brow the road went fairly abruptly to the right, the popular vote of my passengers was that we back off to 70 at least. It was on this and other similar occasions where the works teams had a tremendous advantage; most of them had been over the route previously, and they were all equipped with pace notes that covered every inch of the route.

Much of the road—track would be a better word—was completely unmarked, there being no hedges or grass verges to stand

I let in the clutch and we roared off into the night.

out as a definition. As the track was more or less hewn out of the sides of the hills this meant that there was a very real danger of sliding off the edge where invariably there was a sheer—or near sheer—drop to whatever lay below. To say the least of it, a mistake of this sort would put paid to our chances of getting further in the rally, to say nothing of personal injuries.

All too soon the road surface deteriorated as we started to climb the pass which rose to well over 6,000 feet. It was mud and loose stones all the way, twisting to the right and left in an unending series of corners which kept me twirling the steering wheel and making opposite lock corrections when I would find the corner a lot tighter than it looked. Needless to say I was getting endless criticisms from the other two seats, and I must say I didn't blame them—I would have been cringing on the floor whimpering had one of them been driving.

We passed a considerable number of other competitors in the early stages, and then had a fairly lonely run until we came on a Ford of some sort which had failed to make a corner and shot straight on into what looked like somebody's front garden. They were up to their hubs in mud and it looked as if they would be there for some time. Next we wound down a series of corners through a wooded section with a right angle bend over a bridge at the bottom. I had a glimpse of lights on the bridge as I slithered onto it, and as my headlamps swung round I could see an 1800 BMC car which was stationary across the bridge with its front end hanging over the river, having crashed through the balustrade.

Normally there would have been no problem stopping, but the construction of the bridge combined with the muddy, greasy surface almost piled us into the side of the car, which would undoubtedly tip it into the river below. Apart from the balustrades on either side, the part one had to drive over consisted of two planks about 15 inches wide, these being about 4 inches thick with other planks fixed across the underside. I had managed to get on the planks, and not wanting to risk swerving off or leaving my rear wheels on their wrong side to try and scrape past the obstruction, I had to stop in a straight line. Then I backed off the bridge, and by driving forward with the right side almost touching the railing, we managed to squeeze through. We had lost at least one precious minute.

Further on one of the Australian entries came up behind and I pulled over to let him through. I was able to hang onto his tail for quite a long way taking advantage of his reconnaissance notes, but finally lost him on a long uphill section where his big, powerful engine pulled him away from us. We were further hampered on these competitive stages by the wide ratios of the gearbox. It was a perfectly standard one, and I just longed for a close ratio box which would allow me to use the power available to me to the best advantage.

Then we ran out of brakes. I was using them pretty hard for each corner we approached, and on many occasions I had to use them to brake the back end away in order to get round. Now they started fading horribly and soon I could push the pedal to the floor without a vestige of retardation. I had to ease off considerably earlier than before on approaching a corner, for now my only way of slowing up was to put the car sideways and it wasn't possible to judge accurately the degree of severity of the corner.

After five minutes or so of not touching the brake pedal, the brakes returned to normal, but I was to suffer a repetition of this failure once more before getting to Erzincan. There was one corner I remember distinctly where I was very glad the brakes were functioning normally. We were hurtling downhill at some ridiculous speed on loose stones, and it looked as if the road went straight on for some way. I had my right foot fairly well planted on the throttle, when suddenly, without any warning, I could see the road took a sharp right handed hairpin and there was a nasty, murky darkness in front. Instantly I remembered a conversation I once had with Paddy Hopkirk about this kind of situation and had no alternative but to try and make the theories work for me. I braked as hard as the surface would allow, then, some way short of the hairpin, I threw the car sideways with the front end pointing in the opposite direction to the way the road went. This slowed us down considerably and, when I threw the car back to get the front pointing at the corner, the pendulum effect got the back end sufficiently wide for us to slither round.

I distinctly recall hearing the comment 'bloody hell' from somewhere in the car!

This road was full of many such surprises of deception. In several places the road would be quite cambered into the apex of a corner, and I would approach on the high side of the camber, set the car up aiming at the apex I couldn't see and then, just as we would be sliding nicely on the line that seemed to be indicated, I could see that the apex I was aiming at just didn't exist. In its place there would be a sheer drop over the edge into obscurity. Having been forced to make several rapid changes of direction, which usually put the tail end uncomfortably close to some other hazard, like a vertical rock face, I learned to aim a little wide of apexes unless they were very clearly defined.

Eventually the road surface improved as we descended from the pass, and we were back onto a hardish dirt road which was fairly straight. The first few miles had a series of bridges and, as with the blind humps earlier, I backed off to about 70 mph in case there was a jump-up onto the bridge, but always found that this was much too slow—again the lack of notes was losing us time. Finally, as another bridge loomed up, I decided that I would just keep my foot down and hold the speed at between 90 and 100 mph. But this was the one bridge with a jump-up. As we got to the top of the incline onto the bridge there was an edge which shot the poor Mercedes three or four feet up into the air; we never even touched the bridge, nor did we touch the decline running off it until the road levelled off again. We hit the road with the most monumental crash and as the sump guard took the impact, a liver-crippling jar went all the way from my feet to my head. But at least I was ready for it, whereas poor Mikey in the back didn't even see it coming, and I had been unable to shout a warning. He hit the roof with an almighty crash, which unfortunately put his neck out of joint. This was the one thing he feared, for in 1960 he had broken his neck and back when the steering column of his Lotus sheared during practice for the Belgian Grand Prix at Spa. How the car survived the return to terra firma without damage, I cannot for the life of me imagine.

The last few miles were tarmacadam with a loose surface of gravel chippings, but fairly straight with fast corners. We had been running over the pass with four headlamps, two long range halogen beams, and the two Cibie roof lights all illuminated, and very gradually the load began to drain the battery. I had been finding it progressively more difficult to see where I was going, for we all believed it was mud on the lamp glasses that was causing the dimness.

One of the works Fords came up behind us on the last stretch, and although I was able to use his lights for a short while, I couldn't keep too close for fear of getting our lamps or windscreen shattered by flying stones. As it was we had already been hit by several, and the screen was scarred by numerous star-shaped cracks. Had we been able to see properly, we could have kept up 100–110 mph on this stretch instead of feeling our way along at 90-ish.

At last the Shell petrol station, where the control was located, loomed up as a blaze of light; I braked hard, we skittered to a halt and Mikey dived into the control to have our time recorded in the route book.

JIM'S BIG DREAM

Mark Twain

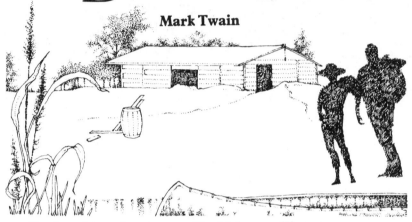

During his adventures, Huckleberry Finn teams up with Jim; and together they venture down-river on a raft . . .

We judged that three nights more would fetch us to Cairo, at the bottom of Illinois, where the Ohio River comes in, and that was what we was after. We would sell the raft and get on a steamboat and go way up the Ohio amongst the free States, and then be out of trouble.

Well, the second night a fog begun to come on, and we made for a tow-head to tie to, for it wouldn't do to try to run in fog; but when I paddled ahead in the canoe, with the line, to make fast, there warn't anything but little saplings to tie to. I passed the line around one of them right on the edge of the cut bank, but there was a stiff current, and the raft come booming down so lively she tore it out by the roots and away she went. I see the fog closing down, and it made me so sick and scared I couldn't budge for most a half a minute it seemed to me—and then there warn't no raft in sight; you couldn't see twenty yards. I jumped into the canoe and run back to the stern and grabbed the paddle and set her back a stroke. But she didn't come. I was in such a hurry I hadn't untied her. I got up and tried to untie her, but I was so excited my hands shook so I couldn't hardly do anything with them.

As soon as I got started I took out after the raft, hot and heavy, right down the tow-head. That was all right as far as it went, but the tow-head warn't sixty yards long, and the minute I flew by the foot of it I shot out into the solid white fog, and hadn't no more idea which way I was going than a dead man.

Thinks I, it won't do to paddle; first I know I'll run into the bank or a tow-head or something; I got to set still and float, and yet it's mighty fidgety business to have to hold your hands still at such a time. I whooped and listened. Away down there, some-wheres, I hears a small whoop, and up comes my spirits. I went tearing after it, listening sharp to hear it again. The next time it come, I see I warn't heading for it but heading away to the right of it. And the next time, I was heading away to the left of it—and not gaining on it much, either, for I was flying around, this way and that and t'other, but it was going straight ahead all the time.

I did wish the fool would think to beat a tin pan, and beat it all the time, but he never did, and it was the still places between the whoops that was making the trouble for me. Well, I fought along, and directly I hears the whoop *behind* me. I was tangled good, now. That was somebody else's whoop, or else I was turned around.

I throwed the paddle down. I heard the whoop again; it was behind me yet, but in a different place; it kept coming, and kept changing its place, and I kept answering, till by and by it was in front of me again and I knowed the current had swung the canoe's head downstream and I was all right, if that was Jim and not some other raftsman hollering. I couldn't tell nothing about voices in a fog, for nothing don't look natural nor sound natural in a fog.

The whooping went on, and in about a minute I come a-booming down on a cut bank with smoky ghosts of big trees on it, and the current throwed me off to the left and shot by, amongst a lot of snags that fairly roared, the current was tearing by them so swift.

In another second or two it was solid white and still again. I set perfectly still, then, listening to my heart thump, and I reckon I didn't draw a breath while it thumped a hundred.

I just give up, then. I knowed what the matter was. That cut bank was an island, and Jim had gone down t'other side of it. It warn't no tow-head, that you could float by in ten minutes. It had the big timber of a regular island; it might be five or six mile long and more than a half a mile wide.

I kept quiet, with my ears cocked, about fifteen minutes, I reckon. I was floating along, of course, four or five mile an hour; but you don't ever think of that. No, you *feel* like you are laying dead still on the water; and if a little glimpse of a snag slips by, you don't think to yourself how fast *you're* going, but you catch your breath and think, my! how that snag's tearing along. If you think it ain't dismal and lonesome out in a fog that way, by yourself, in the night, you try it once—you'll see.

Next, for about a half an hour, I whoops now and then; at last I hears the answer a long ways off, and tries to follow it, but I couldn't do it, and directly I judged I'd got into a nest of two-heads, for I had little dim glimpses of them on both sides of me, sometimes just a narrow channel between; and some that I couldn't see, I knowed was there, because I'd hear the wash of the current against the old dead brush and trash that hung over the banks. Well, I warn't long losing the whoops, down amongst the tow-heads; and I only tried to chase them a little while, anyway, because it was worse than chasing a jack-o'-lantern. You never knowed a sound dodge around so, and swap places so quick and so much.

I had to claw away from the bank pretty lively, four or five times, to keep from knocking the islands out of the river; and so I judged the raft must be butting into the bank every now and then, or

'Hallo, Jim, have I been asleep?'

else it would get further ahead and clear out of hearing—it was floating a little faster than what I was.

Well, I seemed to be in the open river again, by and by, but I couldn't hear no sign of a whoop nowheres. I reckoned Jim had fetched up on a snag, maybe, and it was all up with him. I was good and tired, so I laid down in the canoe and said I wouldn't bother no more. I didn't want to go to sleep, of course; but I was so sleepy I couldn't help it; so I thought I would take just one little cat-nap.

But I reckon it was more than a cat-nap, for when I waked up the stars was shining bright, the fog was all gone, and I was spinning down at a big bend stern first. First I didn't know where I was; I thought I was dreaming; and when things begun to come back to me, they seemed to come up dim out of last week.

It was a monstrous big river here, with the tallest and the thickest kind of timber on both banks; just a solid wall, as well as I could see, by the stars. I looked away downstream, and seen a black speck on the water. I took out after it; but when I got to it it warn't nothing but a couple of saw-logs made fast together. Then I see another speck, and chased that; then another, and this time I was right. It was the raft.

When I got to it Jim was sitting there with his head down between his knees, asleep, with his right arm hanging over the steering oar. The other oar was smashed off, and the raft was littered up with leaves and branches and dirt. So she'd had a rough time.

I made fast and laid down under Jim's nose on the raft, and begun to gap, and stretch my fists out against Jim, and says:

'Hallo, Jim, have I been asleep? Why didn't you stir me up?'

'Good gracious, is dat you, Huck? En you ain' dead—you ain' drownded—yous back agin? It's too good for true, honey, it's too good for true. Lemme look at you, chile, lemme feel o' you. No, you ain' dead! you's back agin', live en soun', jis de same old Huck—de same ole Huck, thanks to goodness!'

'What's the matter with you, Jim? You been a-drinking?'

'Drinkin'? Has I had a chance to be a-drinkin?'

'Well, then, what makes you talk so wild?'

'How does I talk wild?'

'*How?* why, hain't you been talking about my coming back, and all that stuff, as if I'd been gone away?'

'Huck—Huck Finn, you look me in de eye; look me in de eye. *Hain't* you ben gone away?'

'Gone away? Why, what in the nation do you mean? *I* hain't been gone anywheres. Where would I go to?'

'Well, looky here, boss, dey's sumf'n wrong, dey is. Is I *me*, or who *is* I? Is I heah, or what *is* I? Now dat's what I wants to know.'

'Well, I think you're here, plain enough, but I think you're a tangle-headed old fool, Jim.'

'I is, is I? Well, you answer me dis. Didn't you tote out de line in de canoe, fer to make fas' to de tow-head?'

'No, I didn't. What tow-head? I hain't seen no tow-head.'

'You hain't seen no tow-head? Looky here—didn't de line pull loose en de raf' go a-hummin' down de river, en leave you en de canoe behine in de fog?'

'What fog?'

'Why, *de* fog. De fog dat's ben aroun' all night. En didn't you whoop, en didn't I whoop, tell we got mix' up in de islands en one un us got los' en t'other one was jis' as good as los', 'kase he didn' know whah he wuz? En didn't I bust up agin a lot er dem islands en have a turrible time en mos' git drownded? Now ain' dat so?'

'Well, this is too many for me, Jim. I hain't seen no fog, nor no islands, nor no troubles, nor nothing. I been setting here talking with you all night till you went to sleep about ten minutes ago, and I reckon I done the same. You couldn't a got drunk in that time, so of course you've been dreaming.'

'Dad fetch it, how is I gwyne to dream all dat in ten minutes?'

'Well, hang it all, you did dream it, because there didn't any of it happen.'

'But Huck, it's all jis' as plain to me as—'

'It don't make no difference how plain it is, there ain't nothing in it. I know, because I've been here all the time.'

Jim didn't say nothing for about five minutes, but set there studying over it. Then he says:

'Well, den, I reck'n I did dream it, Huck; but dog my cats ef it ain't de powerfullest dream I ever see. En I hain't ever had no dream b'fo' dat's tired me like dis one.'

'Oh, well, that's all right, because a dream does tire a body like everything, sometimes. But this one was a staving dream—tell me all about it, Jim.'

So Jim went to work and told me the whole thing right through, just as it happened, only he painted it up considerable. Then he said he must start in and ''terpret' it, because it was sent for a warning. He said the first tow-head stood for a man that would try to do us some good, but the current was another man that would get us away from him. The whoops was warnings that would come to us every now and then, and if we didn't try hard to make out to understand them they'd just take us into bad luck, 'stead of keeping us out of it. The lot of tow-heads was troubles we was going to get into with quarrelsome people and all kinds of mean folks, but if we minded our business and didn't talk back and aggravate them, we would pull through and get out of the fog and into the big clear river, which was the free States, and wouldn't have no more trouble.

It had clouded up pretty dark just after I got onto the raft, but it was clearing up again, now.

'Oh, well, that's all interpreted well enough, as far as it goes, Jim,' I says; 'but what does *these* things stand for?'

It was the leaves and rubbish on the raft, and the smashed oar. You could see them first rate, now ...

HIDING FROM THE
RED COATS

Robert Louis Stevenson

'**H**oot, hoot,' said Alan, looking mighty silly. 'Tomorrow there'll be a fine to-do in Appin, a fine riding of dragoons, and crying of "Cruachan!"[1] and running of red-coats; and it behoves you and me to be the sooner gone.'

Thereupon we set out, in an easterly direction, over broken country . . .

Sometimes we walked, sometimes ran; and as it drew on to morning, walked ever the less and ran the more.

Though, upon its face, that country appeared to be a desert, yet there were huts and houses of the people, of which we must have passed more than twenty, hidden in quiet places of the hills.

[1] The rallying-word of the Campbells.

For all our hurry, day began to' come in while we were still far from any shelter. It found us in a prodigious valley, strewn with rocks and where ran a foaming river. Wild mountains stood around it; there grew there neither grass nor trees; and I have sometimes thought since then, that it may have been the valley called Glencoe, where the massacre was in the time of King William. But for the details of our itinerary, I am all to seek; our way lying now by short cuts, now by great detours; our pace being so hurried, our time of journeying usually by night; and the names of such places as I asked and heard being in the Gaelic tongue and the more easily forgotten.

The first peep of morning, then, showed us this horrible place, and I could see Alan knit his brow.

'This is no fit place for you and me,' he said. 'This is a place they're bound to watch.'

And with that he ran harder than ever down to the water-side, in a part where the river was split in two among three rocks. It went through with a horrid thundering that made my belly quake; and there hung over the lynn a little mist of spray. Alan looked neither to the right nor to the left, but jumped clean upon the middle rock and fell there on his hands and knees to check himself, for that rock was small and he might have pitched over on the far side. I had scarce time to measure the distance or to understand the peril before I had followed him, and he had caught and stopped me.

So there we stood, side by side upon a small rock slippery with spray, a far broader leap in front of us, and the river dinning upon all sides. When I saw where I was, there came on me a deadly sickness of fear, and I put my hand over my eyes. Alan took me and shook me; I saw he was speaking, but the roaring of the falls and the trouble of my mind prevented me from hearing; only I saw his face was red with anger, and that he stamped upon the rock. The same look showed me the water raging by, and the mist hanging in the air: and with that I covered my eyes again and shuddered.

The next minute Alan had set the brandy bottle to my lips, and forced me to drink about a gill, which sent the blood into my head again. Then, putting his hands to his mouth, and his mouth to my ear, he shouted, 'Hang or drown!' and turning his back upon me, leaped over the farther branch of the stream, and landed safe. I was now alone upon the rock, which gave me the more room; the brandy was singing in my ears; I had this good example fresh before me, and just wit enough to see that if I did not leap at once, I should never leap at all. I bent low on my knees and flung myself forth, with that kind of anger of despair that has sometimes stood me in stead of courage. Sure enough, it was but my hands that reached the full length; these slipped, caught again, slipped again; and I was sliddering back into the lynn, when Alan seized me, first by the hair, then by the collar, and with a great strain dragged me into safety.

Never a word he said, but set off running again for his life, and I must stagger to my feet and run after him. I had been weary before, but now I was sick and bruised, and partly drunken with the brandy; I kept stumbling as I ran, I had a stitch that came near to overmaster me; and when at last Alan paused under a great rock that stood there among a number of others, it was none too soon for David Balfour.

A great rock I have said; but by rights it was two rocks leaning together at the top, both some twenty feet high, and at the first sight inaccessible. Even Alan (though you may say he had as good as four hands) failed twice in an attempt to climb them; and it was only at the third trial, and then by standing on my shoulders and leaping up with such force as I thought must have broken my collar-bone, that he secured a lodgment. Once there, he let down his leathern girdle; and with the aid of that and a pair of shallow footholds in the rock, I scrambled up beside him.

Then I saw why we had come there; for the two rocks, being both somewhat hollow on the top and sloping one to the other, made a kind of dish or saucer, where as many as three or four men might have lain hidden.

All this while Alan had not said a word, and had run and climbed with such a savage silent frenzy of hurry, that I knew that he was in mortal fear of some miscarriage. Even now we were on the rock he said nothing, nor so much as relaxed the frowning look upon his face; but clapped flat down, and keeping only one eye above the edge of our place of shelter scouted all round the compass. The dawn had come quite clear; we could see the stony sides of the valley, and its bottom, which was bestrewed with rocks, and the river, which went from one side to another, and made white falls; but nowhere the smoke of a house, nor any living creature but some eagles screaming round a cliff.

Then at last Alan smiled.

'Ay,' said he, 'now we have a chance'; and then looking at me with some amusement, 'ye're no very gleg[1] at the jumping,' said he.

At this I suppose I coloured with mortification, for he added at once, 'Hoots! small blame to ye! To be feared of a thing and yet to do it is what makes the prettiest kind of a man. And then there was water there, and water's a thing that daunts even me. No, no,' said Alan, 'it's no you that's to blame, it's me.'

I asked him why.

'Why,' said he, 'I have proved myself a gomeral this night. For first of all I take a wrong road, and that in my own country of Appin; so that the day has caught us where we should never have been; and thanks to that, we lie here in some danger and mair discomfort. And next (which is the worst of the two, for a man that has been so much among the heather as myself) I have come wanting a water-bottle, and here we lie for a long summer's day with naething but neat spirit. Ye may think that a small matter: but before it comes night, David, ye'll give me news of it.'

I was anxious to redeem my character, and offered, if he would pour out the brandy, to run down and fill the bottle at the river.

'I wouldnae waste the good spirit either,' says he. 'It's been a good friend to you this night; or in my poor opinion, ye would still

[1] Brisk.

I took but one look at them and ducked again into my place.

be cocking on yon stone. And what's mair,' says he, 'ye may have observed (you that's a man of so much penetration) that Alan Breck Stewart was perhaps walking quicker than his ordinar'.'

'You!' I cried, 'you were running fit to burst.'

'Was I so?' said he. 'Well, then, ye may depend upon it, there was nae time to be lost. And now here is enough said; gang you to your sleep, lad, and I'll watch.'

Accordingly, I lay down to sleep; a little peaty earth had drifted in between the top of the two rocks, and some bracken grew there, to be a bed to me; the last thing I heard was still the crying of the eagles.

I dare say it would be nine in the morning when I was roughly awakened, and found Alan's hand pressed upon my mouth.

'Wheesht!' he whispered. 'Ye were snoring.'

'Well,' said I, surprised at his dark face, 'and why not?'

He peered over the edge of the rock, and signed to me to do the like.

It was now high day, cloudless, and very hot. The valley was as clear as in a picture. About half a mile up the water was a camp of red-coats; a big fire blazed in their midst, at which some were cooking; and near by, on the top of a rock about as high as ours, there stood a sentry, with the sun sparkling on his arms. All the way down along the riverside were posted other sentries; here near together, there widelier scattered; some planted like the first, on places of command, some on the ground level and marching and counter-marching, so as to meet half-way. Higher up the glen, where the ground was more open, the chain of posts was continued by horse-soldiers, whom we could see in the distance riding to and fro. Lower down, the infantry continued; but as the stream suddenly swelled by the confluence of a considerable burn, they were more widely set, and only watched the fords and stepping-stones.

I took but one look at them and ducked again into my place. It was strange indeed to see this valley, which had lain so solitary in the hour of dawn, bristling with arms and dotted with the red coats and breeches.

'Ye see,' said Alan, 'this was what I was afraid of, Davie: that they would watch the burn-side. They began to come in about two hours ago, and, man! but ye're a grand hand at the sleeping! We're in a narrow place. If they get up the sides of the hill they could easy spy us with a glass; but if they'll only keep in the foot of the valley, we'll do yet. The posts are thinner down the water: and, come night, we'll try our hand at getting by them.'

'And what are we to do till night?' I asked.

'Lie here,' says he, 'and birstle.'

That one good Scotch word, 'bristle', was indeed the most of the story of the day that we had now to pass. You are to remember that we lay on the bare top of a rock, like scones upon a girdle; the sun beat upon us cruelly; the rock grew so heated, a man could scarce endure the touch of it; and the little patch of earth and fern, which kept cooler, was only large enough for one at a time. We took turn about to lie on the naked rock, which was indeed like the position of that saint that was martyred on a gridiron; and it ran in my mind how strange it was, that in the same climate and at only a few days' distance, I should have suffered so cruelly, first from cold upon my island and now from heat upon this rock.

All the while we had no water, only raw brandy for a drink, which was worse than nothing; but we kept the bottle as cool as we could, burying it in the earth, and got some relief by bathing our breasts and temples.

The soldiers kept stirring all day in the bottom of the valley, now changing guard, now in patrolling parties hunting among the rocks. These lay round in so great a number, that to look for men among them was like looking for a needle in a bottle of hay; and being so hopeless a task, it was gone about with less care. Yet we could see the soldiers pike their bayonets among the heather, which sent a cold thrill through my vitals; and they would sometimes hang about our rock, so that we scarce dared to breathe.

It was in this way that I first heard the right English speech; one fellow as he went by actually clapping his hand upon the sunny face of the rock on which we lay, and plucking it off again with an oath. 'I tell you it's 'ot,' says he; and I was amazed at the clipping tones and the odd sing-song in which he spoke, and no less at that strange trick of dropping out the letter h. My surprise was all the greater to hear that manner of speaking in the mouth of a grown man; and indeed I have never grown used to it; nor yet altogether with the English grammar, as perhaps a very critical eye might here and there spy out even in these memoirs.

The tediousness and pain of these hours upon the rock grew only the greater as the day went on; the rock getting still the hotter and the sun fiercer. There were giddiness, and sickness, and sharp pangs like rheumatism to be supported. I minded then, and have often minded since, on the lines in our Scotch psalm:—

'The moon by night thee shall not smite,
    Nor yet the sun by day';

and indeed it was only by God's blessing that we neither of us were sun-smitten.

At last, about two, it was beyond men's bearing, and there was now temptation to resist, as well as pain to thole. For the sun being now got a little into the west, there came a patch of shade on the east side of our rock, which was the side sheltered from the soldiers.

'As well one death as another,' said Alan, and slipped over the edge and dropped on the ground on the shadowy side.

I followed him at once, and instantly fell all my length, so weak was I and so giddy with that long exposure. Here, then, we lay for an hour or two, aching from head to foot, as weak as water, and lying quite naked to the eye of any soldier who should have strolled that way. None came, however, all passing by on the other side; so that our rock continued to be our shield even in this new position.

Presently we began again to get a little strength; and as the soldiers were now lying closer along the riverside, Alan proposed that we should try a start. I was by this time afraid of but one thing in the world; and that was to be set back upon the rock; anything else was welcome to me; so we got ourselves at once in marching order, and began to slip from rock to rock one after the other, now crawling flat on our bellies in the shade, now making a run for it, heart in mouth.

The soldiers, having searched this side of the valley after a fashion, and being perhaps somewhat sleepy with the sultriness of the afternoon, had now laid by much of their vigilance, and stood dozing at their posts or only kept a look-out along the banks of the river; so that in this way, keeping down the valley and at the same time towards the mountains, we drew steadily away from their neighbourhood. But the business was the most wearing I had ever taken part in. A man had need of a hundred eyes in every part of him, to keep concealed in that uneven country and within cry of so many and scattered sentries. When we must pass an open place, quickness was not all, but a swift judgment not only of the lie of the whole country, but of the solidity of every stone on which we must set foot; for the afternoon was now fallen so breathless that the rolling of a pebble sounded abroad like a pistol shot, and would start the echo calling among the hills and cliffs.

By sundown we had made some distance, even by our slow rate of progress, though to be sure the sentry on the rock was still plainly in our view. But now we came on something that put all fears out of season; and that was a deep rushing burn, that tore down, in that part, to join the glen river. At the sight of this we cast ourselves on the ground and plunged head and shoulders in the water; and I cannot tell which was the more pleasant, the great shock as the cool stream went over us, or the greed with which we drank of it.

We lay there (for the banks hid us), drank again and again, bathed our chests, let our wrists trail in the running water till they ached with the chill; and at last, being wonderfully renewed, we got out the meal-bag and made drammach in the iron pan. This, though it is but cold water mingled with oatmeal, yet makes a good enough dish for a hungry man; and where there are no means of making fire, or (as in our case) good reason for not making one, it is the chief stand-by of those who have taken to the heather.

As soon as the shadow of the night had fallen, we set forth again, at first with the same caution, but presently with more boldness, standing our full height and stepping out at a good pace of walking. The way was very intricate, lying up the steep sides of mountains and along the brows of cliffs; clouds had come in with the sunset, and the night was dark and cool; so that I walked without much fatigue, but in continual fear of falling and rolling down the mountains, and with no guess at our direction.

The moon rose at last and found us still on the road; it was in its last quarter, and was long beset with clouds; but after a while shone out and showed me many dark heads of mountains, and was reflected far underneath us on the narrow arm of a sea-loch.

At this sight we both paused; I struck with wonder to find myself so high and walking (as it seemed to me) upon clouds: Alan to make sure of his direction.

Seemingly he was well pleased, and he must certainly have judged us out of ear-shot of all our enemies; for throughout the rest of our night-march he beguiled the way with whistling of many tunes, warlike, merry, plaintive; reel tunes that made the foot go faster; tunes of my own south country that made me fain to be home from my adventures; and all these, on the great, dark, desert mountains, making company upon the way.

FIRST FLIGHT

John Evangelist Walsh

**Upon Kitty Hawk Sands—off the North Carolina coast—
on 17 December 1903, the Wright Brothers, Orville and
Wilbur, took the first steps to making man's dream of
flying by motor-powered aircraft a reality . . .**

At 10 a.m. the signal flag was run up and the two brothers began
laying the track in the sand about sixty yards to the west of
the large shed, pointing due north. So cold was it that they had to
return to the stove in the shed at intervals to warm their hands.
Four men from the lifesaving station braved the cold to watch, and
assist if needed. Two of them had been present on the fourteenth,
John T. Daniels and W. S. Dough. Two others had been occasional visitors to the camp, A. D. Etheridge and W. C. Brinkley.
With them came a seventeen-year-old who had stopped at the
station to talk; Johnny Moore of Nags Head.

By ten thirty the Flyer stood poised on the takeoff rail, the engine
sputtering in a warmup. Behind it and a few feet to the right,

Orville had set up a tripod camera, aimed at a point near the end of the track, the point from which he expected the Flyer to rise. John Daniels volunteered to operate it; as the Flyer lifted he was to snap the shutter.

When all was ready Wilbur motioned to his brother and the two walked a little apart from the others, where they stood talking quietly for a few minutes. 'After a while they shook hands,' remembered Daniels, 'and we couldn't help notice how they held on to each other's hand, sort o' like they hated to let go; like two folks parting who weren't sure they'd ever see each other again.' The substance of this conversation was not recorded, though it probably included a reminder from Wilbur that Orville was to be careful not to let the Flyer get too high; between ten and fifteen feet was the height they had agreed on.

Orville climbed aboard and adjusted himself in the hip cradle. Wilbur, before taking his place at the right wing tip, walked over to the five spectators who were standing a short distance to the rear of the Flyer. He told them, as Daniels recalled, 'not to look sad, but to laugh and hollo and clap our hands and try to cheer Orville up when he started.' As Wilbur walked back to the Flyer the five set up a noisy demonstration.

Above the sound of motor and propellers rose Orville's shout of readiness. The restraining wire was slipped. The Flyer started forward, Wilbur's grasp on the right wing tip struts keeping it level. He had no trouble in staying with the machine since the strong wind kept the Flyer's ground speed under ten miles an hour. Just before reaching the end of the track Orville's left hand moved the elevator control, opening the two-surfaced elevator to nearly full positive. The Flyer lifted, tilting a little to the left. As it passed the end of the track the skids were less than three feet above the sand. Wilbur came to a halt, gazing apprehensively.

Levelled out, the Flyer continued to rise until it had reached a height of about ten feet, then it dipped sharply down to four or five feet, rose again, dipped again, came up again. At about one hundred feet from the end of the track it made a last downward

The Flyer lifted, tilting a little to the left.

dart, in which it covered another twenty feet, then the skids made contact with the sand. The Flyer's full weight came down on them, cracking one slightly as the machine came to a straight sliding halt. Orville reached over and turned off the petrol supply. The engine died as the propellers slowed to circular blurs, to single blades, then stopped. Now the sound of the wind whistling through the wire bracing could be heard.

Wilbur and the others ran up, congratulating Orville. While the spectators were probably not overly impressed with the 120-foot flight (they had seen the Wright's *gliders* go much farther) Wilbur knew that something significant had been accomplished. The Flyer had been in the air twelve seconds, had flown forty yards against a twenty-seven-mile-an-hour wind. If the speed of the retarding wind was added to the Flyer's true ground speed, then the air-speed came to something like thirty-five miles an hour. In a flight of twelve seconds this would be the equivalent of a distance of 600 feet or so. Technically, then, it could be said that Orville had flown the longer distance, surely enough to prove that the Flyer had stayed up by means of its own power.

And yet, of course, the Flyer had not really flown for 600 feet, nor could any amount of mathematical calculation substitute for actual performance, particularly where a first flight was concerned. To those watching, the laymen as well as the expert, a first flight could only mean a flight in which sufficient ground was actually covered, one in which human eyes could *see* a machine maintaining itself in the air, proceeding on and on until all doubts evaporated in the unarguable sight of the wondrous thing being *done*.

Although Orville's flight of 120 feet in twelve seconds is today universally accepted as the first flight in history, that is only another of the myths that managed to spring up during those long, silent decades following the death of Wilbur. It is based on a purely technical position, reached by a curious species of behind-hand reasoning: since the Flyer later flew, then its first flight from level ground, when corrected mathematically, was the first flight. But at Kitty Hawk on December 7 neither brother accepted the first trial as, incontestably, a proper flight. It had simply been too short.[1]

With the help of the spectators, the Flyer was picked up and carried back to the starting rail. The cracked skid was soon spliced with strong cord and at that point the Wrights and their guests gave in to the cold. They had been outside for nearly an hour and were chilled to the bone; all retired to the shed to warm up.

His undulating progress, Orville explained to his brother, had been caused by control difficulties, not any basic deficiency in the Flyer. To begin with, it appeared that the elevator was not balanced adequately. The fulcrum was too near the centre, so that the elevator 'had a tendency to turn itself when started . . . too far on one side, and then too far on the other.' This condition would have been promptly uncovered if the Flyer had been tested as a glider, and there would have been time to correct it. Stopping now to make a structural change was out of the question.

Then, also, the brothers' experience on the glider had not prepared them for dealing with winds of such great strength, even if the elevator had been properly balanced. During the trial Orville had been nonplussed to find that a slight change in the elevator's attitude was enough to exert a powerful directional change on the machine, much more powerful than anything he had encountered when gliding in lighter winds. Wilbur, who would be making the next attempt, would have to use a subtler touch to compensate for both the skittish elevator and the wind.

At twenty minutes past eleven Wilbur took his place on the lower wing of the Flyer, Orville moving over to the right wing tip struts. The start and the take-off were duplicates of the first effort, smooth and sure. At an altitude of about ten feet Wilbur levelled off but quickly found that his brother had not exaggerated the touchiness of the elevator. As the Flyer drove forward it alternately rose and fell exactly as it had done before, not once

---

[1] This fact can be appreciated even today by anyone who visits the Kitty Hawk site, where markers now stand at the takeoff spot and at the landing points.

achieving straight flight. Passing over the spot at which Orville had landed, it went on for another fifty feet or so, then swooped low, touched down and came to an easy stop. Time in the air was thirteen seconds. History's first official flight had not yet taken place. The Flyer was lugged back to the rail and set up again.

At twenty minutes to twelve Orville took off. To those watching, it was immediately apparent that he had the machine under good control, with very little undulation in the attitude. The Flyer churned its way ahead, zooming over Wilbur's landing spot and appearing very much as if it would go on indefinitely. Then, abruptly, it jumped up to a height of more than fifteen feet as the right wing lifted, tilting in a manner alarming to those on the ground.

Orville had to make two hasty corrections, in two directions, simultaneously. He had to apply negative elevator to prevent the machine from rising any higher and in fact to bring it down to what the brothers had agreed was a safe altitude. He had also to apply warp to bring the right wing level. Not surprisingly, he overdid both controls. The Flyer came down fast, the wings levelling off so rapidly that the right tip, which had been climbing only a split second before, made first contact with the ground, though lightly. The machine slid to a halt about 200 feet from takeoff. Time in the air was only fifteen seconds.

At precisely twelve noon Wilbur began the fourth trial of the day. It did not start well. With Wilbur overcorrecting on the controls, the undulations immediately set in. Passing the 200-foot mark, the Flyer was dipping and rising fairly violently, once coming within a foot of the ground. But it kept going and at 300 feet the lifting and falling became less pronounced. By the time it had reached 400 feet the watchers back at the starting point could see that Wilbur had got it under much better control. About ten feet above the sand, it was boring straight into the wind, the mingled snarl of propellers and engine diminished as the distance lengthened.

It was now, at approximately twenty seconds after twelve noon, with the Flyer calmed to level flight, that everyone knew, without need of stopwatches or measurement, that the machine was flying, was sustaining itself in steady progress through the air. On it flew: 500 feet, 600 feet, 700 feet, the bright spread of the wings growing smaller and smaller against the grey background of sand and sky. To those gazing happily after the shrinking Flyer it seemed that Wilbur was going to make good his intention of landing at the village of Kitty Hawk, nearly four miles away.

Aboard the Flyer, Wilbur, too, had his eyes set on the sprawling cluster of trees and houses directly ahead of him. Between lay only the open sands. Then, at about 800 feet, as he tried to rise a bit to clear a slight hummock, the machine began pitching again. This time he could not settle it down. Dipping low, it touched the sand. The skids dug in, tipping the Flyer forward and putting all the weight on the elevator's substructure. To the sound of cracking, twisting wood, the machine bounced to a halt as the surfaces of the elevator tilted brokenly out of line. The Wright luck still held, for if the descent had been a few degrees steeper the Flyer might have flipped over, certainly it would have been much more badly damaged.

Man's first flight was over. It had lasted a second less than one minute, covering 852 feet.

Not all great moments enter history accompanied by the rolling drum and the swelling chorus. This was one of those that didn't. When the Flyer came to a stop, sand kicking up from the ploughing elevator frame, Wilbur cut the engine and climbed off. What thoughts may have gone through his mind as he stood looking at the machine he never said—was there perhaps some fleeting memory of that young invalid of long ago who thought his life a ruin? For two or three minutes, before Orville and the others ran up, Wilbur stood there alone. Only the wind, still sweeping roughly over the solitary sands, sighing against Flyer and pilot, whispered its acceptance of man's new status as a denizen of the air.

It was a grudging acceptance, however, and the wind had one last petulant bit of mischief to perform. With the broken elevator removed, the Flyer was carried back to camp where it was temporarily set down in the open. Repairs would take a day or two, then it would be Orville's turn again. For a few minutes all stood in a little group talking about the successful flight. The wind had picked up and was now over thirty miles an hour.

Someone shouted and everyone turned to look. The wind had lifted the Flyer by its front edges and was throwing it over backwards. Wilbur rushed to the front, grabbed at a skid but couldn't hold on. Orville and John Daniels ran behind as the big wings tumbled 'like an umbrella turned inside out and loose in the wind.' The lower wing, weighted by the engine, came down heavily. Orville jumped clear but Daniels was caught between the wings, trapped by the wire bracing.

'I can't tell to save my life,' he said later, 'how it all happened, but I found myself caught up in them wires, and the machine flowing across the beach and heading for the ocean, landing first on one end and then the other, rolling over and over, and me getting more tangled up in it all the time.' He had been caught near the centre of the span and found himself repeatedly thrown against the motor and the propeller chains. 'When the thing did stop for a second I nearly broke up every wire and upright getting out of it.'

The others ran up to examine the badly frightened man. Aside from torn clothes, a good many bruises, scratches, and cuts, and wobbly legs, he was not badly hurt. Wilbur and Orville 'pulled my legs and arms, felt of my ribs, and told me there were no bones broken.' The Flyer, of course, was done for. The motor had been broken loose, the chain guides bent, struts and ribs broken. There could be no more flying that season.

The machine was stored away, the other men drifted back to their work, taking Daniels to be patched up. The brothers sat down to a well-earned lunch. About the middle of the afternoon they set out along the beach for the Kitty Hawk weather station, to send a telegram to their father.

CROSSING THE FRONT LINES

John Buchan

Richard Hannay and 'The Companions of the Rosy Hours' have stolen a German-Turkish staff-map. The map reveals a glaring weakness in the enemy defence system.

Peter Pienaar, the old Boer hunter, is sent to cross the enemy lines and warn the Russians.

Now hurry in a job of this kind was abhorrent to Peter's soul, for, like all Boers, his tastes were for slowness and sureness, though he could hustle fast enough when haste was needed. As he pushed through the winter fields he reckoned up the things in his favour, and found the only one the dirty weather. There was a high, gusty wind, blowing scuds of snow but never coming to any great fall. The frost had gone, and the lying snow was as soft as butter. That was all to the good, he thought, for a clear, hard night would have been the devil.

The first bit was through farmlands, which were seamed with little snow-filled water-furrows. Now and then would come a house and a patch of fruit trees, but there was nobody abroad. The roads were crowded enough, but Peter had no use for roads. I can picture him swinging along with his bent back, stopping every now and then to sniff and listen, alert for the foreknowledge of danger. When he chose he could cover country like an antelope.

Soon he struck a big road full of transport. It was the road from Erzerum to the Palantuken pass, and he waited his chance and crossed it. After that the ground grew rough with boulders and patches of thorn-trees, splendid cover where he could move fast without worrying. Then he was pulled up suddenly on the bank of a river. The map had warned him of it, but not that it would be so big.

It was a torrent swollen with melting snow and rains in the hills, and it was running fifty yards wide. Peter thought he could have swum it, but he was very averse to a drenching. 'A wet man makes too much noise,' he said, and besides, there was the off-chance that the current would be too much for him. So he moved up stream to look for a bridge.

In ten minutes he found one, a new-made thing of trestles, broad enough to take transport wagons. It was guarded, for he heard the tramp of a sentry, and as he pulled himself up the bank he observed a couple of long wooden huts, obviously some kind of billets. These were on the near side of the stream, about a dozen yards from the bridge. A door stood open and a light showed in it, and from within came the sound of voices . . . Peter had a sense of hearing like a wild animal, and he could detect even from the confused gabble that the voices were German.

As he lay and listened someone came over the bridge. It was an officer, for the sentry saluted. The man disappeared in one of the huts. Peter had struck the billets and repairing-shop of a squad of German sappers.

He was just going ruefully to retrace his steps and try to find a good place to swim the stream when it struck him that the officer who had passed him wore clothes very like his own. He, too, had had a grey sweater and a Balaclava helmet, for even a German officer ceases to be dressy on a mid-winter's night in Anatolia.

The idea came to Peter to walk boldly across the bridge and trust to the sentry not seeing the difference.

He slipped round a corner of the hut and marched down the road. The sentry was now at the far end, which was lucky, for if the worst came to the worst he could throttle him. Peter, mimicking the stiff German walk, swung past him, his head down as if to protect him from the wind.

The man saluted. He did more, for he offered conversation. The officer must have been a genial soul. 'It's a rough night, Captain,' he said in German. 'The wagons are late. Pray God, Michael hasn't got a shell in his lot. They've begun putting over some big ones.'

Peter grunted goodnight in German and strode on. He was just leaving the road when he heard a great halloo behind him.

The real officer must have appeared on his heels, and the sentry's doubts had been stirred. A whistle was blown, and, looking back, Peter saw lanterns waving in the gale. They were coming out to look for the duplicate.

He stood still for a second, and noticed the lights spreading out south of the road. He was just about to dive off it on the north side when he was aware of a difficulty. On that side a steep bank fell to a ditch, and the bank beyond bounded a big flood. He could see the dull ruffle of the water under the wind.

On the road itself he would soon be caught; south of it the search was beginning; and the ditch itself was no place to hide, for he saw a lantern moving up it. Peter dropped into it all the same and made a plan. The side below the road was a little undercut and very steep. He resolved to plaster himself against it, for he would be hidden from the road, and a searcher in the ditch would not be likely to explore the unbroken sides. It was always a maxim of Peter's that the best hiding-place was the worst, the least obvious to the minds of those who were looking for you.

He waited until the lights both in the road and the ditch came nearer, and then he gripped the edge with his left hand, where some stones gave him purchase, dug the toes of his boots into the wet soil and stuck like a limpet. It needed some strength to keep the position for long, but the muscles of his arms and legs were like whipcord.

The searcher in the ditch soon got tired, for the place was very wet, and joined his comrades on the road. They came along, running, flashing the lanterns into the trench, and exploring all the immediate countryside.

Then rose a noise of wheels and horses from the opposite direction. Michael and the delayed wagons were approaching. They dashed up at a great pace, driven wildly, and for one horrid second Peter thought they were going to spill into the ditch at the very spot where he was concealed. The wheels passed so close to the edge that they almost grazed his fingers. Somebody shouted an order and they pulled up a yard or two nearer the bridge. The others came up and there was a consultation.

Michael swore he had passed no one on the road.

'That fool Hannus has seen a ghost,' said the officer testily. 'It's too cold for this child's play.'

Hannus, almost in tears, repeated his tale. 'The man spoke to me in good German,' he cried.

'Ghost or no ghost he is safe enough up the road,' said the officer. 'Kind God, that was a big one!' He stopped and stared at a shell-burst, for the bombardment from the east was growing fiercer.

They stood discussing the fire for a minute and presently moved off. Peter gave them two minutes' law and then clambered back to the highway and set off along it at a run. The noise of the shelling and the wind, together with the thick darkness, made it safe to hurry.

He left the road at the first chance and took to the broken country. The ground was now rising towards a spur of the Palantuken, on the far slope of which were the Turkish trenches. The night had begun by being pretty nearly as black as pitch; even the smoke from the shell explosions, which is often visible in darkness, could not be seen. But as the wind blew the snow-clouds athwart the sky patches of stars came out. Peter had a compass, but he didn't need to use it, for he had a kind of 'feel' for landscape, a special sense which is born in savages and can only be acquired after long experience by the white man. I believe he could smell where the north lay. He had settled roughly which part of the line he would try, merely because of its nearness to the enemy. But he might see reason to vary this, and as he moved he began to think that the safest place was where the shelling was hottest. He didn't like the notion, but it sounded sense.

Suddenly he began to puzzle over queer things in the ground, and, as he had never seen big guns before, it took him a moment to fix them. Presently one went off at his elbow with a roar like the Last Day. These were Austrian howitzers—nothing over 8-inch, I fancy, but to Peter they looked like leviathans. Here, too, he saw for the first time a big and quite recent shell-hole, for the Russian guns were searching out the position. He was so interested in it all that he poked his nose where he shouldn't have been and dropped plump into the pit behind a gun-emplacement.

Gunners all the world over are the same—shy people, who hide themselves in holes and hibernate and mortally dislike being detected.

A gruff voice cried, '*Wer da*?' and a heavy hand seized his neck.

Peter was ready with his story. He belonged to Michael's wagon-team and had been left behind. He wanted to be told the way to the sappers' camp. He was very apologetic, not to say obsequious.

'It is one of those Prussian swine from the Marta bridge,' said a gunner. 'Land him a kick to teach him sense. Bear to your right, mannikin, and you will find a road. And have a care when you get there, for the Russkoes are registered on it.'

Peter thanked them and bore off to the right. After that he kept a wary eye on the howitzers, and was thankful when he got out of their area on to the slopes up the hill. Here was the type of country that was familiar to him, and he defied any Turk or Boche to spot him among the scrub and boulders. He was getting on very well, when once more, close by, came a sound like the crack of doom.

It was the field-guns now, and the sound of a field-gun close at hand is bad for the nerves if you aren't expecting it. Peter thought he had been hit, and lay flat for a little to consider. Then he found the right explanation, and crawled forward very warily.

Presently he saw his first Russian shell. It dropped half a dozen yards to his right, making a great hole in the snow and sending up a mass of mixed earth, snow, and broken stones. Peter spat out the dirt and felt very solemn. You must remember that never in his life had he seen big shelling, and was now being landed in the thick of a first-class show without any preparation. He said he felt cold in his stomach, and very wishful to run away, if there had been anywhere to run to. But he kept on to the crest of the ridge, over which a big glow was broadening like sunrise. He tripped once over a wire, which he took for some kind of snare, and after that went very warily. By and by he got his face between two boulders and looked over into the true battlefield.

He told me it was exactly what the predikant used to say that Hell would be like. About fifty yards down the slope lay the Turkish trenches—they were dark against the snow, and now and then a black figure like a devil showed for an instant and disappeared. The Turks clearly expected an infantry attack, for they were sending up calcium rockets and Verey flares. The Russians were battering their line and spraying all the hinterland, not with shrapnel, but with good, solid high-explosives. The place would be as bright as day for a moment, all smothered in a scurry of smoke and snow and debris, and then a black pall would fall on it.

Peter felt very sick. He had not believed there could be so much noise in the world, and the drums of his ears were splitting. Now, for a man to whom courage is habitual, the taste of fear—naked, utter fear—is a horrible thing. It seems to wash away all his manhood. Peter lay on the crest, watching the shells burst, and confident that any moment he might be a shattered remnant. He lay and reasoned with himself, calling himself every name he could think of, but conscious that nothing would get rid of that lump of ice below his heart.

Then he could stand it no longer. He got up and ran for his life. But he ran forward.

It was the craziest performance. He went hell-for-leather over a piece of ground which was being watered with HE, but by the mercy of heaven nothing hit him. He took some fearsome tosses in shell-holes, but partly erect and partly on all fours he did the fifty yards and tumbled into a Turkish trench right on top of a dead man.

The contact with that body brought him to his senses. That men could die at all seemed a comforting, homely thing after that unnatural pandemonium. The next moment a crump took the parapet of the trench some yards to his left, and he was half buried in an avalanche.

He crawled out of that, pretty badly cut about the head. He was quite cool now and thinking hard about his next step. There were men all around him, sullen dark faces as he saw them when the flares went up. They were manning the parapets and waiting tensely for something else than the shelling. They paid no attention to him, for I fancy in that trench units were pretty well mixed up, and under a bad bombardment no one bothers about his neighbour. He found himself free to move as he pleased. The ground of the trench was littered with empty cartridge-cases, and there were many dead bodies.

The last shell, as I have said, had played havoc with the parapet. In the next spell of darkness Peter crawled through the gap and twisted among some snowy hillocks. He was no longer afraid of shells, any more than he was afraid of a veld thunderstorm. But he was wondering very hard how he should ever get to the Russians. The Turks were behind him now, but there was the biggest danger in front.

Then the artillery ceased. It was so sudden that he thought he had gone deaf, and could hardly realize the blessed relief of it. The wind, too, seemed to have fallen, or perhaps he was sheltered by the lee of the hill. There were a lot of dead here also, and that he couldn't understand, for they were new dead. Had the Turks attacked and been driven back? When he had gone about thirty yards he stopped to take his bearings. On the right were the ruins of a large building set on fire by the guns. There was a blur of woods and the debris of walls round it. Away to the left another hill ran out farther to the east, and the place he was in seemed to be a kind of cup between the spurs. Just before him was a little ruined building, with the sky seen through its rafters, for the smouldering ruin on the right gave a certain light. He wondered if the Russian firing-line lay there.

Just then he heard voices—smothered voices—not a yard away and apparently below the ground. He instantly jumped to what this must mean. It was a Turkish trench—a communication trench. Peter didn't know much about modern warfare, but he had read in the papers, or heard from me, enough to make him draw the right moral. The fresh dead pointed to the same conclusion. What he had got through were the Turkish support trenches, not their firing-line. That was still before him.

He didn't despair, for the rebound from panic had made him extra courageous. He crawled forward, an inch at a time, taking no sort of risk, and presently found himself looking at the parados of a trench. Then he lay quiet to think out the next step.

The shelling had stopped, and there was that queer kind of peace which falls sometimes on two armies not a quarter of a mile distant. Peter said he could hear nothing but the far-off sighing of the wind. There seemed to be no movement of any kind in the trench before him, which ran through the ruined building. The light of the burning was dying, and he could just make out the mound of earth a yard in front. He began to feel hungry, and got out his packet of food and had a swig at the brandy flask. That comforted him, and he felt a master of his fate again. But the next step was not so easy. He must find out what lay behind that mound of earth.

Suddenly a curious sound fell on his ears. It was so faint that at first he doubted the evidence of his senses. Then as the wind fell it came louder. It was exactly like some hollow piece of metal being struck by a stick, distinctly musical and oddly resonant.

He concluded it was the wind blowing a branch of a tree against an old boiler in the ruin before him. The trouble was that there was scarcely enough wind now for that in this sheltered cup.

But as he listened he caught the note again. It was a bell, a fallen bell, and the place before him must have been a chapel. He remembered that an Armenian monastery had been marked on the big map, and he guessed it was the burned building on his right.

The thought of a chapel and a bell gave him the notion of some human agency. And then suddenly the notion was confirmed. The sound was regular and concerted—dot, dash, dot—dash, dot, dot. The branch of a tree and the wind may play strange pranks, but they do not produce the longs and shorts of the Morse Code.

This was where Peter's intelligence work in the Boer War helped him. He knew the Morse, he could read it, but he could make nothing of the signalling. It was either in some special code or in a strange language.

He lay still and did some calm thinking. There was a man in front of him, a Turkish soldier, who was in the enemy's pay. Therefore he could fraternize with him, for they were on the same side. But how was he to approach him without getting shot in the process? Again, how could a man send signals to the enemy from a firing-line without being detected? Peter found an answer in the strange configuration of the ground. He had not heard a sound until he was a few yards from the place, and they would be inaudible to men in the reserve trenches and even in the communication trenches. If somebody moving up the latter caught the noise, it would be easy to explain it naturally. But the wind blowing down the cup would carry it far in the enemy's direction.

There remained the risk of being heard by those parallel with the bell in the firing trenches. Peter concluded that that trench must be very thinly held, probably only by a few observers, and the nearest might be a dozen yards off. He had read about that being the French fashion under a big bombardment.

The next thing was to find out how to make himself known to this ally. He decided that the only way was to surprise him. He might get shot, but he trusted to his strength and agility against a man who was almost certainly wearied. When he had got him safe, explanations might follow.

Peter was now enjoying himself hugely. If only those infernal guns kept silent he would play out the game in the sober, decorous way he loved. So very delicately he began to wriggle forward to where the sound was.

The night was now as black as ink around him, and very quiet, too, except for soughings of the dying gale. The snow had drifted a little in the lee of the ruined walls, and Peter's progress was naturally very slow. He could not afford to dislodge one ounce of snow. Still the tinkling went on, now in greater volume. Peter was in terror lest it should cease before he got his man.

Presently his hand clutched at empty space. He was on the lip of the front trench. The sound was now a yard to his right, and with infinite care he shifted his position. Now the bell was just below him, and he felt the big rafter of the woodwork from which it had fallen. He felt something else—a stretch of wire fixed in the ground with the far end hanging in the void. That would be the spy's explanation if anyone heard the sound and came seeking the cause.

Somewhere in the darkness before him and below was the man, not a yard off. Peter remained very still, studying the situation. He could not see, but he could feel the presence, and he was trying to decide the relative position of the man and bell and their exact distance from him. The thing was not so easy as it looked, for if he jumped for where he believed the figure was, he might miss it and get a bullet in the stomach. A man who played so risky a game was probably handy with his firearms. Besides, if he should hit the bell, he would make a hideous row and alarm the whole front.

Fate suddenly gave him the right chance. The unseen figure stood up and moved a step, till his back was against the parados. He actually brushed against Peter's elbow, who held his breath.

There is a catch that the Kaffirs have which would need several diagrams to explain. It is partly a neck hold, and partly a paralysing backward twist of the right arm, but if it is practised on a man from behind, it locks him as sure as if he were handcuffed. Peter slowly got his body raised and his knees drawn under him, and reached for his prey.

He got him. A head was pulled backward over the edge of the trench, and he felt in the air the motion of the left arm pawing feebly but unable to reach behind.

'Be still,' whispered Peter in German; 'I mean you no harm. We are friends of the same purpose. Do you speak German?'

'*Nein*,' said a muffled voice.

'English?'

'Yes,' said the voice.

'Thank God,' said Peter. 'Then we can understand each other. I've watched your notion of signalling, and a very good one it is. I've got to get through to the Russian lines somehow before morning, and I want you to help me. I'm English—a kind of English, so we're on the same side. If I let go your neck will you be good and talk reasonably?'

The voice assented. Peter let go, and in the same instant slipped to the side. The man wheeled round and flung out an arm but gripped vacancy.

'Steady, friend,' said Peter; 'you mustn't play tricks with me or I'll be angry.'

'Who are you? Who sent you?' asked the puzzled voice.

Peter had a happy thought. 'The Companions of the Rosy Hours?' he said.

'Then are we friends indeed,' said the voice. 'Come out of the darkness, friend, and I will do you no harm. I am a good Turk, and I fought beside the English in Kordofan and learned their tongue. I live only to see the ruin of Enver, who has beggared my family and slain my twin brother. Therefore I serve the *Moscov ghiaours*.'

'I don't know what the Musky Jaws are, but if you mean the

Russians I'm with you. I've got news for them which will make Enver green. The question is, how I'm to get to them, and that is where you shall help me, my friend.'

'How?'

'By playing that little tune of yours again. Tell them to expect within the next half-hour a deserter with an important message. Tell them, for God's sake, not to fire at anybody till they've made certain it isn't me.'

The man took the blunt end of his bayonet and squatted beside the bell. The first stroke brought out a clear, searching note which floated down the valley. He struck three notes at slow intervals. For all the world, Peter said, he was like a telegraph operator calling up a station.

'Send the message in English,' said Peter.

'They may not understand it,' said the man.

'Then send it any way you like. I trust you, for we are brothers.'

After ten minutes the man ceased and listened. From far away came the sound of a trench-gong, the kind of thing they used on the Western Front to give the gas-alarm.

'They say they will be ready,' he said. 'I cannot take down messages in the darkness, but they have given me the signal which means "Consent".'

'Come, that is pretty good,' said Peter. 'And now I must be moving. You take a hint from me. When you hear big firing up to the north get ready to beat a quick retreat, for it will be all up with that city of yours. And tell your folk, too, that they're making a bad mistake letting those fool Germans rule their land. Let them hang Enver and his little friends, and we'll be happy once more.'

'May Satan receive his soul!' said the Turk. 'There is wire before us, but I will show you a way through. The guns this evening made many rents in it. But haste, for a working party may be here presently to repair it. Remember there is much wire before the other lines.'

Peter, with certain directions, found it pretty easy to make his way through the entanglement. There was one bit which scraped

Peter grunted goodnight in German and strode on.

a hole in his back, but very soon he had come to the last posts and found himself in open country. The place, he said, was a graveyard of the unburied dead that smelt horribly as he crawled among them. He had no inducements to delay, for he thought he could hear behind him the movement of the Turkish working party, and was in terror that a flare might reveal him and a volley follow.

From one shell-hole to another he wormed his way, till he struck an old ruinous communication trench which led in the right direction. The Turks must have been forced back in the past week, and the Russians were now in the evacuated trenches. The thing was half full of water, but it gave Peter a feeling of safety, for it enabled him to get his head below the level of the ground. Then it came to an end and he found before him a forest of wire.

The Turk in his signal had mentioned half an hour, but Peter thought it was nearer two hours before he got through that noxious entanglement. Shelling had made little difference to it. The uprights were all there, and the barbed strands seemed to touch the ground. Remember, he had no wire-cutter; nothing but bare hands. Once again fear got hold of him. He felt caught in a net, with monstrous vultures waiting to pounce on him from above. At any moment a flare might go up and a dozen rifles find their mark. He had altogether forgotten about the message which had been sent, for no message could dissuade the ever-present death he felt around him. It was, he said, like following an old lion into bush when there was but one narrow way in, and no road out.

The guns began again—the Turkish guns from behind the ridge—and a shell tore up the wire a short way before him. Under cover of the burst he made good a few yards, leaving large portions of his clothing in the strands. Then, quite suddenly, when hope had almost died in his heart, he felt the ground rise steeply. He lay very still, a star-rocket from the Turkish side lit up the place, and there in front was a rampart with the points of bayonets showing beyond it. It was the Russian hour for stand-to.

He raised his cramped limbs from the ground and shouted, 'Friend! English!'

A face looked down at him, and then the darkness again descended.

'Friend,' he said hoarsely. 'English.'

He heard speech behind the parapet. An electric torch was flashed on him for a second. A voice spoke, a friendly voice, and the sound of it seemed to be telling him to come over.

He was now standing up, and as he got his hands on the parapet he seemed to feel bayonets very near him. But the voice that spoke was kindly, so with a heave he scrambled over and flopped into the trench. Once more the electric torch was flashed, and revealed to the eyes of the onlookers an indescribably dirty, lean, middle-aged man with a bloody head, and scarcely a rag of shirt on his back. The said man, seeing friendly faces around him, grinned cheerfully.

'That was a rough trek, friends,' he said; 'I want to see your general pretty quick, for I've got a present for him . . . '

DÉDÉE
RESISTANCE FIGHTER

Airey Neave

On a hot afternoon in August 1941, Little Cyclone swept into the British Consulate at Bilbao. She had marched all the way from Brussels on a mission which no one had thought possible. The over-worked Consul rose courteously from his chair and faced the young girl, with no sign on his face of the suspicion which he felt about her.

'Mademoiselle Andrée de Jongh?'

The girl nodded. Her eyes did not waver under his stern gaze.

'It is safer to call me Dédée,' she said.

The Consul laid down his pipe and looked closely at his visitor.

'I have heard about you from our Consul at San Sebastian. Tell me your story.'

'I am a Belgian, and I have come all the way from Brussels,' she said. 'I have brought you two Belgians who want to fight for the Allies, and a Scottish soldier. We left Brussels last week and crossed the Pyrenees two nights ago.'

The Consul looked warily at the small figure, dressed in a simple blouse and skirt and flat shoes with white ankle-socks. He tapped his pipe meditatively.

'Where is the Scotsman?' he asked.

'He is downstairs with the two Belgians.' The girl smiled at the Consul.

'How long did your journey take?'

'I have told you. About a week.'

There was an incredulous tone in his voice:

'How did you get over the Pyrenees?'

The girl's blue eyes shone with triumph.

'I have friends near Bayonne who were able to get a Basque guide. He brought us through without difficulty. It was a good trip.'

Her hands clutched the side of the leather armchair and, leaning forward eagerly, she continued:

'There are many British soldiers and airmen hidden in Brussels, most of them survivors from Dunkirk. I can bring them through to you here if you will let me. My father and I have already formed an escape line all the way from Brussels to St Jean de Luz. With money, we will be able to find guides to get them cross the mountains.'

The Consul did not betray his unbelief.

'How old are you?' he shot at her.

'I am twenty-five.'

The Consul noticed her bare arms. They were slim and delicate. Her face, without make-up, was intelligent. Her mouth and nose were not beautiful, but determined and arresting. There was an eagerness and power about her that impressed him.

'But you—you are a young girl. You are not going to cross the Pyrenees again?'

'But, yes. I am as strong as a man. Girls attract less attention in the frontier zone than men. The Basque guide, Thomas, I have found, will take me back. With your help I can bring through more Englishmen. I beg of you to let me.'

The Consul turned his impassive face to the window and for several moments there was no sound but the whirr and rattle of the trams outside.

'We are more interested in British Servicemen,' he said.

The young woman laughed.

'Naturally. My father and I have agreed that we shall concentrate on bringing through as many trained fighting men as we can. All we need is money to pay our guides, and for feeding and housing the men on the long route from Brussels to Bilbao.'

'How much does it cost you to bring a man from Brussels?' said the Consul.

He looked at her searchingly. He still doubted that this slip of a girl had really crossed the Pyrenees on foot. It was an arduous journey, and he had never heard of anyone except smugglers attempting it before. The ugly thought came to him that the Germans might have sent her. Could she be a stool-pigeon? And yet, she looked too innocent to be a traitor.

She answered without hesitation:

'Six thousand Belgian francs from Brussels to St Jean de Luz.'

The Consul grimly pencilled the figure on his blotting-pad.

'That should be about two thousand and twenty-one pesetas. What about mountain guides?'

'Fourteen hundred pesetas.'

He stood up and looked fixedly at her:

'That seems very expensive.'

'I agree, but the guides are nervous of taking Allied soldiers through Occupied territory, particularly the Coastal Zone.'

The Consul was silent for a moment, writing at his desk. There was the heady smell of good tobacco. The girl waited tensely.

'I must refer all this to my superiors. When do you think you can come back with another party?'

The girl was delighted.

'In three or four weeks' time.'

'Then bring three more men with you.'

The Consul held out his hand. There were many refugees to whom he must attend. He must dismiss this strange visitor and hope that in fact she would return in three or four weeks with more rescued men.

'*Au revoir, Mademoiselle.*'

'*Au revoir, Monsieur le Consul.*'

The Little Cyclone walked swiftly from the room and down the stairs. Her disappointment at this cautious reception mingled with pleasure at the prospect of establishing an escape route that became the famous Comet Line.

Private Cromar of the 1st Gordons, a survivor of St Valéry, stood waiting outside with two young Belgians. They made a modest group, disguised in rough working clothes. Their faces revealed their joy at the first exquisite taste of liberty.

The girl shook their hands. Private Cromar held hers for a moment.

'Goodbye, Colin.'

'Good luck, Miss,' he said. 'And God bless you!'

She waved to the three men and was gone, like some kindly sprite. She was soon lost in the crowd of office-workers, hurrying home. It was still very hot and the dust of the streets of Bilbao was in her eyes and throat.

The tram to San Sebastian gave time for reflection as she gazed out over the shimmering sea. Why had the Consul seemed so unimpressed? She felt a sharp pang of disappointment. She wondered if the British suspected her of working for the Germans. Did they think that she was being used to bring enemy agents to neutral territory? No, that could not be true, otherwise the shrewd Consul would never have allowed her to return to France. For a moment there were tears in her eyes. Then she remembered her triumphant conquest of the mountains.

Dédée did not know that, despite his early misgivings, the

Consul was already won over. He had made up his mind to obtain the support of the British Foreign Office for her plan. His kindly encouragement was to be of the greatest·value to the Comet Line.

She resolved to go back to Brussels and tell her father, Frédéric de Jongh, that what had seemed impossible had been achieved. There had been faint-hearts among her friends who sheltered soldiers and airmen in Belgium, who had said that there could never be an escape route all the way to Spain.

The Comet Line was her dream. In the next few months she created it. It became the greatest escape route of all. In its three years of life, eight hundred Allied airmen and soldiers were saved from captivity and returned to England to fight again.

She thought of her early life as a student designing posters, and of training to be a nurse. Posters! She looked at her fine hands and smiled.

In 1940 war had come and offered her adventure. There was the hospital in Belgium where she had worked as a nurse among wounded British soldiers. There were the prisoners in Germany to whom she had sent parcels. Their helplessness had moved her deeply.

The invasion of the Germans had released her from a humdrum existence. As a young girl, she had loved from afar the great French pilot, Mermoz, who had flown for thousands of miles over uncharted land and sea. His brave story thrilled her. It helped her in her decision to aid Allied soldiers and airmen, hiding in Belgium.

Early in 1941 she began to gather friends around her, who agreed to house and feed young Belgians and servicemen of the Allies who wished to escape to England. Her foremost comrade in this dangerous work was her father, Frédéric de Jongh. In 1915 he had found inspiration in the sacrifice of Edith Cavell. A generation later it was the spirit of his own daughter which fired him.

He liked to think of her as 'Little Cyclone', the name he had given her as a child. It marked her lively nature and high spirits. She was always rushing to and fro. But to her friends she was Dédée, the affectionate name given to girls named Andrée in

The consul tapped his pipe meditatively.

Belgium. It was as Dédée that she was known to hundreds of members of the Comet Line which she created. To the British Foreign Office she became the 'Postman', who delivered secret parcels at Bilbao.

It was a misfortune to be a woman, she thought.

'But,' she said to herself, 'I can walk as far and as fast as any man.'

She laughed with pleasure as she recalled that night of summer a few weeks earlier. With a young countryman named Arnold de Pé, she had set out with her first party of fugitives from Brussels to the Spanish frontier. This was the pioneer effort which led to the formation of the Comet Line.

On one daring adventure Dédée took with her ten Belgians, wanted by the Gestapo, and a plump, middle-aged Englishwoman in a Panama hat. Miss Richards, as she was called, though Dédée never knew her real name, was threatened with internment.

In Brussels the spring sun shone warmly. Arnold and Dédée, dividing their forces, split up the party, and boarded different compartments in the train for Lille. As the train, packed with passengers, left Brussels, Dédée felt her heart beat wildly. This was her first bold stroke. Would it succeed?

Miss Richards evidently considered that a clandestine voyage to the Spanish frontier should be treated like any other journey. Her luggage consisted, despite the entreaties of Dédée and Arnold, of a substantial suitcase, a handbag and an umbrella. The thought of crossing the Pyrenees on foot did not deter her from regarding this experience as similar to any other form of travel.

Miss Richards sat, pink and indignant, in the corner of her compartment. Dédée, on her first adventure, thought how easy it all seemed. They would have to leave the train at Quievrain and cross from Belgium into France. Then would come two more train journeys and the crossing of the River Somme by boat at La Corbie, near Amiens. Arnold had chosen the crossing-place near La Corbie. With the aid of Nenette, a farmer's wife, a boat had been hidden among the reeds on the east bank of the river.

They left the train at Quievrain, and their false identity cards, forged by hand, were not examined. Then they tramped through a meadow to avoid further controls, borne down with Miss Richards' luggage, to Blanc-Misseron to take the train to Lille.

The sky was very blue as Dédée strode cheerfully beside Arnold, the others following.

After two hours in a local train they reached Lille and changed for La Corbie, where they stopped for a meal. At sunset the escapers and their guides in single file made their way towards the bank of the Somme. There was the sharp snap of twigs as Arnold, leading the party, forged towards the river.

Arnold, leaving them crouching in a copse, moved forward to search for the boat hidden by Nenette, who was waiting on the far bank. It was now dark and there was a faint red glow among the trees. Groping forward, Arnold stumbled on a group of holiday-makers round a camp-fire. Their tents had been pitched in a clearing a few yards from the spot where the boat was concealed. Arnold, frustrated, clenched his fists. It would be impossible to guide the escapers past the campers or the German patrols without attracting attention.

Arnold returned to the copse.

'There is nothing for it, Dédée,' he whispered. 'We must swim across.'

Miss Richards's white Panama, faintly outlined against the sky, betrayed her still-indignant presence. The Belgians were whispering nervously.

'Six of the men and Miss Richards are non-swimmers,' said Dédée. 'Arnold, we must ferry them over. We want a length of wire or rope and something like a lifebelt.'

Arnold disappeared again to search for means of improvizing a ferry. There was still time before daylight to find the necessary materials from neighbouring farms.

Dédée crept silently to the river, knelt beside it and peered across. The water flowed calmly by, leaving a black sludge on the bank. The breeze blew softly through the rushes. Dédée looked towards a cluster of tall trees on the far side.

There Nenette must be anxiously waiting, unaware of what had gone wrong. Suddenly, Dédée flung herself into the brambles, as the light of a bicycle lamp came silently towards her along the towpath. Its beams swung from right to left, and cast strange shadows. As it passed her, she glimpsed the shape of a German helmet. Slowly, terribly slowly, the light vanished along the bank.

The party, crouching by the river, awaited Arnold's return. Dédée had already formed her plan, which was to run a line across the river from trees on either bank so that the men and Miss Richards, clinging to a floating object, could be towed across.

At two in the morning, someone hoarsely whispered Dédée's name. Arnold was back with a length of good wire and the inflated inner tube of a motor tyre.

After a short conference Arnold fastened the wire round a tree. Then came another lamp winking along the towpath. Everybody fell flat until it had passed.

When all was clear Arnold splashed into the water and quietly swam across the river, uncoiling the line. Five minutes passed and there was a tugging on the wire—the signal for Dédée to start sending passengers across on the rubber tyre.

The first to cross, a stout, panting youth, floundered through the oozing mud and clambered on to the tyre, desperately embracing the line. Dédée, knowing that he could not swim, tore off her tartan skirt and blouse and waded into the water. She swam easily across the river, propelling the rubber tyre and the fat youth in front of her. Her vision was obscured by the large behind of her ungainly passenger. She knew that she had reached the other side when her feet touched the mud and she saw the stout youth scramble forward. She swam back to the east bank to collect her next passenger.

There was little current, and Dédée, untiring and excited, swam the river to and fro eleven times. The Belgians, who could swim, crossed alone and were hustled, shivering, by Nenette to her home a hundred yards away. It was a dangerous operation. The splashing they made caused Dédée anxiety, for at any moment another German patrol might appear.

But in spite of the danger there was one delicious moment. Dédée, years afterwards, could never think of the crossing of Miss Richards without chuckling. Her suitcase, which had encumbered the party, was left among the trees, partly emptied, and a pile of tweed skirts and underclothes and shoes was ferried across on a large piece of wood. In spite of her protests, Miss Richards was advised to take off her skirt in order that she should arrive on the other bank with dry clothes. Dédée, in her impatience, nearly tore it off her. Miss Richards took it off and stood, revealed in startling white bloomers. Even at a distance, they formed a ghostly patch of brightness. Picked out in the beam of a German cycle lamp, they would be an easy target.

'Now you must take *them* off, Mademoiselle,' said the anxious Dédée.

'What!'

'They will be seen by the Germans on the towpath.'

'I can't help it,' spluttered Miss Richards; 'I refuse to take them off.'

There was a faint snigger in the trees.

Dédée, having angrily launched Miss Richards on the tyre, swam a side-stroke, half pushing, half pulling her across. She soon changed from this uncomfortable manoeuvre and propelled Miss Richards from behind. This caused Miss Richards to tip forward. Her Panama hat vanished into the darkness and all that Dédée could see was her vast posterior. The tyre began to slip and bulge out from under Miss Richards. There was an anxious few seconds while she was hoisted back onto the tyre.

Dédée was becoming weary after several journeys. Her legs ached and the water seemed bitterly cold.

'Oh, God, look!' said Miss Richards, moaning.

Another bicycle lamp appeared on the towpath.

'Slip into the water and hang on to the tyre,' whispered Dédée.

There was a splash and Miss Richards slid into the river. The two women clung together until the lamplight was gone. Then Miss Richards, wet, panting and terrified, was hauled by Arnold up the bank.

It had taken an hour and a half for the whole party to cross the river. Dédée had been in the water all this time. As she lay exhausted on an old sofa in Nenette's farmhouse, she thought of the night's experience as something she would never forget. Exciting, and at times hilarious, as it had been, everyone had been in danger. But a lesson had been learned. Next time there must be no mistake about the boat. This first crossing of the Somme was a vital landmark in the history of the Comet Line.

DEATH OF A SHIP

John Davies

Ginger, Buster, Gilo, Sharkey, Brock and Drunken Duncan are members of the gun-crew on board the destroyer *Skye.*

'If anything's goin' to 'appen it'll 'ave to 'appen quick!' says Gilo. 'It'll be light soon.'

'Wonder where we are?'

'Dunno. Somewhere pretty close in.'

Slower now, as though we have all but reached our destination. Then whistles shrill on the mess deck below and there is the sound of men moving.

'Pongo action stations,' says Brock. 'Now we shan't be long.'

Ten minutes later *Skye* stops completely, lying easily on the water and rolling slightly. There are sounds of activity amidships, but the mass of the bridge structure aft of B gun prevents our seeing what is going on.

The small noises continue, the sound of moving men, and occasionally a faint creak which sounds as though it may be coming from the davits as the boats are lowered. Then silence. Another short period of activity and then silence once again.

Skye still lies stopped. We can do nothing but wait, and every minute the eastern sky seems to clear slightly as though dawn is not far off. Our work must be completed before daylight betrays us, and there is very little time left . . .

Still we wait, and now there is no doubt but that dawn is upon us. The darkness is lifting slightly from the surface of the sea, and a white mist begins to show palely over the water. On our starboard beam a dark shape moves slowly past us, visible for a few seconds before it vanishes into the vaporous remains of the night. A destroyer. We do not know which one, but as she idles past she seems to regard us enquiringly. 'Has anything gone wrong?' she seems to ask.

Has anything gone wrong?

We have no means of knowing. The eastern sky continues to brighten, but *Skye* lies as though dead. Sharky tries to get some information over the inter-com. system, but the TS remains obstinately silent. And we on B gun, standing beneath the twin barrels trained shoreward, peer out across the sea to try to find some sign of a potential target. And as we gaze we are equally silent. Our life of watching and waiting has once more culminated in a period of sharp suspense. Surely something must happen soon! I find myself more eager than ever before for the familiar crash of B gun, for the sustaining sound of *Skye*'s salvos and her confident rush through the water.

But relief does not come, the suspense does not end. And every moment the daylight is growing relentlessly. In a matter of minutes the bright Mediterranean morning will be striding across the surface of the sea, the white mist will vanish like magic, and we shall see, and be seen.

The darkness seems to gather rather than disperse in the shadows on our port beam, and as it gathers it begins to assure a certain solidity, until finally we know that what we are looking at is land.

Gradually the coast-line grows into being, and *Skye* has still shown no sign of life. Each minute we wait and hope for the pulsation of her engines and the growing hiss of the water cleft by her bows, but it does not come.

Four sudden bright flashes from landward, and, an instant later, 'COMMENCE! COMMENCE! COMMENCE!' The silent dawn is rent by the abrupt crash of salvos. *Skye* is in full and furious action again, and the sound of her guns has come at last to comfort us. But something is still gravely wrong, for her engines are still idle..

White water leaps into the air close on our port bow, and a second later I hear two sharp whines overhead in rapid succession. Vaguely I realize what a sitting target we are. Why doesn't *Skye* get going? Why is she wantonly throwing herself away? In her speed is her only hope.

And at this instant she steams ahead again. Beyond the guard-rail I catch a momentary glimpse of white vapour streaming past as though we are almost awash in a sea of mist, and no sight could better lift the heart. Exhilarated, I turn to the gun.

Now from seaward comes the sound of heavier firing. We must have at least one cruiser with us further out, and firing over us at the enemy. A further cause for satisfaction . . .

There comes a colossal crash, followed closely by another, and then the deafening roar of escaping steam from somewhere aft of the bridge. The slight vibration of the deck ceases, and we know instantly that *Skye* has been hit. She has had no time to gather speed, and now her engines are stopped again, under the very muzzles of the shore batteries.

But, mercifully, the barrage from the sea continues. No time to stop, to think, to let fear creep in. All *Skye*'s guns are still firing, hurling shells shoreward in a smother of smoke and flame every few seconds. In the urgency of the moment my mind will not function properly. We have been hit. *Skye* has been hit. All the guns are firing. Hit. Hit amidships. Amidships. Engines. Engines . . .

A shattering roar from aft, a roar mounting unbearably in intensity. A tremendous column of smoke rushes up into the thinning mist. *Skye* is burning. She is afire aft.

Suddenly our salvos sound thin and empty, although B gun is still firing furiously, and from time to time I catch sight of the flash and yellow smoke from the muzzles of A gun below us. The guns aft are silent. Half of our main armament is no longer in action.

There is a tremendous confusion of sound smashing at us from all sides. There is a shattering crash above, and something tinkles on the deck beside me. Glass. Involuntarily I look up. The port side of the bridge is wrecked. Twisted streamers of metal are hanging down in front of the wheel-house.

A crescendo of gun-fire swells up astern, growing every moment. Then a sudden roar from Buster, 'CHECK! CHECK! CHECK!' B gun stops firing, and after one more salvo A gun on the foc'sle below is also silent.

Amori is coming up close on our port side, firing rapidly shore-ward. As she closes us she reduces speed. Figures are leaning over the starboard side of her bridge. Then a voice comes thinly across the intervening space but is lost in the gun-fire. There is an up-thrust of water in front of her bows as a shell falls.

Now one of *Skye*'s signalmen is standing precariously on the wreckage of the port wing of the bridge. The red and yellow signal flags flutter in his hands. The message is rapidly passed. In the noise and confusion the robot-like movement of the signalman's flags looks strangely out of place.

There is a rush of *Skye*'s hands forrard onto the foc'sle beneath us. The flare hides them from sight. *Amori* closes us still more and then begins to draw slowly past. Although all her guns are still firing there is much other activity on her upper deck. She is preparing to tow.

'COMMENCE! COMMENCE! COMMENCE!' Now she is past, close ahead, and B gun's field of fire is unobstructed once more. We dash again to serve the gun, to keep it firing, to give what little cover we can to the desperate endeavour on the foc'sle. A gun is still silent.

Suddenly I feel foolishly and selfishly proud that B gun is the only four-seven still in action.

The enemy ashore can never have dreamed of a better target. Shells are falling around us constantly, but by a miracle *Skye* has not been hit again. Then I see once more that gradual, slow drift past the guard-rail, and know that the miraculous has been achieved, the tow has been secured. A faint but undaunted cheer floats up thinly from the foc'sle, a cheer which momentarily proves too much for B gun's crew, for we must pause a moment and look ahead. Between *Skye* and *Amori* stretches the seemingly frail black link of the hawser, whipping the water. But at the very moment of looking, even as it tautens with the dead weight of *Skye*, there is a crash and a smother of water just beyond our bows, and when the water subsides the tow has disappeared. All *Skye*'s former good luck seems to vanish instantly in that one impossible accident of ill fortune.

Motionless again, and the shore batteries still fire relentlessly. A sharp explosion tears the air somewhere above us, followed by a shriek of metal, and Sharky slides quietly down off his seat. B gun is still firing, and now comes the sound of A gun once more in action also. *Amori* is steaming impotently seaward in a wide circle. She looks as though she is coming in again, though God knows what she can do to help us now. The miracle of the tow cannot be achieved twice.

Another crash aft, and *Skye* shudders throughout her length, and then we know that this is the end. She has no list, but the gun deck is tilted slightly aft. She is settling by the stern.

Slowly, slowly the angle of inclination of the gun deck increases. There is silence aft. God only knows what has happened there. It is an overwhelming labour now to carry ammunition from the hoist to the gun. But it shall be done as long as it is possible. We cannot tell what has happened elsewhere in the ship. The communication system has gone. Sharky lies motionless on the deck. Drunken Duncan took a look at him when he fell, and now we know that he is dead. Someone shouts down from the bridge, but it is utterly impossible to hear what is being said. We can only keep the gun firing until the end.

Slowly a furious anger takes possession of me. B gun is firing slowly now, waiting silent between salvos while we struggle up the sloping deck from the hoist to the tray. The round goes home. The gun fires. The next wait is longer. Then as I bend again to the hoist it is empty. I shout below, but there is no answer, no movement.

A vast cloud of steam rushes out from amidships. For a moment we stand and watch it. There is nothing more to be done. The shore batteries are no longer firing at us. They know we are finished.

Buster gives the final, bitter order. 'All right, boys—jump for it! Starboard side.' We obey without question. Across the gun deck to the starboard ladder. Buster stands beside it as we climb down. He looks at me as I pass him. 'Blow up yer lifebelt!' he says.

Down the ladder to the foc'sle. I try to blow up my lifebelt, but there is something wrong with it. No use as it is. I take it off and drop it with my tin hat on the deck. Then I climb over the guard-rail and hold onto it as I lean out over *Skye*'s side. Some of the others are already in the water, but I feel a great and inexplicable reluctance to leave. I am seized by a sudden wild impulse to rush back to my locker on the mess deck, but God knows what I intend to do when I get there. Then someone pushes me from behind and I fall into the water in an ungraceful heap.

The water is not cold, and only faintly oily. There is a great sense of quiet. Shells are now going over to the other ships, and they are urgently replying. Strangely enough this is my first real opportunity to take a look at them. One cruiser and three destroyers. I do not recognize any of them except *Amori*. For the moment I feel quite happy, absolved temporarily from the necessity of doing anything more than keep myself afloat. The water is very calm. I must get rid of my duffel coat. It is lucky I am not wearing sea boots. There are perhaps twenty men in the water, some of them in khaki, together with a few small bits of wreckage and patches of oil. I cannot see any more leaving the ship. I do not know how many have

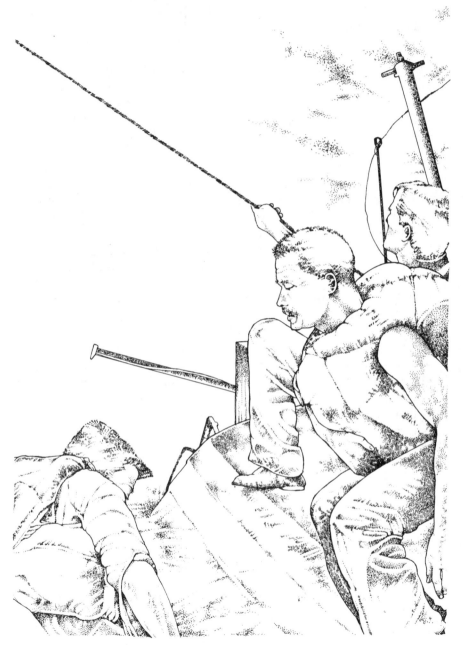

'All right, boys – jump for it! Starboard side!'

managed to get off on the other side. That is the landward side. We are better off here.

I feel no apprehension. I have no thought of what is going to happen next. Fear is even more in abeyance than it ever has been during action. What is there to fear anyway? It is all over. *Skye* is going. I will stay here, and keep myself afloat, and watch her go. It's all pure nonsense.

Buster, swimming near me, looks at me for a moment and then shakes his head and shoulders like a dog, spitting oil and water out of his mouth. He shouts something which I cannot hear. Then he points out to sea and turns and starts to swim away from *Skye*.

Skye is going. That is the only thought that registers in my brain. But I don't believe it. *Skye* was never destined to be sunk. She is a lucky ship. I am very tired. I was very tired when I turned in at midnight. The First Watch was long and dreary. I am very tired, but in a moment I shall be wakened again. 'A-ll the Starboard Watch! . . . A-ll the Starboard Watch! . . .'

I am quite comfortable if I lie on my back. *Skye* is sinking. Her quarter-deck is now under water, and the paint on her forefoot is glistening in the sunlight. Soon she will slip quietly down. Slip down, and take me with her.

In that moment I realize the urgent need to get away from her before it is too late.

I turn to follow Buster, and simultaneously comes the realization that I am no longer comfortable. The water is colder than I thought, and I am beginning to feel my clothes heavy upon me. My trousers seem a dead weight on my legs and my arms ache as I move them through the water. And with the discomfort comes the first cold finger of fear. Are we, am I, going to be picked up? *Amori* is the ship nearest to us, but she is moving away. I realize with some surprise that her guns are still in action. It seems pointless. *Skye* is sinking. Slowly *Amori* moves out of my field of vision and I turn wearily to keep her in view, and there, some twenty yards behind me, is a Carley raft. There are several men in it and others in the water around.

Twenty yards. So short a distance, and yet I can make no progress. My arms move futilely, and the distance is no less. Perhaps it would be better not to bother. But unless I continue to move my arms I cannot keep my head above water.

Then suddenly I am within a yard of the raft. One of the men in the water reaches out a hand and pulls me to the life-lines. My body is drawn on under the raft, but I grasp the life-line with a desperate effort and manage to retain my grip.

The raft is comforting. There are other men on and around it and that is comforting also. *Skye* is sinking but the raft will not sink. I will not sink if I can keep my grip on the life-line. For the moment that is enough. I cannot grapple with the thought of what will happen next.

A sudden, inarticulate cry from someone above me. A man on the edge of the raft is pointing. Slowly I turn my head but I can see nothing. Nothing? Where *Skye* was sinking the sea is empty. She has gone and I did not see her go. Very sadly I turn back to the raft.

The sound of gun-fire draws nearer again, the guns of our ships still blazing away at the shore. But what is the use now that *Skye* has gone? My arms are becoming numb, but they are twisted in the life-line and I shall not slip away. I do not want to move. I want to end here. There can be nothing more.

The firing, increasing in volume every moment, becomes thunderous and apparently close above us. A cloud of smoke drifts down. Then a destroyer's bows loom close above the raft. *Amori*, at infinite peril to herself, has come in again to help. She passes slowly between us and the shore. The raft begins to heave gently in the water she displaces. Then in the intervals of her salvos voices are shouting from her quarter-deck. Something drops from her side and trails in the water, causing a small ripple which fascinates me. A net, a scrambling net. *Amori*'s side suddenly looms very close. The raft rocks and there is a splash as someone jumps. Then the others begin to leave. Buster lets go and pushes slowly away. But I do not want to move. The Carley raft is more comforting than the net on the steep steel side of the ship. But someone is splashing close beside me. Buster. He is pulling at my arms. I try to tell him that I don't want to go, but he still pulls at me, and then my arms are free. I make a tremendous effort to keep my head above water, but I can feel myself going down. And in that instant my fingers touch and cling to the net.

Buster is beside me. A tremendous heave and we are both half out of the water. The ship is already increasing speed. The ripple of the net in the water is becoming a tremendous and terrifying surge around our half-submerged bodies. Another heave and we are a little further out, but the sea still drags insistently at my legs. There are other men higher up on the net, all of them motionless, clinging like flies. Before my eyes there is a boot glistening with rainbow colours from the oil. Then it disappears.

There is a lot of shouting above me. Someone leans over the side and bellows down at us, but I cannot tell what he is saying. Then a hand grasps me painfully by the forearm, and a moment later I am sprawling across the sharp edge of the deck. I try to move further inboard but cannot. Again I am seized and dragged over to the bulkhead.

An immediate sensation of warmth from the sun-warmed deck, and with the warmth a great weariness. Gradually my breath comes more easily and at last I can look around. This is not *Skye*. *Skye* has gone. There are ten or a dozen other bedraggled figures on the deck. How many of them are alive? For the moment none of them are moving.

The sound of shells again, or perhaps bombs. I cannot tell. I only know that I have very little left with which to combat them, and I cower to the deck with each explosion. *Amori*'s salvos seem to burst with intolerable pain inside my head. But life is returning to my arms.

More heavy concussions, quite definitely bombs this time. I try to look up into the sunshine, but an acute pain stabs through my neck. Then more bombs, very close astern. I can see the water heave up in our wake. *Amori* turns violently to port and sends me sprawling, but now I have strength enough to sit up again. I can hear aircraft engines, a sustained roar through the gun-fire. We turn sharply to starboard, but while the ship is still heeling there is a terrific explosion and a sudden roar from forrard. A leaping sheet of flame dazzles my eyes, and a second or so later another rushes up nearer amidships. Then I realize that *Amori* already lies stopped, and is down by the head.

Figures come running from the wreckage forrard. The bridge is enveloped in flame. A man runs by me with both hands over his face and cannons violently into the bulkhead. Then there is a noise, an attempt at speech from the man on the deck beside me and he begins to crawl slowly aft. I turn to follow him, instinctively retreating from the inferno forrard. We are crawling uphill, and the slope seems to increase with every yard we cover.

The quarter-deck is crowded. Someone is taking down the guard-rails. Then beyond the quarter-deck I can see the bows of another ship coming up from astern. She is moving fast and looks as though she must certainly collide with us.

A heavy thump close at hand, but I have no idea what caused it. Then the other ship is upon us. Her bows swing past, almost within reach, her length slides by, and then there is a bump as the two quarter-decks come together. Her after part bumps ours and stays there, by what means I do not know. Already men are moving across to her from *Amori*. A number of the newcomer's crew spring across onto our quarter-deck. I cannot make it without help, but they are coming to help. I feel myself half lifted, half dragged to the side. A moment later I am sprawling upon her quarter-deck.

In a matter of seconds she is sliding away from *Amori*. Someone is shouting. I can distinguish nothing but the words 'Get forrard!' many times repeated. 'Get forrard!' Once more on my hands and knees I crawl away from the stern. This is a small ship, 'K' class, I think, but it is an interminable distance to the waist. I reach the narrow deck between the after deck-house and the rail. She is moving very fast. The water seething past her sides is an infinite comfort . . .

A strange mess deck. My head is aching thunderously. A mess deck much smaller than *Skye*'s. *Skye* is sunk. *Skye* is gone, and I did not see her go. I think I am all right apart from my head.

Someone gives me a drink of water and I am immediately violently sick. I feel I want to weep with misery and mortification. In all my seasickness I have never before been sick on the deck. But strangely enough no one seems to mind. No one takes any notice. I lie down again and close my eyes.

It is a dishevelled and gloomy party that now stands on the *Keely*'s quarter-deck, waiting to go ashore. We got safely back to Alex. about an hour ago. I have no knowledge of what happened on the rest of that fateful trip. When I awoke we had already passed through the boom.

Buster, Gilo, Ginger, Brock. We have very little to say to each other. It is no use wondering what has happened to the others. We know what happened to Sharky. The others simply vanished. Perhaps some of them are prisoners. We were so close inshore when it all happened that the enemy must have been able to take many prisoners—if many were left alive. If we had gone over the other side into the water we might have shared that fate. But Buster had said the starboard side.

And *Skye* has gone. At last we are beginning to accept the fact. The ship herself has gone, but, more than that, her ship's company has vanished for ever as a unit, that strangely composite yet united body of men which through trial and tribulation and triumph took on a character transcending that of the individuals of which it was composed. What remains? New ships, new crews. The beginning of a new life of mutual hardship and experience out of which another ship's company will gradually be evolved.

BENEATH NIAGARA

E. Z. Burns

There is an extensive drainage system in connection with the great tunnel by which the water power of Niagara Falls has been recently made to furnish an enormous current of electricity in Buffalo and other places. The outlet for this drainage system is a particularly interesting piece of work, being itself a tunnel, which is eight feet high and eight feet wide. It is excavated in the solid rock, seventy-five to eighty feet below the surface of the ground, and is at present over a mile and a half in length.

This tunnel ends at the gorge below the cataract in a vertical well, or shaft, fifty feet deep. This well overflows into a second well, and this in turn overflows into the river, which is over one hundred feet below the level of the tunnel.

In order to help the work of excavation, several deep shafts were sunk from the surface of the ground to the tunnel. Shaft four is about one mile from the river gorge. It was in the construction of this drainage tunnel, which I planned and have in part executed as engineer, that the following incidents occurred.

In February 1894, I received a notice from the contractor to the effect that the men employed in the tunnel at shaft four had suffered inconvenience from some kind of gas. Soon after, however, he informed me that the compressed air used in running the drills seemed to renew the air in the tunnel sufficiently for the men to work.

In the spring of 1895 this tunnel had progressed, under another contractor, till it reached a point nearly half a mile eastward from shaft four. Still farther to the east shaft six had been sunk, and from this shaft a tunnel was being excavated to meet the one from shaft four. The headings of the two tunnels were at this time several hundred feet apart.

One day the contractor, with his foreman, entered my office, and informed me that the gas had lately grown so unbearable that his men could hardly be induced to go to work. It was determined after considerable discussion that the foreman, Mr Baxter, and I should go into the tunnel about six o'clock that evening and take samples of the gas, samples of the water, and samples of rock near the heading.

I desired not only to test the composition of the gas and learn its quantity, but also its source—whether from the water which was coming into the tunnel, or from pockets in the rocks, or from the chemical action of the water on some substance in the rock.

From the conversation which took place at this time, I gained the impression that nothing more serious than a disagreeable sensation, resulting in sickness, had ever been experienced by the workmen, even after breathing the air of the tunnel for several hours. It was therefore with no concern whatever for our safety that I met Mr Baxter at the appointed time at shaft four. Only a few of the workmen were loitering about the shaft when we arrived, and neither to them nor to the engineer of the hoisting engine did we state our object, nor say how long we expected to be in the tunnel.

After providing ourselves with candles and matches, we stepped into the square box which served as a hoist, and were quickly lowered. As we left the hoist at the bottom of the shaft, there came to me an odour that no chemist could mistake. It was the smell of a gas well known to chemists, which, when breathed, is quite poisonous. It has the offensive smell of rotten eggs.

Probably the first effect of this gas on the person breathing it is to paralyse the nerves of smell. It was this property, in the present instance, that deceived me into venturing farther; for after a few moments I no longer noticed the odour, and therefore supposed that a very small quantity of the gas was present. Indeed, I had no feeling of insecurity, for I called to mind that the workmen had been free from any serious ill.

As soon as our candles were lighted, we walked leisurely in towards the heading. The way was impeded by a roughly constructed, narrow railway track used for drawing the excavated material from the heading to the shaft. A stream of water was silently flowing in the bottom of the tunnel. At places an obstruction made the water nearly or quite a foot deep.

We soon reached the heading; here lay a great mass of the shattered rock, where it had been left by the last blast. My companion explained that the gas usually seemed to be worse while the workmen were digging up this material in the process of removing it. Therefore, while he stirred up the material with a pick, I filled several flasks with air from different positions in the tunnel, and sealed each one air tight by means of paraffin.

The tears began to flow while we were doing this, and interfered with our work. We were not alarmed, but Mr Baxter remarked once or twice about feeling badly, and when we had collected our samples of air and water, I told him he could place them in the basket and go to the shaft, while I would remain and examine the rock and gather samples from the pile.

I was thus busily engaged, and my companion had gone about

fifty feet towards the shaft, when I heard a slight noise. I looked in the direction of the shaft. There was a flash from Mr Baxter's light; then it was as suddenly extinguished. The sound of his steady tramp, tramp had ceased, and there was an ominous silence.

I called to him, asking if he could not get a light. To this I received no reply. The silence seemed oppressive. I gathered up my things, and with my dimly burning candle walked towards the shaft. I had but a slight feeling of concern.

When I came to my companion, I experienced a momentary sense of relief. He was apparently sitting down, and leaning against the side wall in a very natural posture. In the uncertain light of the candle he seemed to be looking directly into my eyes.

I spoke to him. He did not reply.

A feeling of impending disaster came over me as I looked more closely at my companion. He had a strange, fixed look. I took him by the arm; it was limp and lifeless; the gas had done its work. I grew dizzy as the truth flashed upon me. We were half a mile from all human aid.

A small pipe for conveying compressed air to the rock drills extended from the engine house to the surface into the heading, and Mr Baxter was at that moment actually leaning against it. To get air from this pipe meant preservation from a terrible death; but Baxter had shut off the compressed air at the surface just before descending the shaft.

No search for us was likely to be made for hours, probably not before morning. It seemed as if we could not have more effectually cut ourselves off from every means of preservation and succour.

I put my free arm underneath my companion's, intending to carry him to the shaft. I could not raise him. Then I realized that I, too, was nearly overcome with the gas.

In that instant I knew that both our lives hung on my ability to reach the shaft and give the alarm. It was terrible to leave my companion so mute and helpless, but my judgment told me it was his only chance, as well as my own, and I could not hesitate. Death seemed to be striding toward us with each passing second.

He was apparently sitting down, and leaning against the side wall.

My candle was still burning, and I started towards the shaft, setting my teeth with determination to throw off the paralysis that seemed to be creeping over me. But the poison was surely telling on me. I had taken only a few steps from my companion when my head seemed to reel; the light in my hand danced before my eyes, then receded to a great distance, and I fell backward unconscious upon the rock bottom of the tunnel.

It may have been the severe shock of falling upon the rock bottom, or it may have been that my head fell so that the cold water of the tunnel flowed over my face; at any rate, for one blessed moment I regained consciousness. I remembered that this gas is slightly heavier than air, and must consequently vitiate the air of the lower part of the tunnel more than the upper. For this reason I concluded to hold my head as high as possible. I also stopped breathing as much as I was able.

I struggled to my feet, but had hardly strength to stand. I reached for the side of the tunnel, and so supporting myself, began to make my way towards the shaft. In my fall I had lost my oilskin cap and my light had been extinguished, but I still held my candle firmly grasped in my left hand. Only those who have been in an unlighted mine or tunnel can know how complete was the darkness.

I thought I would try to light my candle, but I could not control my hand to get a match from my pocket. As I released my grasp of the rock in the side of the tunnel, again the dreadful feeling of paralysis came over me, and again I could not resist. Probably the same cause as before mercifully brought me back to consciousness, and once more began the desperate struggle.

I must have made considerable progress, always holding my breath with all the determination at my command, and clinging to the jagged rock at the side, but my recollection of this part of my struggle is marked only by one slight occurrence. When I became unconscious the second time, I held the unlighted candle in my left hand, but when I roused, it was no longer there.

After exerting all my energy for what seemed a very long time, a numb feeling, and with it a great weariness, came over me once more. My breath came in short gasps. Finally I stumbled and fell headlong. A long time seemed to go by now before I was roused by a great smarting about my face and eyes. Either in falling, or by some convulsive movement after falling, my face had been plunged in the water, which contained much acid, and so caused the smarting sensation.

I think I must have revived more completely this time than before, for I remember the sense of pain with which I again grasped at the projections at the side of the tunnel, and tried to drag myself along. The skin on my fingers where I had grasped at the projecting rock had worn through, leaving the flesh raw and bleeding.

A new horror came to torment me. I could not be sure that when falling unconscious I had not turned around in rising; if I had done so, I was going back towards the heading. I pictured the finding of my body, and wondered if the terrible fight I was making for life would or could be traced. I continued, however, to move along, thinking, in a dull way, that the chances of my direction being right, were as favourable as I could make them.

The thought occurred to me at that awful time that night and darkness must have come on, so that I might, in case the hoist had been raised, walk right by the shaft without seeing it. Then I might walk on and on till I came to the brink of the first well near the gorge; one step more, a plunge, a crash against some jutting rock of the shaft, a rebound, and all would be over. The yawning shaft at the mouth of the tunnel seemed to be waiting for me; it was transformed into a demon, and was beckoning me on.

Instinctively I clung more closely to the projections of the rock, and put forward my foot with care, to be sure of its receiving support, before trusting my weight upon it. I wondered if my body would remain in the well, or be washed out into the river, and thence down through the Whirlpool Rapids.

The idea that I might be blind came to me, suggested no doubt by the intense smarting of my eyes. The darkness was so complete, that I could not put the illusion to test. This dread was by no means the least of the terrors that assailed me.

Choking, gasping for breath, how I longed for the pure air above! It seemed such a great, priceless boon, this air that is given to us, without stint and without care on our part, all through life.

Sometimes my thoughts drifted to Baxter. I wondered if he would be alive if I succeeded in giving the alarm. I saw him so plainly, his ghastly face upturned, and his wide, open eyes staring straight before him! He might have been aware of passing events, but without the power to speak or move. In that case he knew when I left him, and might have thought I was leaving him like a coward, but held in that overpowering sleepiness that weighted down his lips and limbs, he could not call to me, and beg me to save him, too. It tortured me to think I had left him without trying to give him the hope that I was going for help.

Then I became terror stricken with the thought that I might be incapable of letting anyone know of the disaster which had befallen my companion, and I fell to repeating his name in a mechanical way.

This is all of that terrible journey that I remember with any distinctness. I have a shadowy recollection of falling and rising many times. Everything seemed to be carried forward, up and down, as on a mighty billow. In a confused way I was conscious of going on and on, but my motions were in large measure involuntary. Finally it seemed to me that all I had passed through was only a dream; that I was still lying where I had first fallen; that I was held by a dreadful, oppressive power which I was trying in vain to throw off.

Suddenly I was conscious of a change. There was an obstruction in my way. One last dreadful agony assailed me—was the obstruction the form of my prostrate companion, and had I retraced my steps? This was more than I could bear, and all hope and life seemed to leave me.

The obstruction was, in fact, the hoisting box at the shaft, and I had fallen over one edge and into it. Someone loitering near heard the muffled noise, peered down into the darkness of the shaft, and listened. All was quiet, but the noise had been so unmistakable that at his suggestion the engineer raised the hoist. As the fresh air came to me more and more, I revived, and began, even before I was helped from the hoist, to say, 'Baxter! Baxter! Baxter!'

My bruised appearance, together with the repetition of his name, told very plainly that something was wrong with my companion. A party was organized, the compressed air was turned on, and in due time my companion in this perilous adventure was brought to the surface.

After hours of work by the hastily summoned doctors he was brought out of his deathlike stupor. He lived, but may never fully recover from the effects of the poisonous gas.

As for myself, my story ends with the rescue.

HUNTING THE
HAMMERHEAD
SHARK

Trevor Housby

The biggest Hammerhead I ever had was with my brother-in-law, the intrepid Valerio, who is, like myself, shark mad. We are both obsessive shark fishermen. We love the sharks first and foremost. I think catching them is just a minor part of the whole thing. Whether it is the danger element, or just that sharks as shark appeal to us, we just don't know. Valerio will go anywhere for a big shark, and I am just the same. You could say that we are slightly retarded, but there is no denying it, sharks do turn us on.

This story concerns one trip I made to Madeira. I, strictly speaking, shouldn't have been there on a fishing trip at all, but Valerio told me that some of the local fishermen working close to the Pont San Laurenco Lighthouse had on three or four occasions that week seen a big Hammerhead working on bait fish close to shore.

When a Madeiran fisherman says that a shark is a big one, it pays to believe him. They know sharks as well as anybody and have caught a fair number of big ones over the years, so they don't make too many mistakes. They had seen this fish come to the surface, cruise, come around the boat, snatch at hooked fish and do all sorts of things. He had clearly taken up temporary residence in the area, which was rich in food, and would probably stay for a week or a month, until the food thinned out or it simply got bored.

Ever keen to help get a big fish, Valerio suggested we should take the boat and go up there. I always keep a spare set of big-game tackle in his house in Madeira. There is a shark rod, 10–0 type reel loaded with heavy line, all the usual things, and Valerio always has the traces, gaffs and other equipment for his own trade. Anyway, we sailed out of Funchal harbour very early one morning, just as the sun was coming up. We cleared the harbour leaving the big white passenger liners behind us, turning away up the coast for the long run up to Canical, up past the whaling station and on to the final extremity where the Pont San Laurenco Lighthouse stands out against the skyline.

This is obviously a big fish area. Tide rips come in around the corner of Madeira, the bait fish build up in these places and the big fish, tuna, sharks and all sorts come in to feed on them. I have always been fascinated by fishing this corner of Madeira, where the great volcanic rocks with their rusty stains of long-gone fire sweep down into the ocean. The sea here is always blue, the surf is always white against the rugged rocks.

We had brought some mashed fish with us, and we feathered a lot of bait. The idea was to get as much mackerel aboard as we could, the Spanish mackerel, the small bonito, everything we needed. We wanted a bait fish weighing about ten pounds; we got that very quickly in the form of a bonito about this weight. Then we got a dorado, one of the dolphin fish and to me one of the most beautiful fish in the world. It has a blunt square head and beautiful sides. This one was a male, a brilliant golden fish, unbelievably beautiful. The gold was shot with blue flecks, a flickering fire of a fish, just what I needed for bait. It was a pity to kill it, but these dorados do make first-class shark-bait.

Having established our position we began to drift. We chopped up buckets of mackerel and fed it over the side to lay a constant trail of bait-size chunks through the water to bring the shark in (there was only one shark that we wanted). We fished two rods, mine on the surface and Valerio's way down in the depths. As it happened the surface rod finally picked up the fish.

We were excited to be able to watch the shark for some while before it moved in to take the bait, about ten o'clock in the morning with the sun burning down really hot. The shark came to the surface, lying idly awash, just moving enough to push himself back and forth some fifty yards away. He was obviously interested, and fascinated by the trail of chopped-up mackerel. This one was going to feed sooner or later; he wasn't too bothered; I'm sure he'd had plenty of good fish for breakfast, but still he gave every sign of a shark that would feed before the day was out.

He looked a good specimen. We both put him at over ten feet long. A Hammerhead of this size is a pretty big fish. The maximum size for a Hammerhead is something like fifteen feet, but a fifteen-footer is a rarity. Even at ten feet they are quite a handful. Gradually the shark eased in towards us. Sharks can come in at a deceptively slow pace, and you are not really aware that they are making progress towards you, until abruptly you see them within five or ten yards. It's rather like being mesmerized.

And so our Hammerhead came in, until all of a sudden we found ourselves looking almost down on top of him. With the clear water and the bright morning sunshine we could see every detail of the fish as he cruised alongside. We could see his big fins, beautiful shape and quaint hammerhead with the eyes on each angle of the hammer. These Hammerheads have a peculiar characteristic of banking away from you, as if they need to do this to see you. They

We caught a dorado for a bait.

lean over to one side very steadily, and the eye comes up, so that the fish can take a good look at the boat and even the occupants. This one seemed untroubled by our presence. I would say that across the head the fish measured a little over two feet.

A Hammerhead is a deceiving shape because the hammerhead itself is so broad, and the base of the head behind it is so narrow, that you can get a distorted impression of the size of the head. The actual body of the fish is very bulky.

This fish appeared to watch us for a second or two, and then cruised around in a circle, and as it did so I began to ease my bait towards the boat. Hammerheads aren't really active feeders in this respect, but like most sharks they are attracted by movement. As I began to wind the bright dorado bait back, this one saw it. He didn't do anything too fast to start with, but he began to bristle noticeably once he had seen the bait. You get this impression of a build-up, a concentration of potential energy. They seem to charge themselves like a battery. A torpid fish can suddenly be transformed into one electrified and ready to pounce. I don't quite know how to describe it, but you could see it; the fins began to bristle, and he was obviously bunching for an attack.

Suddenly he came in really fast. The dorsal fin went down, the tail lashed the surface and he hit the bait with everything he'd got. He didn't waste any time—and the line went out accordingly. He left the surface and went straight down into deep water. I knew we had two or three hundred feet of water beneath our keel and I wasn't too worried about the fish getting into heavy rock and fouling the line. Hammerheads usually go straight to the bottom and then begin to cruise three or four feet above the sea bed.

This one did just about that. Valerio started the motor and gently put the boat into gear, and we began to follow the fish. He didn't do anything very spectacular to begin, he just went along at a steady pace with us in tow. I kept maximum pressure on him, making him work for every inch of line, and pull every ounce of his strength. With a shark you have to make him work hard from the moment you set the hook; if you let him relax in any way then you will never catch him. They don't seem to tire unless forced to fight the spring of the rod, the power of the angler, and every inch of line and drag between rod tip and mouth.

This one didn't take too much notice of me to begin with, but I wasn't too worried yet by his complacency. Gradually we manoeuvred ourselves above him. I like to get right above a shark if I can, and when one is down deep the whole object is to bring him to the surface. If you can get him up on a line he begins to panic, and starts to fluster. When in danger fish run for cover just like any other creature, and cover to a big fish means deep water. He wants to get down there where no light penetrates; it must be like hiding in a dark cave where you feel that danger cannot reach you.

So my object now was to get him up. Valerio brought the boat directly above him and I began to try and give the fish a hard time. I bent the rod as hard as I could; I got back every inch of line I could, though I often lost five inches for every inch gained, but I made him pay for every bit of it, and if you can keep this sort of strain up, and if your shoulders will stand it, this is the one thing that will get you your shark.

After a little while we had got him on the move. He was coming up slowly and very reluctantly, but the line was inexorably creeping back through the rod rings. Creeping is the only word: the tautness of the line was incredible, you could have played tunes on it. Drops of water were being squeezed out of the fibres of the line. Although the rod was creaking, and me too for that matter, I knew the fish was coming up.

This was the hardest part. You are lifting a fish weighing between five hundred and nine hundred pounds out of deep water, out of his own element, and brute force alone will get him up. On a rod it really is hard work; you cannot force it. I use a rod with an eighty-pound test for this sort of fishing and there is no man in the world who can pull much more than that strain. When you are lifting a fish on a rod like this, all you can do is bend the rod to its maximum weight to make the fish ease up in the water, and as the rod tip gradually begins to straighten again then get an inch or two of line back on the reel. It may take an hour to raise a fish, but every inch gained is an inch that the fish will never get back again.

Gradually this one began to spiral up. They normally come up in this way, in little short circles. They go round and round, occasionally going into a flurry, trying to get back down. The thing I fear at this stage is the tremendous power of the tail. When a fish goes down like that it often brings the tail into play against the trace with all its strength. You can feel that great big tail wrenching the rod sideways all the time, banging, thumping, crashing against the line and this is a danger point on a tight line, because a breakage is so easy.

The other thing that bothered me was that when a big shark gets tired it is apt to roll; the trace may wind itself around its body, and nine times out of ten you lose the fish, because the line winds round the body too, and the rough denticles on the skin of the shark will chafe through it in seconds. I must have lost a hundred sharks in this way. Hammerheads in particular will roll very quickly.

But Valerio was superb. Like a magician he kept manoeuvring the boat round in little circles, seeming to sense every movement of the shark below us. By keeping the boat turning with the shark, he denied the shark any chance of rolling. I was given every opportunity to pile on the pressure.

Finally we got a glimpse of it. I suppose it was fifty or sixty feet down, a pale ghost of a fish down in the clear water. All we could see, really, was the faint outline of something circling, and a big tail moving. We couldn't see much more, but as it rose inch by inch we began to see the fish as it really was, first the big tail, then the peculiar hammerhead, the great drooping dorsal fin and wide pectoral fins. Each circle seemed to get shorter, and each one brought it closer and closer to the surface. Within ten minutes now I knew the fish would either be ours, or gone forever.

Valerio was mad with delight. To him it was a great game; like me he didn't really care if we lost the fish, we had had a hell of a day fishing already and with most of it still to go. We had hooked the fish we had come for, and he was enjoying the whole thing immensely. Typical Madeiran, he produced a bottle of wine from somewhere and started singing his head off. The fish was coming up very fast now and we could see every detail. It was finished, no question about it; this one was tired and just about ready to surrender the struggle.

As the fish hit surface, Valerio cut the engine of the boat, moved in with the gaff and jammed it solidly into the fish right beneath the pectoral fins. He did it expertly, and we had no more problem. I grabbed the tail rope, slipped it over the big tail and in perhaps two or three seconds the Hammerhead was alongside, lashed down and hardly moving.

It was rather an anti-climax. The fish had had to work so hard that he was beaten already. Normally when you get these big ones alongside there is that terrible moment of flurry when a wall of water comes over the side, and spray goes everywhere; the big tail is beating a tattoo on the side of the boat and the head is swinging trying to get a bite on something. But this fish didn't do anything so dramatic. From stem to stern he was beaten.

Valerio was in seventh heaven, and raving around the boat like a madman, singing and dancing. We had come out for a big shark, done it, and had a lot of fun. What on earth did we do next? I wanted to stay fishing, but Valerio wisely pointed out that to the best of his knowledge there was only one big shark in the area—all the local fishermen had told him that they had only seen the one—and we were unlikely to find another shark of such a size in the area, and what was the point of catching a smaller one? Why not go in to the whaling station, tie the boat up and have a drink?

And we did just that; we went inshore, fell amongst bandits and thieves and the harpooners at the Canical Station and things began to snowball. We collapsed in the local bar, drank aguadenti, wine and the best Madeira, toasted the Hammerhead, toasted the Hammerhead's brothers and cousins, uncles, aunts, grandfathers and future relations and past relations. To put it another way we got terribly and horribly smashed, but we did feel we had every reason to celebrate.

The following morning I realized just how heavily I had celebrated. I had a head like wet concrete. As for the Hammerhead, the local fishermen at Canical took charge of it; they probably used it as bait, or food, but we didn't see it again. We never even weighed it in but it was well over eight hundred pounds. The trouble with fishing sharks in these remote places is that unless you are close to a harbour like Funchal, where we could have weighed the shark within hours of catching it, you never know what it weighs down to the last pound.

But it didn't matter. The object had been to catch it, and we had, and finally we abandoned it to the delighted fishermen at Canical.

A CAPE HORN SNORTER

Capt. W. H. S. Jones

**Rounding Cape Horn is usually a hazardous under-
taking—but for the sailing ship *British Isles* it promised
to be nightmare ... For below deck there was a
shifting cargo of coal threatening to capsize the severely
undermanned vessel; and the treacherous Horn lay
ahead ...**

It was now imperative to get the loose coal in the hold trimmed
and secured and, if possible, get the ship on an even keel again,
so preparations were immediately made to deal with the situation
below.

Heavy sprays and an occasional sea were still breaking on board,
making the opening of the main hatch impossible, so the crew,
including the apprentices, were sent into the hold through the
lazarette door under the Captain's cabin aft. We groped our way
along the top of the coal in the pitch darkness until we were under
the main hatch. It was impossible to use naked lights owing to the
presence of coal-gas in the confined airless hold, and in a sailing-
ship there was no other method of illumination. In the pitch

blackness, sweating and cursing, kneeling in the narrow space between the top of the coal and the deck overhead, on the side where the coal had run down, or sinking to our knees in loose coal on the sloping face on the other side, we shovelled for dear life, occasionally being pitched headlong into a cascade of black diamonds by a violent roll of the ship.

With nostrils and throats choked with the dust thrown up by the shovels, our bodies caked with a mixture of dust and sweat, without food or rest, we laboured on, hour after hour, until gradually the ship's list was reduced; but it was never wholly eliminated, and for the rest of the voyage remained one of the many adverse conditions that would operate to impede our progress.

With the strong fair wind the *British Isles* now ramped and snored along under full sail, logging over 200 miles a day.

On August 7—57 days after our departure from Port Talbot— we passed St John's Point on Staten Island, and headed away south-westward towards Cape Horn, only 150 miles ahead.

The wind from the north-westward had gradually died away, and now a moderate breeze blew from the eastward.

This was the life—rounding the dreaded Cape to the westward, with a fair following wind, all sail set and squared yards and a clear sky!

It was a stroke of luck—something to compensate us for the adversities we had encountered on our long southward run which, being behind us, were now almost forgotten.

If this weather held we would be around the Horn, and into the Pacific Ocean in a day or two, all worries and troubles evaded.

Historians record that Cape Horn was discovered and named, in the year 1616, by the Dutch navigators, Schouten and Lemaire, who, in their ship, *Eendracht*, 220 tons, were the first Europeans to sail around the extreme south of South America.

Before their time ships passing from the Atlantic to the Pacific, or vice versa, used the strait discovered by Magellan, the Spanish circumnavigator of the globe, in the year 1521. Magellan's Strait, separating the large island of Tierra del Fuego ('Land of Fire') from the main, is in 52 degrees South Latitude. It is narrow, landlocked, and difficult of navigation by larger ships, especially under sail. Through this strait, in the year 1578, sailed Francis Drake, the first English circumnavigator of the globe. On emerging into the Pacific Ocean, which had been so named by Magellan fifty-seven years previously, Drake coasted southwards along the western shore of the Land of Fire, expecting to discover a 'Great South Land' (Antarctica) which geographers believed was joined to South America. Instead, he found that 'the Atlantic Ocean and the South Seas meet in a most large and free scope'.

In honour of his discovery the name of 'Drake Strait' was later attached to the passage—about 600 miles wide—between South America and Antarctica. This Strait is blocked by ice-fields on its southern side, but has sea-room, ice-free, of from 200 to 400 miles wide, according to the seasons, on its northern side; and this is certainly 'a most large and free scope' for sailing-vessels in any season.

The name of Cape Horn was affixed by the Dutchmen, Schouten and Lemaire, in honour of their native town, Hoorn, on the Zuyder Zee in Holland, the port from which their vessel had sailed. They also discovered Staten Island at the eastern turning into the Strait, and named it in honour of the 'States' of the Netherlands, which had declared independence of Spanish rule a few years before their voyage.

Cape Horn is on an island, in Latitude 56 degrees South, and is therefore about 276 miles further south than Magellan Strait—no great distance extra on a long voyage, considering the 'large and free scope' offered by the open-water passage 'around the Horn'. For this reason, sailing-ships invariably used the route around the Horn, and Magellan's Strait was used only by small steamers.

Very few sailors rounding the Horn ever saw that Cape of fabulous renown. To clear it safely, ships gave it a wide berth in about 57 degrees South, or in still higher Latitudes. The outstanding feature of the passage, for sailing-vessels going in either direction, was that the prevailing winds, at almost all seasons of the year, were 'westerlies', varying from all points between about S.S.W. and N.N.W., but often blowing at gale force for days, and sometimes for weeks on end.

South of 56 degrees South Latitude, the unobstructed belt of ocean, extending entirely around the globe, allows these winds to gather a tremendous velocity. The cause of surface winds is the flow of air from areas of high pressure to areas of lower pressure, modified to some extent by the rotation of the earth, and deflected by continental land-masses. The westerly winds of the Cape Horn region, especially those blowing from the south-west, come off the Antarctic ice, and are bitterly cold, frequently laden with snow, sleet and hail.

To 'round the Horn', voyaging from the Pacific Ocean *eastwards* to the Atlantic, is a comparatively easy matter for a sailing-ship, as the prevailing westerly winds provide a natural propulsion from aft; but there are special difficulties for sailing-ships when a following wind increases to gale or hurricane force—and, of course the westerlies in the High Latitudes of the South frequently do.

In ordinary circumstances it is the *westward* passage around Cape Horn which is fraught with great difficulties for the mariner under sail. To make the transit from the South Atlantic to the South Pacific, he must usually sail into 'the teeth of the wind', which is possible only by making tacks, if sufficient sail can be carried to keep the ship moving.

The ideal way of rounding the Horn to the westward would be by one long tack to the south-west, followed by another long tack to the north-west; but the caprice of the westerlies, variable as they are in direction and velocity, and likely to bear down on the ship in sudden squalls and fierce storms, coming from anywhere in the S.W. or N.W. quadrants, makes any predetermined plan ineffective.

The course set must be adapted to these variable conditions almost from hour to hour. There is plenty of sea-room for tacking, but hidden dangers lurk, to the south, in drifting icefloes and icebergs, especially as visibility is so often obscured for long periods by rain, hail and sleet. Sometimes for days on end it is impossible, because of low and heavy cloud, to fix the ship's position. Between the icefields of the south and the rocky, uninhabited, and unlit islets clustering close to the Patagonian coast of Chile on the north side of the Strait, there is need for all the sea-room available—which is ample on most occasions, but many ships have vanished without trace of wreckage or survivors in that waste of grey and icy waters—either foundered in a gale or squall, or, in their anxiety to give the land a wide berth, going too far to the south and striking an iceberg or floe-ice.

The ship making westing must expect to ride a heavy westerly swell in waters never stilled as they surge round and round the globe in the High Latitudes on the fringe of the ice, unimpeded by land-barriers. This swell, which may be increased by the compression of the oceanic weight of waters into this relatively narrow passage between two oceans, could be affected also by the earth's rotation, by tides, and by the prevailing currents, which off Cape Horn flow continually from West to East.

When the swell is whipped by winds, locally, into waves, which sailors call 'seas', those seas, during a Cape Horn gale, may reach a height of from 30 feet to 40 and even 50 feet, from trough to crest, and then termed 'precipitous' by scientific formula, but 'mountainous' by those who meet them.

When the seas are running from the west, as they usually do off Cape Horn, a sailing-ship making westing cannot ride over them head-on unless she is hove to, and consequently not making progress, and even then the nearest she would probably get to stemming the seas would be an angle of about 70 degrees. If she is on either tack, she must take the sea—or the swell—on the weather side well abeam, and will roll to an alarming extent, especially when the seas are 'precipitous'. No doubt, many of the ships which have disappeared off Cape Horn 'without trace' have simply rolled over and foundered when caught broadside on by precipitous seas which have stove in the hatches.

With this brief explanation of the hazards of the westward passage around the Cape, I may continue my narrative of the voyage of the *British Isles* which, on August 7 1905, passed Staten Island with a fair and following *easterly* breeze and clear skies.

These conditions, by no means usual, sometimes occur for short periods in the winter months in that vicinity, when on occasion an easterly wind can even reach gale force. In our transit from the Northern Hemisphere to the Southern Hemisphere, we had passed from midsummer to midwinter. Cape Horn weather observations have established that there is usually less rainfall there in winter than in summer, but the winter rainfall is in the form of sleet, snow, blizzards and hailstorms. It happened to be just our luck to pass Staten Island with a fair easterly wind and dry skies, but the air had a keen nip of frost in it, a hint of what was to come.

On August 8, in the morning, we passed Cape Horn, well to the southward, in 57 degrees South, out of sight of land. We were now 7,400 miles from home on the shortest calculation of the direct route which steamers, when correctly navigated, can follow, but our actual sailing distance had certainly been about 8,500 or 9,000 miles, in just under two months since we had hauled out of Port Talbot Dock.

Since parting company from the German ship *Susannah* on June 16 we had never sighted her again, and so had no idea whether she had beaten us around the Horn, or whether she was behind.

We had all sail set to the royals as we passed the meridian of the Cape. When a sight of the sun was taken at noon the officers for once made no secret of our position, and the word flew round that we had turned the famous Continental Cornerpost.

During the pleasant run from Staten Island the Captain's wife and children had again appeared on deck, the lady looking pale and wan, but smiling bravely to share in the general elation.

Soon after noon the easterly wind dropped to a light breeze, and presently we were almost becalmed. At the same time the temperature dropped suddenly, the skies clouded and snow began to fall.

The air was now bitterly cold, and icicles formed in the rigging. The long oily-looking swell from the west took on a sinister look and feel as we breasted it. On the far western horizon dense masses of cloud loomed portentous.

Not having access to the barometer readings the crew did not know what was brewing, although the old hands could make a good guess.

But the Captain knew only too well, as the glass continued to fall, and he eyed the portents in the west. His wife and children returned to their quarters, out of sight.

Towards sunset the expected battle-cry rang out:

'All hands on deck!'

As the watch below came out, on the run, the Mates repeated the Captain's orders to take in sail on all the masts:

'Clew the royals up! Look lively there, men!'

'Port-watch forrard, starboard-watch the main, haul away the buntlines!'

'Slack away those b——y halyards; Nelson!'

'Get moving, men. This is not a b——y funeral!'

So, to the urge of bellowed commands, the creak of blocks, and the rhythmical chants of *Haul we Heigh we Ho*, by hard-driven men exerting themselves to the utmost in the oncoming darkness, all the sails were clewed up, except the foresail, the three lower topsails and a jib, to which we were reduced in good time.

The clewed-up sails had now to be furled. They lay in the buntlines in stiff folds, wet by the snow, which had solidified to ice in the fabric, but were fortunately not bellied out by a strong wind. Scrambling aloft, among the icicles on the rigging, I had my first experience of stowing frozen Number One canvas, in the dark.

It was extremely uncomfortable with numbed fingers, in a temperature several degrees below freezing-point, to lay out with one's belly over a steel spar covered in ice, clutching and clawing at the ice-stiffened canvas to roll it up on the yard. This had not been my idea of a life at sea when I had donned the smart monkey-jacket of a brassbounder in my happy home, now so far away.

But I was learning fast . . .

By 10 p.m., everything was snugged down. I was in the watch on deck, standing by, as the Captain and Second Mate peered into the murk to the westward, from where the change of wind was expected. We had not long to wait, and by midnight a real Cape Horn Snorter was upon us.

In the darkness the long oily hills of water we had breasted all day loomed up for a moment before passing from our view as the ship rolled over the crest of each successive advancing sea, to roll back with a violent jerk into the trough behind it. Under her shortened sail, she had practically no headway in the comparative lull that preceded the storm, and lay at the mercy of the sea, while the moan of the whimpering breeze in the rigging rose alternately to a high-pitched note, and subsided to a sob in an eerie manner, as the top-hamper fell away or was driven up against the wind by the ship's rolling motions.

Suddenly, in the wall of darkness to the westward, a line of vivid whiteness is glimpsed advancing relentlessly towards us. It is the surface of the water churned by the violence of the approaching storm, about a mile from us, so that it seethes as though boiling in a gigantic cauldron.

The oily swells are being transformed into dangerous running seas.

'Hard up the helm!' the Captain orders. 'Lee forebrace!'

The seamen move at the run and tail on to the lee braces, hauling the yards round onto the backstays, as, with a roar like the voices of ten thousand suddenly uncaged and ravenous lions, a squall of hurricane force drives down on the ship as though determined to tear her to pieces.

She shudders at the impact, and heels over until the lee rail is under, and the men there, bracing the yards up, are immersed to their waists in the icy-cold flood of water that pours in over the rail.

The black wall to windward bears down relentlessly on the labouring ship, with a deluge of hail and sleet as it expends its pent-up fury.

On 7th August, 1905 we passed Staten Island.

As the squall passes, the sky to windward gradually lightens, revealing to us dense masses of cloud piled one upon the other on the horizon, reaching high into the heavens, where rippling rays of light, among the peaks and valleys of the rain- and snow-laden cloud-masses, cast their shapes into bold relief and deep shadow, in warning of their devastating power soon to be unleashed upon us in another squall.

In that eerie light we see mountains of water rushing towards the ship, their foaming white crests outlined sharply against the blackness behind them, as though they had been trimmed with a gigantic knife.

It seems a miracle that the ship can ride over these ravening seas, one after the other in endless succession. Their crests break and are driven over her by the force of the wind as high as the main yard, in spume and spindrift which freezes to droplets of ice in the shrouds and wherever else it settles.

Squall follows squall in unremitting succession. The Cape Horn Snorter is shaking us in its teeth as a terrier shakes a rat. The drumming of the wind, the wild plunging and rolling of the ship in the cross sea, the masses of cloud hurtling past near the mastheads, the heavens opening to let loose on us a deluge of snow, hail and sleet, would provide an awe-inspiring, perhaps terrifying, spectacle—if we had time to pause and ponder and observe them at leisure.

But, up to our waists in the water swirling across the deck as the ship rolls, we are preoccupied with holding on to the lifelines, to the belaying-pins, to the rail, to anything handy, as we unravel the tangle of ropes in the icy water, and secure them in the rigging beyond the reach of the sea. Like men in battle, we are too busy to have time to be frightened. Our minds are on the immediate tasks we have to do, but we know, without needing to be told, the penalty for failure to surmount the dangers which beset us, as we work on blindly in obedience to the exacting orders of those who have the responsibility of commanding us what to do.

Headed towards the frozen regions of Antarctica, we can make but little westing in the teeth of this gale. While it lasts, and the

Master persists in trying to sail to the westward, the ship is little better than an unmanageable derelict, for she is drifting now, carried to leeward by the set of the current, the pressure of wind against the maze of rigging, and those mighty rollers pounding against her side. We are drifting sideways, drifting, drifting back east of the Cape we had so jubilantly sailed past 24 hours previously, the Continental Corner-post, the meeting-place of the oceans. The Greybeards of Cape Horn are laughing uproariously at us, in derision, because with our puny strength we have dared to challenge their supremacy and invade their solitudes.

In the dawn we are still drifting helplessly, with our wake streaming to windward at an angle of 60 degrees to our keel, and the storm shows no sign of abating.

An albatross appears out of the murk, to examine us in our plight. The gale is of hurricane force, but the bird sails serenely and unhurriedly through the air, within a few feet of the ship's rail, on the windward side.

Then it turns into the eye of the wind, and disappears in the murk—*westward*—without any discernible effort in its aerial gliding, while we are still drifting to leeward, incapable of emulating its brilliant defiance of the gusts.

Cape Horn was astern yesterday, but today it is again ahead of us. We have rounded the Cape twice—once going forward and once drifting back, and all in 24 hours! We have turned the Corner of the Continent, and have been turned back, willy-nilly.

We shall keep on trying, until the Greybeards relent, and let us through. Battling round the Horn, many a sailorman, and many a ship, have perished; but the *British Isles* still floats; and even a Cape Horn Snorter must eventually abate its fury.

STRANGE EVENTS AT ZINDERNEUF

P. C. Wren

'**A**s we rode out of the gate of my fort, I gathered from the still-dying *goum*, on the still-dying camel, that a couple of days before, a large force of Touaregs had been sighted from the lookout platform of Zinderneuf fort. Promptly the wise *sous-officier*, in charge and command since the lamented death of Captain Renouf, had turned the *goum* loose on his fast *mehari* camel, with strict orders not to be caught by the Touaregs if they invested the fort, but to clear out and trek with all speed for help—as it appeared to be a case of too heavy odds. If the Touaregs were only playful, and passed the fort by, after a little sporting pot-shotting, he was to follow them, I suppose, see them safe off the premises for a day or two, and discover what they were out for.

'Well, away went the *goum*, stood afar off on a sand-hill, saw the Touaregs skirmish up to the oasis, park their camels among the palms, and seriously set about investing the place. He thought it was time for him to go when they had surrounded the fort, were lining the sand-hills, making nice little trenches in the sand, climbing the palm trees, and pouring in a very heavy fire. He estimated them at ten thousand rifles, so I feared that there must be at least five hundred of the cruel fiends. Anyhow, round wheeled Monsieur Goum and rode hell-for-leather, night and day, for help . . .

'Like *How we brought the good news from Aix to Ghent*, and *Paul Revere's Ride* and all. I christened the *goum*, Paul Revere, straight away, when I heard his tale, and promised him all sorts of good things, including a good hiding if I found he had not exceeded the speed limit all the way from Aix to Ghent. Certainly his "Roland" looked as if its radiator had boiled all right. And, *Nom d'un nom d'nom de bon Dieu de sort*! but I made a forced march of it, my friend—and when we of the Nineteenth African Division do *that*, even on mules and camels, you can hardly see us go.'

'Oh, come now! I am sure your progress is perceptible,' said Lawrence politely. 'Specially on camels, and all that . . . You're too modest,' he added.

'I mean you can hardly see us go for dust and small stones, by reason of our swiftness . . . Any more than you can see a bullet, witty one,' rebuked de Beaujolais.

'Oh, quite, quite,' murmured the Englishman.

'Anyhow, I was away with the advance-party on swift *mehari* camels, a mule-squadron was following, and a company of Senegalese would do fifty kilometres a day on foot till they reached Zinderneuf. Yes, and, in what I flatter myself is the unbreakable record time between Tokotu and Zinderneuf, we arrived—and riding far on in advance of my men, I listened for the sound of firing or of bugle-calls.

'I heard no sound whatever, and suddenly topping a ridge I came in sight of the fort—below me on the desert plain, near the oasis.

'There was no fighting, no sign of Touaregs, no trace of battle or siege. No blackened ruins strewn with mutilated corpses here. The Tri-couleur flew merrily from the flag-staff, and the fort looked absolutely normal—a square grey block of high, thick mud walls, flat castellated roof, flanking towers, and lofty look-out platform. All was well! The honour of the Flag of France had been well defended. I waved my *képi* above my head and shouted aloud in my glee.

'Perhaps I began composing my Report then and there, doing modest justice to the readiness, promptitude, and dispatch of my little force, which had maintained the glorious traditions of the Nineteenth African Division: giving due praise to the *sous-officier* commanding Zinderneuf (and not forgetting Paul Revere and his Roland) . . . Meanwhile, they should know that relief was at hand, and that, be the Touaregs near or be they far, the danger was over and the Flag safe. I, Henri de Beaujolais of the Spahis, had brought relief. I fired my revolver half a dozen times in the air. And then I was aware of a small but remarkable fact. The high look-out platform at the top of its long ladder was empty.

'Strange! Very strange! Incredibly strange, at the very moment when great marauding bands of Touaregs were known to be about —and one of them had only just been beaten off, and might attack again at any moment. I must offer the *sous-officier* my congratulations upon the excellence of his look-out, as soon as I had embraced and commended him! New as he might be to independent command, this should never have happened. One would have thought he could as soon have forgotten his boots as his sentry on the look-out platform.

'A pretty state of affairs, *bon Dieu*, in time of actual war! Here was I approaching the fort in broad light of day, firing my revolver— and not the slightest notice taken! I might have been the entire Touareg nation or the whole German army . . .

'No, there must be something wrong, in spite of the peaceful look of things and the safety of the Flag—and I pulled out my field-glasses to see if they would reveal anything missed by the naked eye.

'As I halted and waited for my camel to steady himself, that I might bring the glasses to bear, I wondered if it were possible that this was an ambush.

'Could the Arabs have captured the place, put the defenders to the sword, put on their uniforms, cleaned up the mess, closed the gates, left the Flag flying, and now be waiting for a relieving force to ride, in trustful innocence and close formation, up to the muzzles of their rifles? Possible—but quite unlike brother Touareg! You know what *his* way is, when he has rushed a post or broken a square. A dirty fighter, if ever there was one! And as I focused my glasses on the walls, I rejected the idea.

'Moreover, yes, there were the good European faces of the men at the embrasures, bronzed and bearded, but unmistakably not Arab . . .

'And yet, that again was strange. At every embrasure of the breast-high parapet round the flat roof stood a soldier, staring out across the desert, and most of them staring along their levelled rifles too; some of them straight at me. Why? There was no enemy about. Why were they not sleeping the sleep of tired victors, below on their cots in the *caserne*, while double sentries watched from the high look-out platform? Why no man up there, and yet a man at every embrasure that I could see from where I sat on my camel, a thousand metres distant?

'And why did no man move; no man turn to call out to a sergeant that a French officer approached; no man walk to the door leading down from the roof, to inform the Commandant of the fort?

'Anyhow, the little force had been extraordinarily lucky, or the shooting of the Arabs extraordinarily bad, that they should still be numerous enough to man the walls in that fashion—"all present and correct", as you say in your army—and able to stand to arms thus, after two or three days of it, more or less.

'As I lowered my glasses and urged my camel forward, I came to the conclusion that I was expected, and that the officer in charge was indulging in a little natural and excusable *fantaisie*, showing off—what you call "putting on the dog", eh?

'He was going to let me find everything as the Arabs found it when they make their foolish attack—every man at his post and everything *klim-bim*. Yes, that must be it . . . Ah, it was! Even as I watched, a couple of shots were fired from the wall. They had seen me . . . The fellow, in his joy, was almost shooting *at* me!

'And yet—nobody on the look-out platform! How I would prick that good fellow's little bubble of swank! And I smiled to myself as I rode under the trees of the oasis to approach the gates of the fort.

'It was the last time I smiled for quite a little while.

'Among the palm trees were little pools of dried and blackened blood where men had fallen, or wounded men had been laid, showing that, however intact the garrison of the fort might be, their assailants had paid toll to the good Lebel rifles of my friends.

'And then I rode out from the shade of the oasis and up to the gate.

'Here half a dozen or so kept watch, looking out over the wall above, as they leant in the embrasures of the parapet. The nearest was a huge fellow, with a great bushy grey moustache, from beneath which protruded a short wooden pipe. His *képi* was cocked rakishly over one eye, as he stared hard at me with the other, half closed and leering, while he kept his rifle pointed straight at my head.

'I was glad to feel certain that he at least was no Arab, but a tough old legionary, a typical *vieille moustache*, and rough soldier of fortune. But I thought his joke a poor one and over-personal, as I looked up into the muzzle of his unwavering rifle . . .

' "*Congratulations, my children*," I cried. "*France and I are proud to salute you*," and raised my *képi* in homage to their courage and their victory.

'Not one of them saluted. Not one of them answered. Not one of them stirred. Neither a finger nor an eyelid moved. I was annoyed. If this was "*making fantasies*", as they call it in the Legion, it was making it at the wrong moment and in the wrong manner.

' "*Have you of the Foreign Legion no manners?*" I shouted. "*Go, one of you, at once, and call your officer*." Not a finger nor an eyelid moved.

'I then addressed myself particularly to old Grey-Moustache. "*You*," I said, pointing up straight at his face, "*go at once and tell your Commandant that Major de Beaujolais of the Spahis has arrived from Tokotu with a relieving force—and take that pipe out of your face and step smartly, do you hear?*"

'And then, my friend, I grew a little uncomfortable, though the impossible truth did not dawn upon me. Why did the fellow remain like a graven image, silent, motionless, remote—like an Egyptian god on a temple wall, looking with stony and unseeing eye into my puny human face?

'Why were they all like stone statues! Why was the fort so utterly and horribly silent? Why did nothing *move*, there in the fierce sunlight of the dawn? Why this tomb-like charnel-house, inhuman silence and immobility?

'Where were the usual sounds and stir of an occupied post? Why had no sentry seen me from afar and cried the news aloud? Why had there been no clang and clatter at the gate? Why had the gate not been opened? Why no voice, no footstep in all the place? Why did these men ignore me as though I were a beetle on the sand? Where was their officer? . . .

'Was this a nightmare in which I seemed for ever doomed to ride voiceless and invisible, round endless walls, trying to attract the attention of those who could never be aware of me?

'When, as in a dream, I rode right round the place, and beheld more and more of those motionless silent forms, with their fixed, unwinking eyes, I clearly saw that one of them, whose *képi* had fallen from his head, had a hole in the centre of his forehead and was dead—although at his post, with chest and elbows leaning on the parapet, and looking as though about to fire his rifle!

'I am rather near-sighted, as you know, but then the truth dawned upon me—they were *all* dead!

' "*Why were they not sleeping the sleep of tired victors?*" I had asked myself a few minutes before. They *were* . . .

'Yes, all of them. *Mort sur le champ d'honneur!* . . .

'My friend, I rode back to where Grey-Moustache kept his last watch, and, baring my head, I made my apologies to him, and the tears came into my eyes. Yes, and I, Henri de Beaujolais of the Spahis, admit it without shame.

'I said, "*Forgive me, my friend.*" What would you, an Englishman, have said?'

'What about a spot of tea?' quoth Mr George Lawrence, reaching beneath the seat of his tiffin-basket.

After a dusty meal, impatiently swallowed by Major de Beaujolais, that gentleman resumed his story, with serious earnestness and some gesticulation, while, on the opposite side of the carriage, George Lawrence lay upon his back, his clasped hands beneath his head, idly watching the smoke that curled up from his cheroot. But he was paying closer attention to the Frenchman's tale.

'But, of course, it soon occurred to me,' continued that gentleman, 'that someone must be alive . . . Shots had been fired to welcome me . . . Those corpses had not of *themselves* taken up those incredibly life-like attitudes. Whoever had propped them up and arranged them and their rifles in position, must be alive.

'For, naturally, not all had been struck by Arab bullets and remained standing in the embrasures. Nine times out of ten, as you know, a man staggers back and falls, when shot standing.

'Besides, what about the wounded? There is always a far bigger percentage of wounded than of killed in any engagement. Yes, there must be survivors, possibly all more or less wounded, below in the *caserne*.

'But surely *one* of them might have kept a look-out. Probably the Commandant and all the non-commissioned officers were killed.

'Even then, though, one would have expected the senior man—even if the survivors were all *soldats deuxième classe*—to have taken that much ordinary military precaution! . . .

'Well, I would soon solve the problem, for my troop was approaching, my trumpeter with them. I was glad to note that my Sergeant-Major had evidently had a similar idea to mine, for, on

Strange! Very strange! The look-out platform was empty.

coming in sight of the fort, he had opened out and skirmished up in extended order—in spite of the bravely-flying Flag.

'When my men arrived, I had the "rouse", the "alarm", the Regimental Call, sounded by the trumpeter—fully expecting, after each blast, that the gates would open, or at least that someone would come running up from below onto the roof.

'Not a sound nor a movement! . . . Again and again; call after call . . . Not a sound nor a movement!

' "Perhaps the last one or two are badly wounded," thought I. "There may not be a man able to crawl from his bed. The fellow who propped those corpses up may have been shot in the act, and be lying up there, or on his cot," and I bade the trumpeter cease. Sending for the *Chef*, as we call the Sergeant-Major, I ordered him to knot camel-cords, sashes, girths, reins, anything, make a rope, and set an active fellow to climb from the back of a camel, into an embrasure, and give me a hoist up.

'That Sergeant-Major is one of the bravest and coolest men I have ever known, and his collection of *ferblanterie* includes the Croix and the Medaille given on the field, for valour.

' "It is a trap, *mon Commandant*," he said. "Do not walk into it. Let me go." Brave words—but he looked queer, and I knew that though he feared nothing living, he was afraid.

' "The dead keep good watch, *Chef*," said I, and I think he shivered.

' "They would warn us, *mon Commandant*," said he. "Let me go."

' "We will neither of us go," said I. "We will have the courage to remain in our proper place, with our men. It may be a trap, though I doubt it. We will send a man in, and if it is a trap, we shall know— and without losing an officer unnecessarily. If it is not a trap, the gates will be opened in two minutes."

' "The Dead are watching and listening," said the *Chef*, glancing up, and he crossed himself, averting his eyes.

' "Send me that drunken *mauvais sujet*, Rastignac," said I, and the Sergeant-Major rode away.

' "May I go, *mon Commandant?*" said the trumpeter, saluting.

STRANGE EVENTS AT ZINDERNEUF

' "Silence," said I. My nerves were getting a little on edge, under that silent, mocking scrutiny of the watching Dead. When the Sergeant-Major returned with a rope, and the rascal Rastignac—whose proper place was in the *Joyeux*, the terrible Penal Battalions of convicted criminals—I ordered him to climb from his camel on to the roof.

' "Not I, *mon Officier*," replied he promptly. "Let me go to Hell dead, not living. I don't mind joining corpses *as* a corpse. You can shoot me."

' "That can I, of a surety," I agreed, and drew my revolver. "Ride your camel under that projecting water-spout," said I. "Stand on its back, and spring to the spout. Climb into the embrasure, and then go down and open the gates."

' "Not I, *mon Officier*," said Rastignac again. I raised my revolver, and the Sergeant-Major snatched the man's rifle.

' "Have you *le cafard?*" I asked, referring to the desert-madness that, bred of monotony, boredom, misery, and hardship, attacks European soldiers in these outposts—especially absinthe-drinkers—and makes them do strange things, varying from mutiny, murder, and suicide to dancing about naked, or thinking they are lizards or emperors or clock pendulums.

' "I have a dislike for intruding upon a dead Company that stands to arms and keeps watch," replied the fellow.

' "For the last time—*go*," said I, aiming between his eyes.

' "Go yourself, *Monsieur le Majeur*," replied Rastignac, and I pulled the trigger . . . Was I right, my friend?'

'Dunno,' replied Lawrence, yawning.

'There was a click, and Rastignac smiled. I had emptied my revolver when approaching the fort, as I have told you.

' "You can live—to be court-martialled and join the *Bati d' Af*," said I. "You will be well placed among the *Joyeux*."

' "Better among those than the Watchers above, *mon Officier*," said my beauty, and I bade the Sergeant-Major take his bayonet and put him under arrest.

' "You may show this coward the way," said I to the trumpeter, and, in a minute, that one had sprung at the spout, clutched it, and was scrambling onto the wall. He was *un brave*.

' "We will proceed as though the place were held by an enemy—until the gates are opened," said I to the Sergeant-Major, and we rode back to the troop and handed Rastignac over to the Corporal, who clearly welcomed him in the rôle of prisoner.

' "*Vous—pour la boîte*," smiled the Corporal, licking his lips. And then we watched and waited. I could see that the men were immensely puzzled and intrigued. Not an eye wandered. I would have given something to have known what each man thought concerning this unique experience. A perfectly silent fort, the walls fully manned, the Flag flying—and the gates shut. No vestige of a sign from that motionless garrison staring out into the desert, aiming their rifles at nothing—and at *us* . . . .

'We watched and waited. Two minutes passed; five; six; *seven*. What could it mean? *Was* it a trap after all?

' "*That* one won't return!" said Rastignac loudly, and gave an eerie jarring laugh. The Corporal smote him on the mouth, and I heard him growl, "What about a little *crapaudine*[1] and a mouthful of sand, my friend? . . . You speak again!' . . .

'At the end of ten minutes, a very *mauvais quart d'heure*, I beckoned the Sergeant-Major. I could stand the strain no longer.

' "I am going in," said I. "I cannot send another man, although I ought to do so. Take command . . . If you do not see me within ten minutes, and nothing happens, assault the place. Burn down the gates and let a party climb the walls, while another charges in. Keep a half-troop, under the Corporal, in reserve."

' "Let me go, *mon Commandant*," begged the *Chef*, "if you will not send another soldier. Or call for a volunteer to go. Suppose you . . ."

' "Silence, *Chef*," I replied, "I am going," and I rode back to the fort. Was I right, George?'

'Dunno,' replied George Lawrence.

---

[1] Torture. The hands and feet tied together in a bunch in the middle of the back.

'I remember thinking, as I rode back, what a pernicious fool I should look if, under the eyes of all—the living and the dead—I failed to accomplish that, by no means easy, scramble, and had ignominiously to admit my inability to climb up where the trumpeter had gone. It is sad when one's vile body falls below the standard set by the aspiring soul, when the strength of the muscles is inadequate to the courage of the heart . . .

'However, all went well, and, after an undignified dangling from the spout, and wild groping with the raised foot, I got a leg over the ledge, scrambled up and crawled into an embrasure.

'And there I stood astounded and dumbfounded, *tout bouleversé*, unable to believe my eyes.

'There, as in life, stood the garrison, their backs to me, their faces to the foe whom they had driven off, their feet in dried pools of their own blood—watching, watching . . . And soon I forgot what might be awaiting me below, I forgot my vanished trumpeter, I forgot my troop waiting without—*for there was something else.*

'Lying on his back, his sightless eyes out-staring the sun—lay the Commandant, and through his heart, *a bayonet*, one of our long, thin French sword-bayonets with its single-curved hilt! No—he had not been shot, he was absolutely untouched elsewhere, and there he lay with a French bayonet through his heart. What do you say to that, my friend?'

'Suicide,' replied Lawrence.

'And so did I, until I realized that he had a loaded revolver in one hand, one chamber fired, and a crushed letter in the other! *Does* a man drive a bayonet through his heart, and then take a revolver in one hand and a sheet of paper in the other? I think not.

'Have you ever seen a man drive a bayonet through his heart, my friend? Believe me, he does not fumble for letters, nor draw a revolver and fire it, after he has done *that*. No. He gasps, stares, staggers. He grips the handle and the *forte* of the blade with both hands, totters, stretches convulsively, and collapses, crashing to the ground . . . In any case, does a man commit suicide with a bayonet when he has a loaded revolver? . . . Suicide? *Pouf.*

'Was it any wonder that my jaw dropped and I forgot all else, as I stared and stared ... *Voyez donc!* A French fort in the Sahara, besieged by Arabs. Every man killed at his post. The Arabs beaten off. The fort inviolate, untrodden by Arab foot. The gates closed. Within—the dead, and one of them slain by a French bayonet while he held a loaded revolver in his hand! ...

'But *was* the fort inviolate and untrodden by Arab foot? If so, what had become of my trumpeter? Might not the Arabs be hiding below, waiting their opportunity to catch the relieving force unawares? Might not there be an Arab eye at every rifle-slit? Might not the *caserne*, rooms, offices, sheds, be packed with them?

'Absurdly improbable—and why should they have slain the Commandant with a French bayonet? Would they not have hacked him to pieces with sword and spear, and have mutilated and decapitated every corpse in the place? Was it like the wild Touareg to lay so clever a trap with the propped-up bodies, that a relieving force might fall into their hands as well? Never. *Peaudezébie!* Had the Arabs entered here, the place would have been a looted, blackened ruin, defiled, disgusting, strewn with pieces of what had been men. No, this was not Arab work.

'These Watchers, I felt certain, had been compelled by this dead man, who lay before me, to continue as defenders of the fort after their deaths ... He was evidently a *man*. A bold, resourceful, undaunted hero, sardonic, of a macabre humour, as the Legion always is.

'As each man fell, throughout that long and awful day, he had propped him up, wounded or dead, set the rifle in its place, fired it, and bluffed the Arabs that every wall and every embrasure and loophole of every wall was fully manned. He must, at the last, have run from point to point, firing a rifle from behind its dead defender. Every now and then he must have blown the alarm that the bugler would never blow again, in the hope that it would guide and hasten the relieving force and impress the Arabs with fear that the avengers must be near.

'No wonder the Arabs never charged that fort, from each of

whose walls a rifle cracked continuously, and from whose every embrasure watched a fearless man whom they could not kill—or whose place seemed to be taken, at once, by another, if they did kill him . . .

'All this passed through my mind in a few seconds—and as I realized what he had done and how he had died in the hour of victory, *murdered*, my throat swelled though my blood boiled—and I ventured to give myself the proud privilege of kneeling beside him and pinning my own Croix upon his breast—though I could scarcely see to do so. I thought of how France should ring with the news of his heroism, resource, and last glorious fight, and how every Frenchman should clamour for the blood of his murderer.

'Only a poor *sous-officier* of the Legion. But a hero for France to honour . . . And I would avenge him!

'Such were my thoughts, my friend, as I realized the truth—what are yours?'

'Time for a spot of dinner,' said George Lawrence, starting up.

EXPLORING AN UNTAMED WILDERNESS

Samuel Edwards

A howling wind roared down the snow-covered slopes of the towering mountains, bending the trunks of pine trees. The sky overhead was dark and ominous clouds obscured the summits of the great peaks. This sky, in the unknown, uncharted, and untamed wilderness of the Continental Divide in western Canada, was called by Alexander Mackenzie 'the lid of the Universe'.

A few flakes of snow were driven down by the wind. Then, all at once, the great cauldron of the 'Universe' seemed to tip. The air was filled with ice and snow—stinging pellets that burned men's faces, lodged in their clothes, and made them wish they had not abandoned the comfortable hearths, snug log cabins, and food-filled warehouses back east.

At the timber line one man stood alone. A vast sea of trees spread out below him, a rubble of rocks and boulders above. Young, still in his twenties, he was very short, with small bones, a slender build, and the delicate features of a poet. His face, however, was gaunt now after long weeks in the wilderness. The sun and wind had darkened his skin, a week's stubble covered his chin and his buckskins were worn and ripped. But holding his head high, he shook his fist at the elements. Then he laughed, a full-throated, hearty laugh of genuine pleasure.

The men who huddled behind him were not surprised, for they knew that Alexander Mackenzie was possessed by demons. There was no other explanation for his inexhaustible energy, his coldly calculated daring. Nor could the men who accompanied him, in the spring and summer of 1792, on his journey of exploration to find the overland, northwest passage across the North American continent to the Pacific Ocean, understand his insatiable curiosity, his lack of fear, and, above all, his ability to drive others as he drove himself.

His Indian guides were certain that creatures from the netherworld had occupied his body and soul. Each night they prayed to their gods of fire and water, sun and earth and sky, in the forlorn hope that he would turn back. His *voyageurs*, hard-muscled and hard-headed French-Canadians, boasted that their physical strength was unequalled in all the world. Now, however, they had more than met their match. For even though they often paddled their canoes or bateaux eighteen hours a day and marched all day and most of the night across wilderness portages, they needed at least a few hours of rest in each twenty-four. Mackenzie, apparently, needed none at all.

Henry Fuller Bishop of New Haven, Connecticut, a youth of twenty-one, had accompanied Mackenzie on his previous journey of exploration three years earlier. He should not have been surprised by his leader's behaviour. But even Bishop was dazed by Mackenzie's fury. Alexander Mackay, the second-in-command of the expedition and Mackenzie's Scottish compatriot, was a man of good education, blessed with a strong body and a mind and will of his own. But he, too, had lost his individual identity somewhere in the trackless wilderness of plains and hills, deep forests and swift-flowing rivers. His mind was numbed, his legs and arms ached ceaselessly, yet he still responded to the goading of the short, slender man with the flashing eyes and the deep voice who sometimes pleaded and begged, sometimes roared and thundered.

Everyone knew that the Pacific lay somewhere to the west, Mackenzie insisted. And he was determined to find the passage that would take him to its shores, no matter how great the obstacles. Hostile Indians could not halt him. Mackenzie even refused to quit when his guides admitted they were lost. Neither burning heat nor bone-chilling cold slowed his pace.

Had Alexander Mackenzie been a giant, the men might have found it easier to believe him, to follow him blindly. But he was only five feet, five inches tall; his wrists, waist, and ankles were as slim as a girl's. To see him in action was frightening. Arousing his companions at two or three o'clock in the morning, he hurried them through breakfast, then broke trail. Accompanied by guides, he marched all day with two ninety-pound packs of life-sustaining pemmican slung across his narrow shoulders, a small arsenal of weapons jammed into his belt, his telescope and other scientific instruments on his back, and his precious notebooks filling his pockets.

Mackenzie walked bareheaded, exposing himself to torrential rains and the merciless rays of the sun. His hair was long and shaggy, his skin as dark and leathery as that of the savages; his buckskins were worn thin. Whenever the party stopped for a brief meal and rest, he wrote in his notebooks about birds, animals, and plants they had encountered, and described the territory they had covered.

When the *voyageurs* faltered, he helped them carry their heavily laden boats. When the Indians fell ill, he boiled herbs and cured them. When young Bishop became melancholy, he told robust jokes that made the boy laugh. Sometimes he marched at Bishop's

His Indian guides were certain that MacKenzie was possessed by demons.

side and, although only twenty-nine years of age himself, spoke with such mature wisdom that he might have been Bishop's father. When Mackay argued that they were bound on a fool's errand and surely would die, he replied with a stubborn logic of his own: the Pacific was somewhere to the west; they had wits and ability; so they were sure to reach their goal if they kept on.

At night, when the others were rolled up in their blankets and fast asleep, he studied the stars through his telescope. Then, working on his maps by the light of the campfire, he carefully charted their position. Then he laboured some more on his notebooks. The Indians, who sometimes awoke in the night, swore that he never slept. Perhaps they exaggerated, but he was certainly refreshed after remarkably short periods of rest.

Now, after grueling weeks of travel up rushing rivers and portages where boiling rapids made progress by boat impossible, the party faced its most severe test. Mackenzie was leading them, on foot, to the very roof of the world!

They toiled up the slopes of mountains, each higher and more rugged than the one behind it. They plunged into tiny, narrow valleys, then resumed their climb towards peaks covered with pure, white snow. The men staggered beneath their loads, sweat oozed from their pores; they were forced to pause every few minutes to catch their breath. But Mackenzie remained cheerful, smiling when they groaned, encouraging them with a few gentle words when they wept.

Mackay felt certain they were crossing territory never before seen by man. Mackenzie scoffed at the idea. And one afternoon, as the party emerged from a forest of pines and headed towards the timberline of a rugged peak, loud war whoops broke the silence. Indian braves were lurking behind the screen of trees; their hail of arrows forced the explorers to take shelter.

Mackenzie promptly advanced towards the savages, calling to them first in one native dialect, then in another. There was no response, so he called again, swearing that he and his companions had peaceful intentions towards all men.

An arrow cut through the leather of his stained buckskins. Mackenzie drew a pistol, but deliberately fired it into the air. The shot echoed and re-echoed across the mountains. The braves, cowed by this display of might, emerged into the open. Mackenzie then opened a pack containing trading goods and presented each of the five braves with a knife. To their leader he gave an iron cooking-pot, a string of beads, and a burnished square of steel that could be used as a mirror.

Now the other explorers left the shelter of boulders. The two parties sat down together over a fire, the savages willingly sharing their fish and jerked elk meat. The *voyageurs* and guides ate ravenously as did Mackay and Bishop. But Alexander Mackenzie was indifferent to food; he wanted information.

He failed to get it. The braves said they had never reached the crest of the mountain range and doubted that anyone could climb that high. If the strangers went higher, they would find no wild life because there were no forests. The headwaters of rivers churned too rapidly for even the hardiest of fish to survive. There were no plants, no edible roots on the heights where snow lay deep throughout the year. And the savages were reluctant to explain other, mysterious terrors.

Mackenzie, brushing aside their superstitions, persisted in his questioning. Had they ever met men who had actually crossed the mountains? Had they ever heard of anyone who had performed such a feat?

The Indians reluctantly admitted that, many years in the past, three warriors from a strange tribe had suddenly appeared in the highlands, saying that they lived on the far side of the mountains.

Did they resemble other Indians?

No, the braves said, they were taller, huskier, and their skins were paler.

Mackenzie had learned what he wanted most to know: the mountain range could be conquered. He stood apart, his face impassive. No one knew he was finding it difficult to curb his mounting sense of excitement. Soon now he must test the theory on which he was staking the lives of his followers as well as his own.

His thoughts must have turned back to the long winter of 1786–87 which he spent with Peter Pond, his good friend and mentor, in a trading post hut on the Athabaska River. There the grizzled veteran who had explored so much of the northwest had chatted for hours with the young man destined to excel him. Together they had developed a new concept of the geography of the North American continent.

Both knew that a high range of mountains, running north and south, cut them off from the Pacific; they called this range the Great Divide. Apparently the rivers running down the eastern slopes of these mountains all flowed towards the east. They had learned this from personal observation and from questioning savages who had penetrated deeper into the chain of massive peaks.

So the rivers on the far side of this chain must flow towards the west. If their theory was right, these streams emptied into the Pacific Ocean.

Common sense dictated that the idea was correct. But Mackenzie was no longer a neophyte. He had already gained lasting renown on an earlier journey of discovery. And he had found repeatedly that Nature confounded the logic of mere mortals. So he would not believe that the Pacific was somewhere ahead until he saw with his own eyes that the rivers past the summit flowed westward.

And what if he were wrong? Well, in that case he had no guidelines. With luck, he and his party might reach the shores of the world's largest sea. But they also might wander through the maze of mountains until they froze or starved to death.

He had no idea when, if ever, the party would eat another hot meal. He didn't know whether they would find their way out of the snow-glazed morass at the top of the world. But there was only one way to go—forward . . .

Peter Pond had proved so accurate regarding the existence of a great river in the northwest, one originating north of Great Slave Lake, that Alexander Mackenzie's first reaction was to banish from his mind any remaining doubts about the rest of his ideas.

The river, Pond had told him, flowed towards the south-west. On it were located the largest falls in the known world. Cutting through a northern spur of the rugged north-south range known as the Rocky Mountains, the stream made its way between gorges and ravines, narrow valleys and hidden lowlands, and emerged on the western side. From that point it flowed in a straight line towards the Pacific.

In spite of his high hopes, however, Alexander remained a realist. He questioned the Red-Knives closely about falls on the river. At first the Indians hesitated, but they finally agreed that they existed. He was elated until English Chief came to him privately and said that the guides were being amenable only because they wanted a reward. They knew no more than anyone else about such falls in his opinion.

So Alexander discarded Pond's theories. His friend had been right about the existence of the river, but now it would be a mistake to rely on mere conjecture. A meeting was called on the bank of the river, and Alexander explained to his followers, first in English, then in French, and finally in the Chipewyan dialect, that no one really knew where the river led. Anyone who was fearful and wanted to turn back could leave at once.

Bishop and Steinbruck had no intention of returning east, and the *voyageurs* insisted to a man on accompanying their leader. The Chipewyan would not think of abandoning the venture, and the Red-Knives proudly insisted that they had earned the right to lead the expedition.

Tears came to Alexander's eyes as he thanked his companions for their faith in him. He promised to do his best for all of them, no matter what lay ahead.

Excitement ran high now as the canoes, spurred by a moderate current, sailed past an island about fourteen miles long. For a time they travelled due west, then southwest. Alexander wondered what kind of magic Pond had employed. No civilized man, indeed no Indian known to civilized men had ever travelled in these waters, yet Pond's theory seemed accurate.

On both sides of the river the countryside was very low, the river itself so broad that a man could hardly see from one bank to the other. Alexander realized that his party had come into another lake. He made several unsuccessful attempts to find his way out, at last locating the main channel which flowed towards the south.

The area to the north was heavily forested; it seemed to be a low plain. To the south, the leader saw a plateau more sparsely wooded. He could not help wondering whether he was heading towards the spur of the Rockies, the last great barrier standing between him and the Pacific.

When the journey was resumed, the river flowed almost due south. Excitement mounted again when a ridge of low mountains was sighted directly ahead. A new river teeming with trout emptied into the Mackenzie. Alexander marked it on his map as the Trout River, a name by which it has since been known. The party camped there for the night.

The sluggish waters ended a few miles below the Trout River camp, the river narrowing to a width of half a mile. The current increased to about eight miles per hour. Alexander, haunted by fears of falls, frequently paused to take soundings. In the afternoon he lost his lead and part of his sounding line. It was severed by an underwater portion of an ice floe. Ice indeed was piled high on both banks of the river.

To the extreme disappointment of the entire party, the river now turned north and west again, then due north. Hopes of finding an immediate passage to the Pacific faded. Near the junction of another river was a small island with signs of previous habitation—the framework of four separate native lodges.

After the Chipewyan and Red-Knives had examined the site for some time, they decided that the island had been inhabited by people of the Knisteneau nation better known as the Cree. This was a fierce tribe of warriors much feared by all other Indians. There was no way of determining how long a time had elapsed since the Cree had left the island, but Alexander guessed that the lodges had been abandoned at least ten years earlier.

The Chipewyan wanted to go home now, but hated to appear cowardly before the Red-Knives; the two guides themselves, although visibly upset, made no mention of leaving. Alexander was less worried about the Cree than he was about the possibility of coming to the falls unexpectedly. So he ordered another quantity of pemmican buried on the island, explaining that it would be used on the return voyage. The Indians were unable to share his optimism; they felt positive that the winter would be spent in the unknown wilderness. They declared openly that they did not expect to return in less than a year.

The tools and weapons the Cree had left behind them created mixed emotions in Alexander. The savages obviously had not been acquainted with iron, so if he found some Cree villages, he could do a great deal of business with them. The trader in him rejoiced; he hoped to get large quantities of furs in return for firearms and iron knives. On the other hand, his sense of disappointment was far greater, for he reasoned that if the Cree had no iron tools, they had not come in contact with explorers on the Pacific coast.

Late one morning a vast range of snow-capped mountains appeared to the west and south when the sun burned away the haze. The range stretched as far as the explorers could see. Studying the slopes with care, they made out wooded patches, but saw, too, that a great many of the peaks soared high above the timber line. Most of the summits were lost in clouds.

Alexander immediately called a halt, studied the mountains through his telescope, and scribbled furiously in his notebook. Even the Indians sensed his excitement. The *voyageurs* wanted to celebrate with rum, a suggestion that was refused.

No explorer could have known a more thrilling moment. Alexander had discovered a vast range of towering mountains totally unknown to civilized man. Even in those first exhilarating moments, he realized that he had won immortality.

FIRST ASCENT OF MONTE INACCESSIBLE

John Ridgway

John Ridgway, his wife Marie Christine, Richard Shuff and Krister Nylund reach the southern tip of Chile near the Straits of Magellan and prepare for an attempt on Monte Inaccessible . . .

The day dawned grey and misty again, but quite calm. After good helpings of porridge, fried fish and tea, the mountain seemed rather less of a problem, even though we couldn't be sure if we had ever really seen the summit through the cloud. The plan was a quick ascent and back again in time for supper. Marie Christine decided not to come with us and this strengthened the supper prospect for our return. Richard, Krister and I packed our kit quickly, hoping to make the most of the remaining fourteen hours of daylight. A hundred feet of No. 4 climbing rope, plenty of warm clothing and the Helly Hansen suits. A sleeping-bag each and a tent, together with rations for two days. For the snow we took glacier cream and goggles. We each had maps and compasses both to help us on the mountain and to check out possible routes up onto the ice-cap, which lay across the fiord from the mountain. By nine-thirty the weather was improving and we made the decision to leave at ten.

The boat trip across the fiord took only fifteen minutes. On the way we saw and heard porpoises gambolling in the still water. Away to our left close under the condors' nest we caught a glimpse of a stately pair of swans, snow-white save for their black necks.

We carried the dinghy across ten feet of pebble beach and laid it upside down on top of the short bushes at the fringe of the forest. In case of high winds, in our absence on the mountain, we made certain that the boat was tied securely both bow and stern. The little beach had been made in the course of time by a powerful torrent, whose roaring could be heard night and day even right across the fiord at our camp. Somewhere, high above in the mist, was the source of this stream, and higher still the summit of the mountain we had come halfway round the world to climb.

The first part of the climb was up through dense trees and bushes which clutched at our every move; underfoot the going was sometimes rock, sometimes swamp. Every so often we emerged onto the bald face of a rock band, to mop the perspiration from our eyes, and then shed another layer of clothing.

'I reckon this is still only the third band,' grunted Richard, 'we left base about four hours too late.'

In my mind's eye, I tried to visualize how far up we were, against the mental picture of the mountain I had tried to memorize at the camp. The third layer of rock up didn't look too hopeful to me. Trees and brush clung to every inch of soil, and behind each rock band they choked the little valleys. However, Krister steadied us with a quote from Lord Slim, 'It could be worse, it could be raining!' So for the next quarter of an hour it did rain.

At twelve-thirty we stopped for lunch on a rocky ledge; it was bare except for a few large boulders which provided shelter from a cold breeze. Underfoot there was some moss and several pools of water. The climb to this point had been particularly trying; up a steep gully full of slippery wet moss, and tangled with bushes which were so insecurely anchored to the rock as to offer little use as hand-holds. Our rucksacks, mounted on their high pack frames, weren't much of a help because they bumped the backs of our heads whenever we tried to look up.

'All in all, I'd rather be in Philadelphia,' quoted Richard as we struggled into our duvet jackets and waterproof suits. Although the rain just managed to hold off, it was pretty chilly. We weren't too optimistic, so no one said much, and the little petrol burner roared away under the tall billy which was carefully placed in the shelter of a boulder and the artificial walls made by our rucksacks.

The cloud base had risen a bit during the morning and we could see well up into the tumbled icefields where they clung to the walls of the ice-cap on the far side of the fiord, although the top was still obscured. At our feet lay the fiord, a long narrow strip of milky green water, running from Canal Gajardo and Chandler Island on our left, to a short river which joined a couple of pale grey lakes and a huge glacier on our right. The orange specks of our three tents marked the base of a thin spiral of grey woodsmoke rising from our camp at the edge of the dark green trees directly opposite us on the far side of the fiord. What interested us was the ground between the orange tents and the blue white wall of the ice-cap; for some-where here, if anywhere, lay our route through the towers and ramparts formed by the rumbling ice-falls. The southern ridge appeared to have the easier approach, because the trees quickly fell away where it rose sharply from the edge of the fiord; also there were broad tongues of yellowed winter grass which led through the worst of the woodland. But try as we would, we still could not get a proper view of either ridge, owing to the layers of grey-white cloud clinging to the side of the valley.

We knew by heart that there were eight thin slices in a pack of Kraft cheese, and twenty-two thin wine biscuits in one of Mackay's Vino packs from Santiago. Krister's chilled fingers made three neat little piles on the bare grey rock. Richard had an advantage with the scalding sweet tea, his plastic thermo-mug enabled him to drink comfortably while Krister and I made hasty sips against the hot edges of the empty butter tins. I thought of the old army trick of insulating the edge with silver paper, but Richard's packets of English cigarettes had run out long since, and with them our only source of foil.

It was too cold to sit for long over lunch. I led the next stage which rose sharply into the snowfields and cloud. Sadly the trees didn't end where the snow began, but rather changed into a low flat-topped type of bush which twisted hither and thither across the surface of the snow as if afraid to climb far from the mountainside. Progress became a matter of kicking footholds in the none-too-crisp snow, and wending a way in and out of the wind-blown bushes. To pass too close to one of these serpentine clumps of silver branches usually meant sinking through the icy crust until one leg was thigh deep in wet snow. This stage of the climb was rather like a tiring game of snakes and ladders, it didn't take long to exhaust both our interest and our new-found energy. We took it in turns to lead through this wilderness which was interrupted occasionally by rushing streams whose snow-covered banks caved in all too easily.

After an hour or so we were well up in the cloud and the whole project assumed a more stark atmosphere. Apart from one solitary snipe we had seen no living thing. I was cold and our world had shrunk to black rock and white snow. We stopped to eat a bar of Kendal Mint Cake, hoping it would give us the energy and enthusiasm to face the last assault, up through the cloud. We found a use for the scrub bushes; they made excellent springy seats which stopped us from sinking in the snow. A chill breeze from the north was blowing now through a saddle connecting Monte Inaccessible with another unnamed mountain to the north-west; we sat for only a few minutes in a fairly sheltered place, but the cold soon got us going again.

Ahead the going became much steeper, the bushes stopped and we were faced with sharp rocky spurs interspersed with gullies full of loose shale or gneiss. Snow lay in drifts here and there, and it blanketed every piece of sheltered flat ground; luckily the crust was hard and we were able to chip footholds in it without difficulty. Finished was the floundering about in wet snow up to our thighs. The best approach to the summit of Inaccessible appeared to be by way of the spur running up from the saddle, which joined the two mountains. Richard led us up in a general direction which would link with it. Once on the spur we would turn sharply to the right and follow it, hopefully to emerge on the summit soon after.

'If you wait here out of the wind I'll nip up and take a look,' called Richard, when we were about thirty feet below the edge of the spur. Krister and I huddled together between a couple of big rocks and cracked jokes to take our minds off the cold. Soon Richard came into sight and clambered down to join us.

'You'd better go up and take a look, John. It's grim. I reckon we'll need a lot more time and a helluva lot more kit,' he said, and Krister and I looked at each other. I could tell we were both thinking the same thing—"Oh no, not all the way down, to come up and go through all this again."

I left them there and crawled up on my own to see the way ahead, fearing the worst. As soon as I reached the crest of the spur the cold wind hit me, probing at every join in my clothing as if anxious to find a way in and freeze me. Across on the other side of the saddle there was a great area of snow-covered peaks, not at all like the friendly fiord and green trees below on the side from which we had come. The sky was above and all round me, like a huge grey blanket. Glancing urgently on up towards the summit of Monte Inaccessible, I could see a stern sight. The ridge of the spur disappeared from sight only thirty yards farther on, over what I guessed would be a false crest. Looking across up the other side of the spur I could see a great bowl of sheer black rock against which fields of snow clung, just ripe for avalanche. Across all this the grey clouds drifted in a most mysterious, melancholy fashion.

Laziness drove me on. I had no plans to go through this again on another day. We had come up here to climb the mountain and climb it we would. I scrambled down to Richard and Krister.

I led the next stage which rose sharply into the snowfields and cloud.

'Well, we've seen Foinavon look like that,' I said. 'If the cloud clears for a few minutes it will look very different. I'm for going on. I'm sure the spur will lead to the top.' Krister looked relieved, Richard cautious and unconvinced, but they both needed assent and we set off.

Once firmly on the spine of the spur, we found the going tricky in the cold wind. It was so steep that we could only move very slowly.

'See the condor, John,' called Krister. I looked up and the great bird seemed close enough to touch. While we struggled for every foot of ground he sailed along with unconcerned ease, bending his ugly bald neck to peer intently at those whom he hoped "are about to die". From below he looked all black save for the bright white collar, but when he banked to turn for another run close over our heads we could see that the tops of his wings had a lot of white on them. Twice he lowered his legs as if about to land but changed his mind, content to circle above us until one or all of us finally lay still.

The loose rock on the spur was nervously and physically exhausting, and it was with some relief that I saw a substantial patch of snow ahead. But when we reached the point where it began I wished that we could simply carry on across rock instead of the time-consuming rope work that would be necessary to cross the insecure area of the snow cornice.

'This is the top of the big snowfield, John. Do you remember we saw it from the camp—the day we thought we saw the top of the mountain?' shouted Krister against the wind.

'Yes, I remember; this bit on the right will be where the avalanches were coming from,' I shouted back, thinking the left windward side of the cornice looked pretty unstable as well.

While Richard belayed himself to the rock at the edge of the thirty-yard horseshoe snow walk, he explained how the formation had occurred. Basically this was a point on the spur where there was a sharp dip, rather like a bite taken out of a slice of melon. The winter snows had filled in the bite and drifting powder snow had found an overhang on the right-hand or sheltered leeward side of the spur. Now that summer was coming (believe it or not) the overhang would collapse and avalanche down the main snowfield which we had seen from the camp. On the left or windward side, the snow fell so steeply with the angle of the spur's side that it too might come unstuck and slide away down the face of the bowl.

Krister went first, with Richard carefully paying out the rope so that there was never too much slack. Watching him plod methodically across the glaring white, prodding the snow with the handle of his ice axe before each step to test the depth, reminded me to slide my sun visor down off my woolly hat to shield my eyes. The sun doesn't necessarily have to be out to cause snow blindness. He reached the rock on the far side of the cornice with only just enough rope to spare and Richard shouted to me that he wished we had brought the three hundred-foot length of 9-mm Kernmantel instead of the hundred feet of No. 4 nylon rope.

By the time we were all three safely on the far side, almost fifteen minutes had elapsed, and we were numb with cold from the biting wind. We struck out for the top at a brisk rate, hoping that we might warm up a bit by the time we reached the summit. As always it took longer than we thought, and another half hour had passed before we all three strode onto the peak together, feeling for all the world like Hillary and Tenzing.

As if to acknowledge our effort the cloud lifted above us and the sun shone through on parts of the surrounding country. For a while the keen wind seemed to drop, or it might have been just the euphoria of achieving our objective. Every way we looked there were snow-capped mountains of all shapes and sizes, from gracefully rounded mounds to the thrusting pinnacles of the cerros which looked like fairy towers encrusted with icing sugar. Ribbons of bright water wove in and out around the feet of the mountains. Nowhere in all this wilderness was there even the slightest trace of man's having ever existed. Close above, the sinister shape of the black condor wheeled about us, the great splayed feathers at his wing-tips playing the wind like fingers on a piano.

Each one of us remarked on our feelings during the few minutes we spent on the summit. Together with the sense of achievement usually felt on reaching the top of something, there was this extra ingredient at standing where no human foot had ever trod. Richard took the tiny Union Jack from his rucksack and pinned it to the top with a couple of rocks. Krister buried a small Sundsvall badge from his home town in Sweden, and we each took a small chip of rock to remind us of the day we made the first ascent of Monte Inaccessible.

DAVID COPPERFIELD'S
JOURNEY TO DOVER

Charles Dickens

David Copperfield's childhood is blighted by his cruel stepfather, Mr Murdstone, who sends David to work at a bleak warehouse after his mother dies.

Conditions are dreadful, and David decides to escape to Dover, where his aunt lives. En-route he plans to sleep near his old school, perchance to be comforted by memories of happier days . . .

Indeed, I foresaw pretty clearly that my jacket would go next, and that I should have to make the best of my way to Dover in a shirt and a pair of trousers, and might deem myself lucky if I got there even in that trim. But my mind did not run so much on this as might be supposed. Beyond a general impression of the distance before me, and of the young man with the donkey-cart having used me cruelly, I think I had no very urgent sense of my difficulties when I once again set off with my ninepence in my pocket.

A plan had occurred to me for passing the night, which I was going to carry into execution. This was, to lie behind the wall at the back of my old school, in a corner where there used to be a haystack. I imagined it would be a kind of company to have the boys, and the bedroom where I used to tell the stories, so near me: although the boys would know nothing of my being there, and the bedroom would yield me no shelter.

I had had a hard day's work, and was pretty well jaded when I came climbing out, at last, upon the level of Blackheath. It cost me some trouble to find out Salem House; but I found it, and I found a haystack in the corner, and I lay down by it; having first walked round the wall, and looked up at the windows, and seen that all was dark and silent within. Never shall I forget the lonely sensation of first lying down, without a roof above my head!

Sleep came upon me as it came on many other outcasts, against whom house-doors were locked, and house-dogs barked, that night—and I dreamed of lying on my old school-bed, talking to the boys in my room; and found myself sitting upright, with Steerforth's name upon my lips, looking wildly at the stars that were glistening and glimmering above me. When I remembered where I was at that untimely hour, a feeling stole upon me that made me get up, afraid of I don't know what, and walk about. But the fainter glimmering of the stars, and the pale light in the sky where the day was coming, reassured me: and my eyes began very heavy, I lay down again, and slept—though with a knowledge in my sleep that it was cold—until the warm beams of the sun, and the ringing of the getting-up bell at Salem House, awoke me. If I could have hoped that Steerforth was there, I would have lurked about until he came out alone; but I knew he must have left long since. Traddles still remained, perhaps, but it was very doubtful; and I had not sufficient confidence in his discretion or good luck, however strong my reliance was on his good-nature, to wish to trust him with my situation. So I crept away from the wall as Mr Creakle's boys were getting up, and struck into the long dusty track which I had first known to be the Dover Road when I was one of them, and when I little expected that any eyes would ever see me the wayfarer I was now, upon it.

What a different Sunday morning from the old Sunday morning at Yarmouth! In due time I heard the church-bells ringing, as I plodded on; and I met people who were going to church; and I passed a church or two where the congregation were inside, and the sound of singing came out into the sunshine, while the beadle sat and cooled himself in the shade of the porch, or stood beneath the yew-tree, with his hand to his forehead, glowering at me going by. But the peace and rest of the old Sunday morning were on everything, except me. That was the difference. I felt quite wicked in my dirt and dust, with my tangled hair. But for the quiet picture I had conjured up, of my mother in her youth and beauty, weeping by the fire, and my aunt relenting to her, I hardly think I should have had the courage to go on until next day. But it always went before me, and I followed.

I got, that Sunday, through three-and-twenty miles on the straight road, though not very easily, for I was new to that kind of toil. I see myself, as evening closes in, coming over the bridge at Rochester, footsore and tired, and eating bread that I had bought for supper. One or two little houses, with the notice, 'Lodgings for Travellers', hanging out, had tempted me; but I was afraid of spending the few pence I had, and was even more afraid of the vicious looks of the trampers I had met or overtaken. I sought no shelter, therefore, but the sky; and toiling into Chatham—which, in that night's aspect, is a mere dream of chalk, and drawbridges, and mastless ships in a muddy river, roofed like Noah's arks— crept, at last, upon a sort of grass-grown battery overhanging a lane, where a sentry was walking to and fro. Here I lay down, near a cannon; and, happy in the society of the sentry's footsteps, though he knew no more of my being above him than the boys at Salem House had known of my lying by the wall, slept soundly until morning.

Very stiff and sore of foot I was in the morning, and quite dazed by the beating of drums and marching of troops, which seemed to hem me in on every side when I went down towards the long narrow street. Feeling that I could go but a very little way that day, if I were to reserve any strength for getting to my journey's end, I resolved to make the sale of my jacket its principal business.

Accordingly, I took the jacket off, that I might learn to do without it; and carrying it under my arm, began a tour of inspection of the various slop-shops.

It was a likely place to sell a jacket in; for the dealers in second-hand clothes were numerous, and were, generally speaking, on the look-out for customers at their shop-doors. But, as most of them had, hanging up among their stock, an officer's coat or two, epaulettes and all, I was rendered timid by the costly nature of their dealings, and walked about for a long time without offering my merchandise to any one.

This modesty of mine directed my attention to the marine-store shops, and such shops as Mr Dolloby's, in preference to the regular dealers. At last I found one that I thought looked promising, at the corner of a dirty lane, ending in an inclosure full of stinging-nettles, against the palings of which some second-hand sailors' clothes, that seemed to have overflowed the shop, were fluttering among some cots, and rusty guns, and oilskin hats, and certain trays full of so many old rusty keys of so many sizes that they seemed various enough to open all the doors in the world.

Into this shop, which was low and small, and which was darkened rather than lighted by a little window, overhung with clothes, and was descended into by some steps, I went with a palpitating heart; which was not relieved when an ugly old man, with the lower part of his face all covered with a stubbly grey beard, rushed out of a dirty den behind it, and seized me by the hair of my head. He was a dreadful old man to look at, in a filthy flannel waistcoat, and smelling terribly of rum. His bedstead, covered with a tumbled and ragged piece of patchwork, was in the den he had come from, where another little window showed a prospect of more stinging-nettles, and a lame donkey.

'Oh, what do you want?' grinned this old man, in a fierce, monotonous whine. 'Oh, my eyes and limbs, what do you want? Oh, my lungs and liver, what do you want? Oh, goroo, goroo!'

I was so much dismayed by these words, and particularly by the repetition of the last unknown one, which was a kind of rattle in his throat, that I could make no answer; hereupon the old man, still holding me by the hair, repeated:

'Oh, what do you want? Oh, my eyes and limbs, what do you want? Oh, my lungs and liver, what do you want? Oh, goroo!'— which he screwed out of himself, with an energy that made his eyes start in his head.

'I wanted to know,' I said, trembling, 'if you would buy a jacket.'

'Oh, let's see the jacket!' cried the old man. 'Oh, my heart on fire, show the jacket to us! Bring the jacket out!'

With that he took his trembling hands, which were like the claws of a great bird, out of my hair; and put on a pair of spectacles, not at all ornamental to his inflamed eyes.

'Oh, how much for the jacket?' cried the old man, after examining it. 'Oh—goroo!—how much for the jacket?'

'Half-a-crown,' I answered, recovering myself.

'Oh, my lungs and liver,' cried the old man, 'no! Oh, my eyes, no! Oh, my limbs, no! Eighteenpence. Goroo!'

Every time he uttered this ejaculation, his eyes seemed to be in danger of starting out; and every sentence he spoke, he delivered in a sort of tune, always exactly the same, and more like a gust of wind, which begins low, mounts up high, and falls again, than any other comparison I can find for it.

'Well,' said I, glad to have closed the bargain, 'I'll take eighteen-pence.'

'Oh, my liver!' cried the old man, throwing the jacket on a shelf. 'Get out of the shop! Oh, my lungs, get out of the shop! Oh, my eyes and limbs—goroo!—don't ask for money; make it an exchange.'

I never was so frightened in my life, before or since; but I told him humbly that I wanted money, and that nothing else was of any use to me, but that I would wait for it, as he desired, outside, and had no wish to hurry him. So I went outside, and sat down in the shade in a corner. And I sat there so many hours, that the shade became sunlight, and the sunlight became shade again, and still I saw there waiting for the money.

There never was such another drunken madman in that line of business, I hope. That he was well known in the neighbourhood, and enjoyed the reputation of having sold himself to the devil, I soon understood from the visits he received from the boys, who continually came skirmishing about the shop, shouting that legend, and calling to him to bring out his gold. 'You ain't poor, you know, Charley, as you pretend. Bring out your gold. Bring out some of the gold you sold yourself to the devil for. Come! It's in the lining of the mattress, Charley. Rip it open and let's have some!' This, and many offers to lend him a knife for the purpose, exasperated him to such a degree, that the whole day was a succession of rushes on his part, and flights on the part of the boys. Sometimes in his rage he would take me for one of them, and come at me, mouthing as if he were going to tear me in pieces; then, remembering me, just in time, would dive into the shop, and lie upon his bed, as I thought from the sound of his voice, yelling in a frantic way, to his own windy tune, the Death of Nelson; with an Oh! before every line, and innumerable Goroos interspersed. As if this were not bad enough for me, the boys, connecting me with the establishment, on account of the patience and perseverance with which I sat outside, half-dressed, pelted me, and used me very ill all day.

He made many attempts to induce me to consent to an exchange; at one time coming out with a fishing-rod, at another with a fiddle, at another with a cocked hat, at another with a flute. But I resisted all these overtures, and sat there in desperation; each time asking him, with tears in my eyes, for my money or my jacket. At last he began to pay me in halfpence at a time; and was full two hours getting by easy stages to a shilling.

'Oh, my eyes and limbs!' he then cried, peeping hideously out of the shop, after a long pause, 'will you go for twopence more?'

'I can't,' I said; 'I shall be starved.'

'Oh, my lungs and liver, will you go for threepence?'

'I would go for nothing, if I could,' I said, 'but I want the money badly.'

'Oh, go—roo!' (it is really impossible to express how he twisted

'Where do you come from?' asked the tinker.

this ejaculation out of himself, as he peeped round the doorpost at me, showing nothing but his crafty old head) 'will you go for fourpence?'

I was so faint and weary that I closed with this offer; and taking the money out of his claw, not without trembling, went away more hungry and thirsty than I had ever been, a little before sunset. But at an expense of threepence I soon refreshed myself completely; and, being in better spirits then, limped seven miles upon my road.

My bed at night was under another haystack, where I rested comfortably, after having washed my blistered feet in a stream, and dressed them as well as I was able, with some cool leaves. When I took the road again next morning, I found that it lay through a succession of hop-grounds and orchards. It was sufficiently late in the year for the orchards to be ruddy with ripe apples; and in a few places the hop-pickers were already at work. I thought it all extremely beautiful, and made up my mind to sleep among the hops that night: imagining some cheerful companionship in the long perspectives of poles, with the graceful leaves twining round them.

The trampers were worse than ever that day, and inspired me with a dread that is yet quite fresh in my mind. Some of them were most ferocious-looking ruffians, who stared at me as I went by; and stopped, perhaps, and called after me to come back and speak to them, and when I took to my heels, stoned me. I recollect one young fellow—a tinker, I suppose, from his wallet and brazier—who had a woman with him, and who faced about and stared at me thus; and then roared to me in such a tremendous voice to come back, that I halted and looked round.

'Come here, when you're called,' said the tinker, 'or I'll rip your young body open.'

I thought it best to go back. As I drew nearer to them, trying to propitiate the tinker by my looks, I observed that the woman had a black eye.

'Where are you going?' said the tinker, gripping the bosom of my shirt with his blackened hand.

'I am going to Dover,' I said.

'Where do you come from?' asked the tinker, giving his hand another turn in my shirt, to hold me more securely.

'I come from London,' I said.

'What lay are you upon?' asked the tinker. 'Are you a prig?'

'N—no,' I said.

'Ain't you, by G—? If you make a brag of your honesty to me,' said the tinker, 'I'll knock your brains out.'

With his disengaged hand he made a menace of striking me, and then looked at me from head to foot.

'Have you got the price of a pint of beer about you?' said the tinker. 'If you have, out with it, afore I take it away!'

I should certainly have produced it, but that I met the woman's look, and saw her very slightly shake her head, and form 'No!' with her lips.

'I am very poor,' I said, attempting to smile, 'and have got no money.'

'Why, what do you mean?' said the tinker, looking so sternly at me, that I almost feared he saw the money in my pocket.

'Sir!' I stammered.

'What do you mean,' said the tinker, 'by wearing my brother's silk handkercher! Give it over here!' And he had mine off my neck in a moment, and tossed it to the woman.

The woman burst into a fit of laughter, as if she thought this a joke, and tossed it back to me, nodded once, as slightly as before, and made the word 'Go!' with her lips. Before I could obey, however, the tinker seized the handkerchief out of my hand with a roughness that threw me away like a feather, and putting it loosely round his own neck, turned upon the woman with an oath, and knocked her down. I never shall forget seeing her fall backward on the hard road, and lie there with her bonnet tumbled off, and her hair all whitened in the dust; nor, when I looked back from a distance, seeing her sitting on the pathway, which was a bank by the roadside, wiping the blood from her face with a corner of her shawl, while he went on ahead.

This adventure frightened me so, that, afterwards, when I saw any of these people coming, I turned back until I could find a hiding-place, where I remained until they had gone out of sight; which happened so often, that I was very seriously delayed. But under this difficulty, as under all the other difficulties of my journey, I seemed to be sustained and led on by my fanciful picture of my mother in her youth, before I came into the world. It always kept me company. It was there, among the hops, when I lay down to sleep; it was with me on my waking in the morning; it went before me all day. I have associated it, ever since, with the sunny street of Canterbury, dozing as it were in the hot light; and with the sight of its old houses and gateways, and the stately, grey Cathedral, with the rooks sailing round the towers. When I came, at last, upon the bare, wide downs near Dover, it relieved the solitary aspect of the scene with hope; and not until I reached that first great aim of my journey, and actually set foot in the town itself, on the sixth day of my flight, did it desert me. But then, strange to say, when I stood with my ragged shoes, and my dusty, sunburnt, half-clothed figure, in the place so long desired, it seemed to vanish like a dream, and to leave me helpless and dispirited.

I inquired about my aunt among the boatmen first, and received various answers. One said she lived in the South Foreland Light, and had singed her whiskers by doing so; another, that she was made fast to the great buoy outside the harbour, and could only be visited at half-tide; a third, that she was locked up in Maidstone Jail for child-stealing; a fourth, that she was seen to mount a broom, in the last high wind, and made direct for Calais. The fly-drivers, among whom I inquired next, were equally jocose and equally disrespectful; and the shopkeepers, not liking my appearance, generally replied, without hearing what I had to say, that they had got nothing for me. I felt more miserable and destitute than I had done at any period of my running away. My money was all gone, I had nothing left to dispose of; I was hungry, thirsty, and worn out; and seemed as distant from my end as if I had remained in London.

The morning had worn away in these inquiries, and I was sitting on the step of an empty shop at a street corner, near the market-place, deliberating upon wandering towards those other places which had been mentioned, when a fly-driver, coming by with his carriage, dropped a horsecloth. Something good-natured in the man's face, as I handed it up, encouraged me to ask him if he could tell me where Miss Trotwood lived; though I had asked the question so often, that it almost died upon my lips.

'Trotwood,' said he. 'Let me see. I know the name, too. Old lady?'

'Yes,' I said, 'rather.'

'Pretty stiff in the back?' said he, making himself upright.

'Yes,' I said. 'I should think it very likely.'

'Carries a bag?' said he: 'bag with a good deal of room in it: is gruffish, and comes down upon you, sharp?'

My heart sank within me as I acknowledged the undoubted accuracy of this description.

'Why then, I tell you what,' said he. 'If you go up there,' pointing with his whip towards the heights, 'and keep right on till you come to some houses facing the sea, I think you'll hear of her. My opinion is, she won't stand anything, so here's a penny for you.'

I accepted the gift thankfully, and bought a loaf with it. Dispatching this refreshment by the way, I went in the direction my friend had indicated, and walked on a good distance without coming to the houses he had mentioned. At length I saw some before me; and approaching them, went into a little shop (it was what we used to call a general shop, at home), and inquired if they could have the goodness to tell me where Miss Trotwood lived. I addressed myself to a man behind the counter, who was weighing some rice for a young woman; but the latter, taking the inquiry to herself, turned round quickly.

'My mistress?' she said. 'What do you want with her, boy?'

'I want,' I replied, 'to speak to her, if you please.'

'To beg of her, you mean,' retorted the damsel.

'No,' I said, 'indeed.' But suddenly remembering that in truth I came for no other purpose, I held my peace in confusion, and felt my face burn.

My aunt's handmaid, as I supposed she was from what she had said, put her rice in a little basket and walked out of the shop; telling me that I could follow her, if I wanted to know where Miss Trotwood lived. I needed no second permission; though I was by this time in such a state of consternation and agitation, that my legs shook under me. I followed the young woman, and we soon came to a very neat little cottage with cheerful bow-windows: in front of it, a small square gravelled court or garden full of flowers, carefully tended, and smelling deliciously.

'This is Miss Trotwood's,' said the young woman. 'Now you know; and that's all I have got to say.' With which words she hurried into the house, as if to shake off the responsibility of my appearance; and left me standing at the garden-gate, looking disconsolately over the top of it towards the parlour-window, where a muslin curtain partly undrawn in the middle, a large round green screen or fan fastened on to the window-sill, a small table, and a great chair, suggested to me that my aunt might be at that moment seated in awful state.

My shoes were by this time in a woeful condition. The soles had shed themselves bit by bit, and the upper leathers had broken and burst until the very shape and form of shoes had departed from them. My hat (which had served me for a night-cap, too) was so crushed and bent, that no old battered handleless saucepan on a dunghill need have been ashamed to vie with it. My shirt and trousers, stained with heat, dew, grass, and the Kentish soil on which I had slept—and torn besides—might have frightened the birds from my aunt's garden, as I stood at the gate. My hair had known no comb or brush since I left London. My face, neck, and hands, from unaccustomed exposure to the air and sun, were burnt to a berry-brown. From head to foot I was powdered almost as white with chalk and dust, as if I had come out of a lime-kiln. In this plight, and with a strong consciousness of it, I waited to introduce myself to, and make my first impression on, my formidable aunt.

The unbroken stillness of the parlour-window leading me to infer, after a while, that she was not there, I lifted up my eyes to the window above it, where I saw a florid, pleasant-looking gentleman, with a grey head, who shut up one eye in a grotesque manner, nodded his head at me several times, shook it at me as often, laughed, and went away.

I had been discomposed enough before; but I was so much the more discomposed by this unexpected behaviour, that I was on the point of slinking off, to think how I had best proceed, when there came out of the house a lady with her handkerchief tied over her cap, and a pair of gardening gloves on her hands, wearing a gardening pocket like a toll-man's apron, and carrying a great knife. I knew her immediately to be Miss Betsey, for she came stalking out of the house exactly as my poor mother had so often described her stalking up our garden at Blunderstone Rookery.

'Go away!' said Miss Betsey, shaking her head, and making a distant chop in the air with her knife. 'Go along! No boys here!'

I watched her, with my heart at my lips, as she marched to a corner of her garden, and stooped to dig up some little root there. Then, without a scrap of courage, but with a great deal of desperation, I went softly in and stood beside her, touching her with my finger.

'If you please, ma'am,' I began.

She started and looked up.

'If you please, aunt.'

'EH?' exclaimed Miss Betsey, in a tone of amazement I have never heard approached.

'If you please, aunt, I am your nephew.'

'Oh, Lord!' said my aunt. And sat flat down in the garden-path.

THE
RANNOCH MOOR
RESCUE

Hamish MacInnes

Hamish MacInnes, leader of a mountain rescue team recalls one particular rescue operation . . .

Recaptured memories can be rewarding, especially of occasions such as the Rannoch Moor rescue of 1965.

Two professors from Edinburgh had been fishing on the lochs of the Moor; since fishing is very much a solitary occupation they had separated and agreed to meet again at 5 p.m. and return together to their car which was parked on the main road. They had both planned to return to Edinburgh the same evening, after dining at the Kingshouse Hotel. We first suspected that something was amiss when Doris Elliot telephoned me from the hotel to say that one of the professors had come back to the hotel, having failed to make contact with his colleague.

Most of the team members had assembled at the hotel by 8 p.m.

194

The professor gave us details of where he had last seen his companion: a point some four miles north of the A82, across a wild and boggy section of the moor. We had several rescue dogs amongst the company and decided to deploy them in searching over the the vast area which lay to the west of the line that the professors had taken on their outward journey to the fishing grounds on Loch Laidon.

Walter Elliot, George Cormack, Hugh McColl and Eric Moss all took the path, intending to search the area where the professor was last seen by his companion—about a mile from their proposed rendezvous. Willie Elliot and I were going to search the ground to the west of the path, using three dogs: Willie had Corrie, a working border-collie and a trained rescue dog; I had Tiki and Rangi, my two Alsatians. We understood that John Grey and Denis Barclay, fellow team members, would join in the search when they arrived.

Jimmy Ross was then our local police constable and George Cormack, a tall, dark policeman, was his assistant. Sadly, Jimmy and George were not always in perfect accord with one another! On this occasion Jimmy Ross remained at base, providing a fixed point with the flashing blue light of the police Land-Rover from which we could take our bearings if we became lost. A traverse of the moor is daunting, even in daylight, as numerous detours have to be made amongst the myriads of deep, boggy streams. By night, trying to make any progress there can be a heartbreaking task.

Each of our groups had a police walkie-talkie since, at the time, our team possessed none. After about an hour Jimmy informed us that both John Grey and Denis Barclay had arrived and were setting off in the direction which Willie and I had previously taken. We flashed our torches until they had located and joined us. There was now no sign of the Land-Rover or the flashing light.

'I bet he's away for a cup of coffee at the hotel,' said Willie in disgust.

'Well, if he brings some back for us it won't be so bad,' I answered. 'I could do with a cup at the moment; it's ruddy cold.'

Just then Jimmy's voice came over the walkie-talkie: 'Hello there, Hamish. Come in, please.'

'Yes, Jimmy?' I replied. 'We were missing you—where's your flashing light?'

'I had to go to the hotel to telephone,' he explained. 'Can't contact headquarters from here. I'll be back in position shortly. Is there anything to report?'

'Negative here,' I returned. 'Just an abundance of bog. Denis and John Grey have joined forces with our party.'

'Hello, George. Hello, George. Report your position, please,' requested Jimmy.

There was no reply. The message was repeated for the next three or four minutes. At last the exasperated voice of George came over the air: 'My position at the moment is four feet deep in a bog. Two minutes ago it was five feet deep in a bog. Out!'

We had a good laugh over this, picturing the six feet four inches George wallowing in a bog hole.

Working north and west we continued our 'sweep' search; the three dogs quartered the ground ahead, with John on one flank and Denis on the other. Our torches stabbed over black peat hags and tortured remains of the roots of the great Caledonian pines which at one time covered this desolate tract of moorland. Some historians say that the last wolf in Britain was killed on this moor when it was still afforested. There are two theories regarding the disappearance of the forest. One, that it was burned down to get rid of the wolves; the other, that it was burned to rid the area of robbers. That night my large Alsatian, Rangi, looked every inch a wolf as he weaved in and out of the peat bogs, jumping streams and giving an occasional growl.

We were beginning to grow tired and were certainly all wet—in varying degrees—when George's voice came over the walkie-talkie: 'We've got him!'

'What was that?' Jimmy demanded hastily. I could visualize him suddenly starting and becoming officious. 'Repeat your message, please, George,' he requested formally.

'We have found the missing man. Will report further in a few minutes.'

That night, Hugh had our only searchlight, which, due to loose connections, had been flickering off and on—more off than on unfortunately. It had been cursed liberally because, each time the brilliant light went out, the night seemed darker than ever. During one of their illuminated periods Hugh thought he saw something, but it was lost in the enveloping darkness as the light failed yet again. When it came on again he managed to pick out what had previously attracted his attention. It looked like a dismembered head, suspended ten feet above the bog.

'Hey look, chaps. What's that?' he called in amazement. As they approached they heard a strange noise, 'E, E, E, E, E.'

'Cripes,' said Walter. 'It must be a bloody banshee!'

Drawing closer, they saw that the suspended 'head' was the missing man's woollen hat, raised aloft on the end of his fishing rod!

The professor was sitting on an old tree stump, his legs down a bog hole. He was too exhausted even to shout, but had tilted his head backwards and was using the edge of his hand to hit his throat repeatedly, while he emitted a high-pitched scream. This produced the intermittent eerie call which they had heard. Although he saw them approaching, he was too weak to get up and come towards them. Hugh said afterwards that he had hurt his ankle and was obviously suffering badly from exposure. George immediately contacted us on his walkie-talkie.

'Hello there, Hamish,' he called. 'It looks as if this chap has hurt his ankle and won't be able to walk far. We can probably help him a bit; can you have a stretcher set across to us?'

'There's no one else to take it over, George. Our party will have to go back to the road to collect it. But wait a minute,' I added. 'I've an idea; just hold on a tick.' I turned to the others. 'Hey Willie, isn't there a boat in that boatshed on Loch Ba?'

'Yes, I think there is,' he said, musing. 'By Jove, that would be a help, wouldn't it? We could take it right over to the far side of the loch. Just think—the inland lifeboat service!'

'I used that boat last year when I was fishing,' said Denis. 'It belongs to the Flemings at Black Mount.'

'Oh, they won't mind us using it,' I answered.

'Hello, George,' I called. 'Do you think that you could get the prof. to the north end of Loch Ba? We can arrange to meet you there.'

'Righto,' he replied. 'We'll try. Perhaps he'll feel better when he takes some glucose and gets moving.'

'Fine,' I said. 'Standing by.'

I hadn't mentioned the boat to them as I didn't want to raise false hopes, for we still had to get it out of a padlocked boathouse.

'I tell you what,' I spoke to the others, 'I'll go back to the Land-Rover and try to find some suitable tools for breaking and entering. I'll see you at the boathouse—you'd better shine a light when you reach it, though; I'm not sure exactly where it is!'

'Oh, we'll find it,' replied Denis. 'There's a wee path going over to it.'

'Be seeing you,' I called as I set off with the two dogs.

When I reached the Land-Rover, Jimmy was standing outside, stamping his feet on the road.

'Well, thank goodness they've found him,' he began. 'There's nothing worse than being at base on a night like this.'

'Isn't there, Jimmy?' I asked somewhat ironically. 'Have a look at me!'

I was covered in thick, black peat from the chest down.

'Aye, you certainly do look a bit mucky,' Jimmy grudgingly admitted. 'Do you want the stretcher?'

'Yes,' I replied. 'But first of all we could do with a big tyre lever, or perhaps an ice-axe if you've got one?'

'What on earth are you wanting those for?' he asked suspiciously.

'To break into the boatshed,' I answered casually. 'We need the boat to take the prof. back.'

'But man, you can't do that. It's breaking and entering!'

'Aye, and it will be taking the boat as well,' I added with a grin. 'But it's the easiest way.'

In the back of the Land-Rover I discovered a suitably heavy tyre lever. Then, shouldering the stretcher, I made my way to the boathouse.

'Over here,' called Willie, flashing his light.

Beyond the light I could see the black lustre of the loch and, as I approached, the faint outline of the boathouse was visible.

There was splashing in the water.

'Don't tell me you've got the boat out already?' I asked.

'Oh, yes,' replied John Grey, passing an oar down to Denis. 'Denis has had good training at this sort of thing. He had the padlock off before we even arrived here.'

'All it requires is a bit of know-how,' retorted Denis, rather hurt by the implication. 'I remembered that I had my short metal ice-axe in my pack. Anyway, it soon did the trick.'

'Well, we can't all go in that tub,' I said.

'I'm quite willing to stay,' said Denis. 'I could do with a doze in the boatshed for an hour or two. I've got a big job to do tomorrow at the ski-tow and some shut-eye wouldn't do me any harm.'

'All right,' I answered. 'Then the three of us will put ourselves in the hands of the Ancient Mariner here.'

They all knew that I meant John Grey. John had recently purchased a Baltic schooner and started a freight service on the West Coast. His first voyage, bringing the boat across from Norway, was in itself an epic, for they did the trip in a series of force eight and nine gales. However, the initial crew were all fishermen and the boat weathered the storm well. This also proved to be only a foretaste of what was to come during its short and hectic life in Scottish waters. John's subsequent adventures round this rugged and dangerous coast could fill a book which would rival the tales of Para Handy. The stately three-masted schooner, originally built for the Baltic wood trade, shared many a tense moment with John and his often skeletal, certainly usually inexperienced, crew. The boat was christened the *Eala Dhubh* (Black Swan) but, as you can imagine, in moments of stress it was called many other, less endearing names.

On one occasion, as they were sailing down to Oban from Glencoe, they were hit by a violent storm. The shipping forecast had predicted force eight to nine winds for Mallin and Hebrides, but this didn't deter John, who had the utmost faith in his stout-timbered craft. The huge, single-cylinder engine was panting away and spray was cascading over the starboard side as they skirted the coast of Argyll; ahead of them lay the Island of Lismore. Ralph Pierce, who was driving the *Eala Dhubh* that day, was getting worried, for they didn't seem to be making much headway. Suddenly the engine stopped.

It was no disaster, however. They had simply run out of fuel. As if this was not an unknown hazard, John had the lads drop the anchor. Taking the small pram dinghy off the top of the wheelhouse, he dropped it over the side. The only items lacking were the oars and a can—once he had these safely aboard with him, he rowed through the high seas to the shore, while the *Eala Dhubh* bucked at her anchorage. Some locals witnessed this drama from the shore. One of them shouted as he saw the dinghy coming through the spray, 'They're abandoning ship!'

John, however, had no intention of abandoning anything. He rowed ashore to the jetty at Port Appin and, after purchasing a can of diesel fuel, rowed straight back to the boat to continue the voyage.

John is a great lover of folk music and a fine singer and the villages of the West Coast always open their doors to those who enjoy a good ceilidh. There was one small fishing village which was renowned both for its conviviality and for its pride in its newly constructed jetty. John tied up at this new pier, at low tide, while he and his crew—armed with guitar and squeeze-box—repaired to the nearest public house. There they entertained the locals with music and ballads until the small hours of the morning, when high tide was approaching. The appearance of an irate Pier Master broke up the happy occasion. Entering the bar, which, in theory, should have closed at 10 p.m., he announced with evident agitation, 'That bloody boat with the big masts is lifting up the new jetty!'

This statement was no exaggeration: the edge of the boat had

The professor was sitting on an old tree stump, his legs down a bog hole.

caught under the pier and, as the tide came in, was relentlessly raising the entire construction.

Robin Turner, another member of our rescue team, recalls with some trepidation a voyage he made with John to Tiree. They had a cargo of pipes aboard and, again, the voyage coincided with a violent storm. Robin, who is a keen participant of various aqua sports, compares the *Eala Dhubh*'s entrance into harbour that day with a fast run on a surf board towards a rocky shoreline. The locals at the jetty watched with amazement as the tall-masted ship suddenly appeared through the mist of spray and hurtled towards them at breakneck speed. That trip must have strained the *Eala Dhubh*, since, on a later voyage, carrying timber for the Lochaber pulp mill, she started to leak badly and it was probably only her cargo which kept her afloat as she limped into Loch Linnhe.

Eventually the *Eala Dhubh* met her untimely end on the Island of Mull, when John, who was filling a small running generator with petrol, accidentally spilt some and it caught alight. Within minutes the wooden boat was blazing furiously. Luckily no one was injured, but it was the end of the *Eala Dhubh*'s glorious career. John doesn't seem to have much imagination when it comes to his personal exploits, for he tends to dismiss the most hair-raising adventures in an off-hand sentence or two. He has now acquired a new fishing boat to replace the hapless *Eala Dhubh*. John is a great asset to our rescue team, for he's always fit and strong and, though he hasn't done much climbing, he never has difficulty in following up the most treacherous route in bad conditions.

'Well, I suppose I'll have to row,' he said, picking up the oars and pulling on them with the easy rhythm that marks an experienced boatman. As we left the shore a figure with a torch joined Denis at the boatshed. It was Colin Cameron, a policeman who had just arrived from Oban. We experienced some difficulty, navigating the waters of Loch Ba in the middle of the night, but in about an hour we thought we must be nearing the north end of the loch.

'Hello, George,' I called over the walkie-talkie. 'Can you read me?'

'Yes, Hamish, I can, and I can see a strange light on the loch!'

'Aye, that's us,' I confirmed, chuckling. 'The Rannoch Moor Lifeboat crew are on their way to pick up the injured man.'

'Trust you blokes to find an easy way,' he grumbled. 'I suppose we'll have to walk back?'

'That is quite correct, Police Constable Cormach,' I returned. 'Members of the public, or the Police Force, will not be permitted on board!'

Our laughter echoed across the still water of the loch.

It was almost light before we neared the boathouse again. We had been rowing on a direct course towards the light which Denis had hung up at the boathouse; John was now navigating from the bows. There came a grating noise under the boat.

'Hey, John, you've grounded us,' shouted Willie who was in the stern.

'It's just that there isn't enough water below the boat; there's a wee island here,' explained John. 'Take her astern, Hamish, and we'll try farther to the east, round the other side.'

It was my stint at the oars so I eased the boat out into deeper water and we rounded the island, presently drawing alongside the boathouse.

A figure on the bank shouted, 'Have you anything to declare?'

It was Colin Cameron, a born comedian, calling to us in his best official manner.

'One injured professor,' returned Willie cheerfully.

'Well,' replied Colin, 'the duty will be a few drams at the hotel. Payment may be deferred until such time as it may be required!'

By the time we had secured the professor on the stretcher, the others had walked back from the north side of the loch to join us. Jimmy had managed to take the Land-Rover almost all the way down to the boathouse, so it was only a short carry by stretcher. By some act of Providence, Eric Moss had remained quite dry until then; when he saw the Land-Rover's lights ahead he sighed with relief, for he shares the Highlander's aversion to getting wet. But the lights must have distracted him momentarily and he suddenly plunged chest-deep into a slimy bog; as usual, this provided a merry diversion for the rest of the team.

It is likely that the professor would have been in an extremely serious condition by morning, had he not been found, yet when we arrived safely back at Kingshouse he was already much recovered and we knew that he would suffer no serious after-effects from his adventure. However, he retired to bed almost immediately, after arranging that Mr MacDonald, the manager of the hotel, should provide us with sandwiches, tea and whisky. Angus MacDonald would have done so in any case, as he always helped our team in every possible way.

Most of us were standing in our underpants and socks in front of a big wood fire in the main lounge, since our outer clothing was in such a state. Denis, however, had returned to the Land-Rover for his pipe and came back into the room, still wearing his clothes and boots. Suddenly realizing his error, he quickly removed his boots—a deluge of peaty water spread over the rich carpet.

'Ah well,' he said with a cheerful grin, 'we all make mistakes some time or other!'

'Not bad whisky, this Talisker,' said Walter, licking his lips appreciatively. 'You were just telling me something about this whisky when we found the prof., George. What was the story?'

'Oh, yes,' replied George, laughing. 'I was about to illustrate what a fine bunch of law-enforcement officers and detectives you have in these parts!'

Willie let out a loud guffaw. 'Tell us another, George—the "sheer luck" squad?'

'Anyhow,' continued George, ignoring the interruption and settling himself in a large easy-chair. 'A case of whisky was stolen from one of the local pubs—not this establishment, I may add—and we had a fair idea who had taken it: a local fisherman. I'll not mention the name of this alcoholic character, but he's five feet two inches and has a red beard. We had no evidence, you understand, but we knew him to be a man of limited intellect and I had just a hunch that he was responsible. So I tried on him a technique which

I have developed for such thefts. I call it the "Brand Denial Test".
I asked him, quite forcibly'—here I could just imagine the six feet
four inches George towering over the unfortunate man—'with
the correct amount of intimidation in my voice: "Did you steal
that case of Talisker from the pub?"

' "No, no, it wasn't me," the red-bearded man cringed. "It was
Dewar's whisky that I took—I never touched any Talisker!" '

Our laughter was long and loud and some, at least, of the
slumbering guests must have been awakened in time to see a
cloudless dawn.

INCIDENT IN
THE SOUDAN

R. C. Williamson

At the time when the British army, under General Sir Garnet Wolseley, entered the Egyptian Soudan, in the hope of rescuing General Gordon from Khartoum and the native prophet, El Mahdi, a small corps of Canadian river men was employed to man the whaleboats by which the invading British force was transported up the Nile.

The English commander had seen something of the skill of these backwoodsmen at the time when he led a force by water against the half breed rebels of the Red River country, in 1870, and he resolved to avail himself of it for the difficult navigation of the Upper Nile. A few river drivers and boatmen were therefore recruited and taken to Egypt, where they served creditably during one of the Soudanese expeditions; although the extreme heat of African and other conditions, wholly different from those of Canada, tended to impair their usefulness.

Some of them were killed by the heat; others met death at the points of Arab spears; but in the course of two years most of them had returned to America. Among the survivors is Philip Burnet, whose alert bearing and bright, mirthful, black eyes still give him a youthful look. Although not an educated man, he makes use of fairly good English in conversation.

Last April he was at work as a river driver for a New Hampshire lumber company on the upper waters of the Connecticut. I was then scaling lumber in that region, and met Burnet at a drivers' camp on the river bank after work one evening. With several of his fellow drivers, he sat down before the camp fire after supper, and pulled off his heavy, iron-shod drivers' boots to dry his feet. When he rolled up the anklet of his thick, knit drawers, I noticed a long, livid scar on his foot, extending up the inside of his left ankle.

'Was that an axe cut, Burnet?' I asked.

'No,' he replied; and after hesitating a little, he added, 'That's where I got *clawed* when I was in the Soudan.'

'By an Arab?' I inquired.

'No, sir; I was never in a battle. I was mostly with the boats. The soldiers fought those black fellows two or three times, as we got far up the river. But I wasn't anxious to be in it, though I did try a turn at the soldiering.

'Arabs are savage fighters. When they come to attack, they come on the jump, yelling enough to make one's hair stand right up. When they did this, our soldiers would swing into a square, and pile them up with their breechloaders.

'At a place they call Teb, sir, I saw those black fellows lie in heaps four feet high, with their spears sticking up like pins out of a pin ball, all dead, where the infantrymen had shot them as fast as they came on.

'It wasn't an Arab that gave me that scar,' Burnet added; and as he did so he cast a troubled glance at his mates, who were already laughing at him, as they did not believe his story. It was manifest that Burnet did not wholly like to relate his Soudanese adventures in the presence of the river drivers of the Connecticut. I came to his relief by remarking that I knew something of the Soudan, and that it is a country wholly different from Canada and the Northern States; that the Nile is a river ten times as long and twenty times as large as the Connecticut.

I then spoke of the Soudanese people, their manner of fighting, their religion, and the causes of the British and Egyptian war against the Mahdi. Burnet regarded me with an appearance of actual gratitude. As I went on to speak of the ruined cities of Egypt, of the desert, and the great heat of the climate there, he threw a look of triumph on his unbelieving fellow drivers.

'I'm glad you know about the heat there, sir!' he exclaimed. ' 'Twas something terrible. The wind used to break in gusts over the bank of the river, and it scorched us just like heat off a burning building. All our axes and guns got so hot we couldn't touch them without burning our hands to blisters, and that's the truth.

'About that scar,' continued Burnet, noticing that I was still regarding it curiously. 'I will tell you how I came by that. Almost anybody would say that I got it in a queer way.

'They sent us out scouting at daybreak one morning. It was after we had left the river. I was carrying a Martini rifle then, for I had volunteered for soldier duty. Besides me, there were a sergeant and four privates. The sergeant had his orders to go off to some bare, rocky hills we could see four or five miles away, and bring back word what lay beyond, how the country looked, and whether, when the sun rose, he could see any signs of water that way; for water was always the great thing needed out there. It's an awful country to move in, sir. Where the ground isn't bare, hard gravel, it is sure to be covered with thorny stuff, all prickly, creeping over the rocks; and wherever there were any bushes, they were covered with terrible thorns, two or three inches long, and hooked so that if you got amongst brush anywhere, you were sure to be hung up hard and fast.

'We ought to have been given leather clothes to wear, for the thorns tore our trousers all to strings in the course of a few days. We worked round and about through scrub stuff of this sort, and got out to those hills about sunrise; but by the time we reached them, the men were complaining bitterly about the thorns, their feet being badly cut. The sergeant stood and took a long look all around to see what he could report. There was a valley beyond us, but between us and it there were a great many broken cliffs and ledges of red rock—the reddest rock I ever saw—dark red, like old blood, sir.

' "There's a kohr over yonder, I think," said the sergeant; "but I can't see a drop of water in it."

'A khor is one of the queer kind of rivers they have in that country, though mostly there's no water running in them; but there may be a little in some deep hole where once the river ran.

'But we couldn't see very well for the cliffs and crags, where the kohr crooked around below them; and so the sergeant said to me, "Burnet, you're the lightest man in the squad, and the heat does not appear to bother you much. Go down among the crags, where you can look into the bed of this kohr, and see if you can spy any water in it. We will wait here for you; and you needn't go over a mile at most," said the sergeant.

'I made my way down among the crags; and if you had been there, sir, you would have agreed with me that it was the queerest place you ever saw.

'There were those red ledges split apart in all manner of ways, and a kind of plant, with great, thick, green leaves, was creeping all over the rocks, looking like splashes of raw green paint on them; and after every step or two, down you would go knee-deep in a windrow of fine, dry, grey sand, which, the moment your foot touched it, would begin to purr like a cat, and sometimes cause a singing all around you—the queerest kind of sound you ever heard, sir!'

I saw a wink go around among the drivers; but the story of the singing sand was true.

'I soon got down where the crags were higher and fell off faster into the kohr. It was a bad place to make one's way, almost a precipice; but I couldn't see the lowest place in the hollow below me yet, and so I kept on, and pretty soon slid down through a kind of chasm between two upstanding rocks. The first I knew I came out plump on the brink of a dry, red cliff that was as smooth as ice.

'I saw where I was going when I slid down into the sand; I thought that I could pull up on that shelf of rock, but I couldn't. To save me I couldn't stop myself, for a lot of sand went down with me and under me. I threw out both hands and grabbed at the rock, but 'twas so smooth I couldn't get any hold on it, and over I went. I fell perhaps forty feet, and if I had struck on rocks it would have killed me, for certain. But I fell, feet first, into a great heap of dry, loose sand, which had been running down over the cliff for years. I ploughed into that clean up to my shoulders; and was scarcely hurt at all, only shaken up a bit. Then I looked around for my Martini, which I had let go when I tried to save myself from falling over. It had slid out of my hand, off sidewise, and had not fallen off the cliff; I could see about a foot of the barrel sticking out in sight, forty feet over my head.

'There was no way I could get it from where I now stood, for when I came to look around, I saw that I was in a queer sort of bowl-shaped place, with high, smooth, red rocks inclosing it around, except one small fissure between them on the lower side. Partly wallowing in the loose sand, partly crawling, I plodded down through this narrow chasm for as much as a hundred feet, and then came around the corner of a high, overhanging ledge, close to a mud hole in the very bed of the kohr. Almost the first thing my eye fell upon was the head of what I took to be a deer, and a lot of freshly-gnawed bones scattered about. And a little farther back, beneath the great, overhanging red ledge, I spied a yellow-coloured animal curled up in a ball, asleep.

'I wasn't long in making up my mind, then, that I had blundered into some kind of den where there were wild animals, and I began to feel a little creepy. I looked at the sleeping creature for some

Two lions came through the willows.

time, and listened to find out if there were others around. I could not tell what kind of animal it was, and I was thinking to myself how I could get away. There were thick, green bushes like willows all round about the mud hole, and just across it rose another high red rock. As I stood there considering which way I had better go, I heard water a little way farther along the mud hole.

At first I thought it was some animal walking or running in water; but it did not sound quite like that either, and after a moment or two it flashed into my mind that it was some large creature lapping up water with its tongue. That alarmed me more than anything else that I had seen or heard before. I stole along on tiptoe, keeping close up to the foot of the crag, alongside of the mud hole, going in the opposite direction from that of the sound I had heard of lapping water. But I had only gone a few steps when I heard a low growl, and looking back, saw a great yellow creature come out of the willows, its eyes suddenly fixed on me—awful eyes, sir, and the big head he had was something terrible to look at!'

'It must have been a lion,' I exclaimed.

'I suppose it was, sir,' continued Burnet; 'that's what the sergeant afterwards said. The creature stood and stared at me, then gave a sort of sudden bellow like a bull. I heard another bellow and a sort of swishing noise among the willows behind me; and just then I noticed a great slanting crack, running up the side of the crag a few steps ahead.

It looked as if anybody might climb the crag by it, and I made a leap, got hold with my hands, and clambered up for ten or a dozen feet—for I knew by the sounds that the lion was hard after me. He was closer even than I thought, and running to spring, too. When I pulled myself up the rocks, he jumped for me, and struck my leg with his paw. If my fingers hadn't been hard clinched on the sharp edges of the crevice, he would have hauled me down.

One of his claws ripped down my trousers' leg, and tore off my shoe. I think he struck my foot and ankle numb, for I did not know that I was scratched there till I saw the blood trickling down the rock. You see, sir, I wasn't in the crevice. It wasn't wide enough for that. It was a kind of slanting crack, no more than five or six inches wide, and I was working up by it with my hands and feet. I barely hung on when the lion jumped and clawed me; and I then put my bare foot—the one that was bleeding—on the margin of the crevice, and raised myself a little higher; but farther up I could see no good place to get hold with my hands. The rock was too smooth, and I was afraid that I should slide down if I tried it.

'Two lions had come through the willows, and their growling was something fearful to hear. I had no doubt at first that they would get me. They jumped several times, but fell back. They could not quite strike me, but it was awful to hear their claws rake the rocks. They stood on their hind legs, too, and reached up for me, and they could reach a good deal higher than a tall man. One was very shaggy about the head and neck; the other was quite bare and more slim; but this bare, slim one was the worst one for jumping. I had climbed up twelve, maybe fifteen, feet from the sand at the foot of the crag, but the slim one touched me two or three times.

'Then they sat down like dogs and looked at me; and their eyes were so strong that I had to shut mine, to keep from falling down. I braced myself in the crack the best way I could, but it was an uncomfortable place to hold on, and I began shouting for help. I hoped the soldiers back on the hills would hear me, and come to my aid. I shouted more than fifty times, and began to be afraid that, from being so low down in the bed of the kohr, they would not hear me. By and by the small yellow animal that I had seen asleep under the overhanging ledge came along in sight where the two lions sat. The slim lion drove him back and then went after him, to pilot him away, perhaps.

'The shaggy lion sat and watched me, but did not jump again, and it was while the other one was gone that I heard one of the soldiers shouting to me at a distance. They had not heard me at all, but had grown anxious and were looking for me. I now shouted in response, and they answered. The lion probably heard them: he walked to and fro, lashing his sides with his tail, as if uneasy or suspicious; and when the sergeant came out on the crags above the bed of the kohr, the animal walked slowly away, and disappeared among the willows. The men finally descended where I was, by another way, to the south of the place where I slid over the cliff, and you may be pretty sure, sir, that I was very glad to see them.'

THE ADVENTURES OF A SHILLING

Joseph Addison

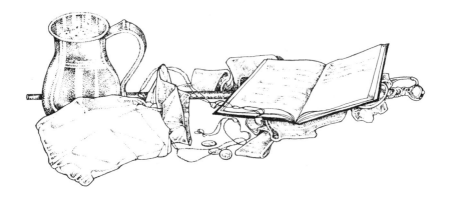

I was last night visited by a friend of mine, who has an in-exhaustible fund of discourse, and never fails to entertain his company with a variety of thoughts and hints that are altogether new and uncommon. Whether it were in complaisance to my way of living or his real opinion, he advanced the following paradox, 'That it required much greater talents to fill up and become a retired life, than a life of business.' Upon this occasion he rallied very agreeably the busy men of the age, who only valued themselves for being in motion and passing through a series of trifling and significant actions. In the heat of his discourse, seeing a piece of money lying on my table, 'I defy,' says he, 'any of these active persons to produce half the adventures that this twelvepenny piece has been engaged in, were it possible for him to give us an account of his life.'

My friend's talk make so odd an impression upon my mind, that soon after I was a-bed I fell insensibly into a most unaccountable reverie, that had neither moral nor design in it, and cannot be so properly called a dream as a delirium.

Methought that the shilling that lay upon the table reared itself upon its edge, and turning the face towards me, opened its mouth, and in a soft silver sound, gave me the following account of his life and adventures:

'I was born (says he) on the side of a mountain, near a little village of Peru, and made a voyage to England in an ingot, under the convoy of Sir Francis Drake. I was, soon after my arrival, taken out of my Indian habit, refined, naturalized, and put into the British mode, with the face of Queen Elizabeth on one side, and the arms of the country on the other. Being thus equipped, I found in me a wonderful inclination to ramble, and visit all parts of the new world into which I was brought. The people very much favoured my natural disposition, and shifted me so fast from hand to hand, that before I was five years old, I had travelled into almost every corner of the nation. But in the beginning of my sixth year, to my unspeakable grief, I fell into the hands of a miserable old fellow, who clapped me into an iron chest, where I found five hundred more of my own quality who lay under the same confinement. The only relief we had, was to be taken out and counted over in the fresh air every morning and evening. After an imprisonment of several years, we heard somebody knocking at our chest, and breaking it open with a hammer. This we found was the old man's heir, who, as his father lay a-dying, was so good as to come to our release: he separated us that very day. What was the fate of my companions I know not: as for myself, I was sent to the apothecary's shop for a pint of sack. The apothecary gave me to an herb-woman, the herb-woman to a butcher, the butcher to a brewer, and the brewer to his wife, who made a present of me to a nonconformist preacher. After this manner I made my way

I thus rambled from pocket to pocket.

merrily through the world; for, as I told you before, we shillings love nothing so much as travelling. I sometimes fetched in a shoulder of mutton, sometimes a play-book, and often had the satisfaction to treat a Templar at a twelvepenny ordinary, or carry him, with three friends, to Westminster Hall.

'In the midst of this pleasant progress which I made from place to place, I was arrested by a superstitious old woman, who shut me up in a greasy purse, in pursuance of a foolish saying, "That while she kept a Queen Elizabeth's shilling about her, she should never be without money." I continued here a close prisoner for many months, till at last I was exchanged for eight and forty farthings.

'I thus rambled from pocket to pocket till the beginning of the civil wars, when, to my shame be it spoken, I was employed in raising soldiers against the king: for being of a very tempting breadth, a sergeant made use of me to inveigle country fellows, and list them in the service of the parliament.

'As soon as he had made one man sure, his way was to oblige him to take a shilling of a more homely figure, and then practise the same trick upon another. Thus I continued doing great mischief to the crown, till my officer, chancing one morning to walk abroad earlier than ordinary, sacrificed me to his pleasures, and made use of me to seduce a milk-maid. This wench bent me, and gave me to her sweetheart, applying more properly than she intended the usual form of, "To my love and from my love." This ungenerous gallant marrying her within a few days after, pawned me for a dram of brandy, and drinking me out next day, I was beaten flat with a hammer, and again set a-running.

'After many adventures, which it would be tedious to relate, I was sent to a young spendthrift, in company with the will of his deceased father. The young fellow, who I found was very extravagant, gave great demonstrations of joy at the receiving of the will: but opening it, he found himself disinherited and cut off from the possession of a fair estate, by virtue of my being made a present to him. This put him into such a passion, that after having taken me

THE ADVENTURES OF A SHILLING

in his hand, and cursed me, he squirred me away from him as far as he could fling me. I chanced to light in an unfrequented place under a dead wall, where I lay undiscovered and useless, during the usurpation of Oliver Cromwell.

'About a year after the king's return, a poor cavalier that was walking there about dinner-time, fortunately cast his eye upon me, and, to the great joy of us both, carried me to a cook's shop, where he dined upon me, and drank the king's health. When I came again into the world, I found that I had been happier in my retirement than I thought, having probably, by that means, escaped wearing a monstrous pair of breeches.

'Being now of great credit and antiquity, I was rather looked upon as a medal than an ordinary coin; for which reason a gamester laid hold of me, and converted me to a counter, having got together some dozens of us for that use. We led a melancholy life in his possession, being busy at those hours wherein current coin is at rest, and partaking the fate of our master, being in a few moments valued at a crown, a pound, or a sixpence, according to the situation in which the fortune of the cards placed us. I had at length the good luck to see my master break, by which means I was again sent abroad under my primitive denomination of a shilling.

'I shall pass over many other accidents of less moment, and hasten to that fatal catastrophe, when I fell into the hands of an artist, who conveyed me under ground, and with an unmerciful pair of shears, cut off my titles, clipped my brims, retrenched my shape, rubbed me to my inmost ring, and, in short, so spoiled and pillaged me, that he did not leave me worth a groat. You may think what a confusion I was in, to see myself thus curtailed and disfigured. I should have been ashamed to have shown my head, had not all my old acquaintance been reduced to the same shameful figure, excepting some few that were punched through the belly. In the midst of this general calamity, when everybody thought our misfortune irretrievable, and our case desperate, we were thrown into the furnace together, and (as it often happens with cities rising out of a fire) appeared with greater beauty and lustre than we could ever boast of before. What has happened to me since this change of sex which you now see, I shall take some other opportunity to relate. In the meantime, I shall only repeat two adventures, as being very extraordinary, and neither of them having ever happened to me above once in my life. The first was, my being in a poet's pocket, who was so taken with the brightness and novelty of my appearance, that it gave occasion to the finest burlesque poem in the British language, entitled from me, "The Splendid Shilling". The second adventure, which I must not omit, happened to me in the year 1703, when I was given away in charity to a blind man; but indeed this was by a mistake, the person who gave me having heedlessly thrown me into the hat among a pennyworth of farthings.'

STRANDED IN A BALLOON

Jules Verne

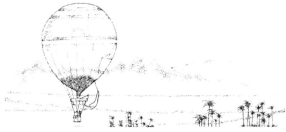

In 1862, Doctor Samuel Fergusson, his servant Joe, and Dick Kennedy, a Scotsman, attempted a new feat of exploration. They hoped to cross the whole of the African continent from East to West in the balloon *Victoria*.

After many adventures they become stranded 400 miles from the West African coast with no food and very little water . . .

'**A**nd not a cloud in this grilling sky. It's enough to drive one mad!'

'Don't let us give in,' said the doctor. 'These fierce heats are always followed by storms in this latitude, and they come with the swiftness of lightning. In spite of the dreadful serenity of the sky at the moment, great changes will very probably come about in less than an hour.'

'But, surely, there would be some sign,' said Kennedy.

'Well,' said the doctor, 'I rather think the barometer shows a slight tendency to drop.'

'Pray Heaven you're right, Sam. We're nailed down here like a winged bird.'

'With the difference, however, old man, that our wings are intact, and I sincerely hope we shall be able to use them yet.'

'Oh, for a wind!' cried Joe. 'Just enough to take us to a stream, and we shall be quite all right. We've got enough grub, and if only we could get some water, we could wait for months without taking any harm. But thirst is awful.'

Thirst, added to the unceasing glare of the desert, was eating into their souls. There was not the slightest break in the ground, not a sand-hill, not a stone to distract their eyes. The flatness sickened them and produced the disorder known as desert sickness. The relentless stillness of the arid blue sky and the yellow immensity of sand eventually struck terror into them. In this burning atmosphere the heat seemed to quiver as over a red-hot furnace. Watching this calm, and seeing no reason why the situation should ever end, for immensity is a kind of eternity, filled their souls with despair. These unfortunate men, deprived of water in this fearful heat, began to experience symptoms of hallucination. Their eyes dilated, their sight became blurred.

When night had fallen the doctor resolved to fight this disquieting mood by means of a sharp walk. He intended to spend a few hours crossing this plain of sand, not with the idea of searching but simply for exercise.

'Come on,' he said to his companions. 'Believe me, it will do you good.'

'It can't be done,' replied Kennedy. 'I couldn't walk a step.'

'I'd much rather sleep,' said Joe.

'But sleep and rest are fatal. Try and rouse yourselves. Now then, come along!'

As the doctor could get no response, he set out alone through the starry clearness of the night. His first steps were painful, the steps of a man weakened and unused to walking; but he soon realized that the exercise would be beneficial. He went on several miles in a westerly direction and his mind was already feeling easier when he was suddenly seized with giddiness. It was as if he were leaning over an abyss. He felt his knees giving way. The vast solitude terrified him. He was as a mathematical point, the centre of an infinite circumference, of the void. The *Victoria* had disappeared completely in the darkness. An uncontrollable panic took possession of the doctor, the impassive, intrepid traveller. He tried to retrace his steps, but in vain. He called aloud, but not the slightest echo answered him, and his voice fell into space like a stone into a bottomless pit. He sank exhausted on the sand, alone amid the great silence of the desert.

At midnight he came round, to find himself in the arms of the faithful Joe, who, uneasy at his master's prolonged absence, had hastily followed his tracks, which were clearly printed in the sand. He had found him unconscious.

'What's happened, sir?' he asked.

'It's nothing, my dear fellow. A momentary weakness, that's all.'

'Nothing, indeed, sir! But get up; lean on me and we'll get back to the *Victoria*.'

Leaning on Joe's arm, the doctor returned the way he had come.

'It was unwise, sir. You shouldn't do these things. You might have been waylaid,' he added, laughing. 'Come, sir, let's be serious.'

'Go on. I'm listening.'

'We must really make up our minds. We can't go on like this for many days more, and if the wind doesn't come, it's all up with us.'

The doctor did not reply.

'Well, someone must sacrifice himself for the rest and it's only natural it should be me.'

'What do you mean? What's your idea?'

'It's quite simple. Take some food and walk straight ahead until I get somewhere. I'm bound to, sooner or later. Meantime, if Heaven sends you a favourable wind, you mustn't wait for me; you must start. As for me, if I come to a village I'll manage to get along with a few Arab words you can write out for me, and I'll bring back help or die in the attempt. What do you think of it, sir?'

'It's mad, but does credit to your heart, Joe. It's out of the question. You're not going to leave us.'

'After all, sir, we must try something. It can't do any harm for, as

I say, you won't wait for me, and at a pinch I may do some good.'

'No, no, Joe; we mustn't separate. It would only make it worse for the others. It was fated that this should be and it's probably arranged that it will be different later. So let us wait patiently.'

'All right, sir, but I'll tell you one thing. I'll give you another day, but I won't wait longer than that. Today is Sunday, or rather Monday, for it's one o'clock in the morning. If we don't get a move on by Monday, I'll risk it. I've quite made up my mind.'

The doctor did not reply. Soon afterwards he reached the car and took his place beside Kennedy, who was lying perfectly still; but that did not mean he was asleep.

In the morning the doctor's first thought was to consult the barometer. At most, there was the faintest drop.

'No good! No good!' he muttered to himself.

He left the car and took a look at the weather. The same heat, the same clear sky, the same implacable conditions.

'Must we give up hope?' he exclaimed.

Joe said nothing. He was wrapped up in his own thoughts, meditating his plan.

Kennedy got up feeling very ill, a prey to an alarming attack of nerves. He was suffering horribly from thirst. His blistered tongue and lips could hardly articulate a sound. There were a few drops of water left. They all knew it. The thoughts of each were drawn towards it as to a magnet, but no one dared go near it.

The three companions, the three friends, looked at one another with haggard eyes and with a feeling of brute greed which betrayed itself most in Kennedy, whose powerful frame succumbed more readily to this intolerable privation. Throughout the day he was in the grip of delirium. He walked up and down, uttering hoarse cries, gnawing his fists, on the point of opening his veins to drink the blood.

'Oh!' he muttered; 'they're right to call this the land of thirst, the land of despair!' Then he relapsed into a state of coma. Nothing was heard from him but the hissing of his breath between his parched lips.

Towards evening Joe began to show symptoms of mania. This vast sea of sand appeared to him as an immense pool of cool and limpid waters. More than once he threw himself down on the scorching sand to drink and got up again with his mouth full of dust.

'Damnation!' he cried angrily. 'It's salt-water!'

Then, while Fergusson and Kennedy lay stretched out motionless, he was seized with an overpowering temptation to drain the few drops of water that were being held in reserve. It grew too much for him. He dragged himself on his knees towards the car, fastened his eyes greedily upon the bottle containing the liquid, looked at it with a desperate glance, seized it, and raised it to his lips.

At this moment he heard the words: 'Water! Water!' in accents that tore the heart. It was Kennedy, dragging himself towards him. The poor fellow was a pitiable sight. He remained on his knees, the tears welling from his eyes. Joe, also in tears, offered him the bottle and, to the very last drop, Kennedy drained the contents. 'Thank you,' he gasped, but Joe did not hear him; he had fallen prone on the sand.

What happened during that dreadful night is known to no one, but on the Tuesday morning, under the douche of fire pouring from the sun, the wretched men felt their limbs gradually shrivelling. When Joe tried to get up he found it impossible. He was unable to carry out his plan. He took a look round him. In the car the doctor lay prostrate, his arms folded over his chest, gazing at an imaginary point in space with imbecile fixity. Kennedy was a terrifying sight. His head swayed from side to side like that of a caged animal.

Suddenly the Scotsman's eye rested upon his carbine, the butt of which was projecting over the side of the car.

'Ah!' he cried, raising himself by a superhuman effort. He dashed at the weapon, desperate, insane, and placed the muzzle to his mouth.

'Sir! Mr Kennedy!' said Joe, throwing himself upon him.

'Leave me alone! Get away!' moaned the Scotsman, and the two struggled desperately.

'Clear out or I'll kill you,' Kennedy went on. But Joe clung to him fiercely. They fought together for nearly a minute, the doctor appearing not to notice them. Then suddenly in the struggle the carbine went off. At the sound of the report the doctor got up, erect as a spectre. He looked around him. Then a sudden light came into his eye. He stretched his hand towards the horizon and, in a voice in which there was nothing human, rasped out: 'Look! Look over there!'

There was such energy in his gesture that Joe and Kennedy broke away and both looked. The plain was rising and falling like a sea lashed by a storm. Waves of sand broke one upon another, throwing up clouds of dust. From the south-east a huge, twisting column was approaching with incredible swiftness. The sun vanished behind a dense cloud whose gigantic shadow extended to the balloon. Grains of fine sand swept along with the quick flow of liquid and, little by little, the rising tide advanced.

A gleam of hope shone in Fergusson's eyes. 'The simoon!' he cried.

'The simoon!' Joe repeated, without much idea of what the word meant.

'Good!' muttered Kennedy, in the delirium of despair. 'All the better. We're going to die.'

'Yes, all the better!' replied the doctor. 'But we're going to live.' And he began rapidly to throw out the sand holding down the car. His companions, at last understanding, rejoined him and took their places at his side. 'And now, Joe,' said the doctor, 'throw out fifty pounds or so of your gold.'

Though he felt a swift pang of regret, Joe did not hesitate. The balloon rose.

'It was time,' said the doctor.

And indeed the simoon was sweeping towards them with the swiftness of lightning. A little longer and the *Victoria* would have been crushed to pieces—Annihilated. The huge column was open them. The *Victoria* was swept by a hail of sand.

'More ballast!' the doctor cried to Joe.

They were right to call this the land of thirst, the land of despair.

'Aye, aye, sir,' replied the latter, hurling out an enormous piece of quartz.

The *Victoria* rose rapidly above the column, but, caught in the great whirlpool of air, she was torn along at dizzy speed over this foaming sea of sand. Samuel, Dick and Joe did not speak but looked and hoped, refreshed by the whirlwind. By three o'clock the tumult had ceased. The sand fell again and formed a great quantity of little hills. The sky resumed its former calm. The *Victoria*, motionless again, was floating within sight of an oasis, an island of trees on the surface of the sandy ocean.

'Water! There's water there!' cried the doctor. And immediately, opening the upper valve, he let the hydrogen escape and came down gently, two hundred yeards from the oasis. In four hours the travellers had covered two hundred and forty miles.

The moment the car came to a halt Kennedy jumped out, followed by Joe.

'Your gun!' cried the doctor. 'Take your guns, and look out.'

Dick seized his carbine and Joe one of the guns. They quickly approached the trees and plunged into the fresh foliage which promised abundant springs. They paid no heed to a number of large, broad footmarks freshly imprinted here and there on the humid earth. Suddenly, twenty yards away, a roar rang out.

'A lion!' said Joe.

'Good!' snapped the exasperated Kennedy. 'We'll fight him. We're strong enough when it's only a question of fighting.'

'Take care, sir. All our lives may depend on the life of one of us.'

But Kennedy was not listening. He strode forward, eyes blazing, carbine cocked, terrible in his audacity. Under a palm an enormous black-maned lion was crouching, ready to spring. Scarcely had he caught sight of Kennedy than he hurled himself through the air; but before he touched the ground a bullet struck him in the heart. He fell dead.

'Hurray!' cried Joe.

Kennedy dashed towards the well, slipping on the wet steps, and threw himself down by a fresh spring into which he greedily plunged his lips. Joe followed his example, and the silence was broken only by the lapping sound similar to that made by thirsty animals.

'Steady, sir,' said Joe, taking a long breath. 'We mustn't overdo it.' But Dick, without answering, went on drinking. He plunged his head and hands into the healing water. He was intoxicated and seemingly oblivious.

'And what about Dr Fergusson?' said Joe. This brought Kennedy to his senses. Filling a bottle he had brought, he dashed up the steps. But what was his amazement when he found a huge opaque body blocking the entrance. Joe, who was following him, had to draw back too.

'We're shut in!'

'Impossible! what does this mean——?'

Dick did not finish. A terrible roar made him realize with what new enemy he had to deal.

'Another lion!' cried Joe.

'No. A lioness. Damn the brute! Wait,' said the hunter, hastily reloading his carbine. An instant later he fired, but the animal had disappeared. 'Come on!' he cried.

'No, sir. You didn't kill her. The body would have rolled down here. She's waiting to spring on whichever of us comes out first, and it will be all up with him.'

'But what's to be done? We must get out. Dr Fergusson's waiting.'

'Let's draw her. You take my gun and pass me the carbine.'

'What's the idea?'

'You'll see.'

Taking off his canvas jacket, Joe stuck it on the end of the gun and held it out above the opening as a bait. The animal dashed at it in fury. Kennedy was ready, and with a shot broke its shoulder. The roaring animal rolled down the steps, knocking Joe over. Joe already imagined he could feel the animal's great claws piercing his flesh, when a second shot rang out, and the doctor appeared at the opening, his gun still smoking in his hand.

Joe got up hastily, climbed over the animal's body and passed the bottle of water to his master. To raise it to his lips and half-empty it was for Fergusson the work of a moment, and from the bottom of their hearts the three travellers thanked Providence, who had so miraculously saved them.

ESCAPE FROM COLDITZ

Alain Le Ray

It was the disgusting Pomeranian winter of 1940–1 when I was back again, a prisoner in Germany's comfortless sheep-fold. I had escaped and had been recaptured.

First, I was subjected to a cunning interrogation by a German security officer but I stubbornly refused to reveal the secret of my escape. There followed twenty days of solitary confinement, when I was lodged far from my comrades, except for Tournon, who had been my partner in escape. We were like people caught in a plague. On roll-call, we had to stand twenty paces in front of our comrades and a special jailer followed us closely wherever we went.

Yet all the time I was working, working at high speed on my new escape-suit. My new trousers were already washed and ready. I had even succeeded in bribing a corporal to buy me a watch for a few marks.

Then one fine morning, three German guards came to us and announced, in their usual roaring voices, that we had ten minutes to pack our things to go to a new camp.

My trousers were not yet dry; my suit not yet complete, so I had no hope of escaping during the journey. I prefer enterprises which are carefully prepared beforehand.

When I found out we were travelling to the west, I felt that at least I was gaining distance and that I should have time in my new camp to prepare more thoroughly for my second attempt.

Tournon and I started this new trip in the highest of spirits. From the train we watched the well-known place names pass before our eyes. We changed at Stettin and Berlin, crossing them like beggars burdened under the weight of the luggage we had to carry. We went on to Cottbus and then to Leipzig where we slept on the tiled floor of a police station.

We left Leipzig by a local train in the early morning of February 24 1941. I was careful to remember the direction we were going and the names of the stations we passed through. Eventually we reached a river in flood, its grey water filled with sheets of floating ice. The railway followed the river up a narrow valley, flanked by rocks and snow-covered forests.

Then we came to Colditz. High above the town, on the right bank of the river Mulde, was a castle with an entanglement of pinnacles, small clock-towers and steep roofs like those of a cathedral. Seen against the bright sky, the fortress appeared gigantic.

Our guards led us up through the town, up a steep and narrow lane, through the castle's heavy gates, which were closed behind us. This marvellous castle became just another prison. Farewell delight and hope.

Now we penetrated deeper through a tunnel which led to the guard-house at the end of a terrace, where a battery of search-lights shone at night in all directions and through every possible angle. Their beams swept along the walls without missing the smallest corner. The windows overlooking the approach-yard were secured by enormous iron bars.

The many guards at this time were young soldiers, not the second-line troops usually used for guard duty. A sergeant-major with an enormous bunch of keys opened the wicket gate in the door leading to the inner courtyard, which was not so much a yard as a pit, about fifty metres deep and paved with stones.

In each corner of this yard was a small door which led to a hundred winding stairs past four floors to the attics. One one side of the pit, a chapel had been built into the castle.

Although the castle had a certain grandeur, it was nevertheless a place of punishment for us. There was no doubt about that. We were isolated, searched and interrogated before we were allowed to join the other prisoners who lived there. At that time, there were twenty-three French, eighty Poles, twenty British and, in the attics, a contingent of Jews. These prisoners were the aristocracy of escape experts and enemies of Germany.

At Colditz I passed some extraordinary weeks which, although filled with despair, gave us hope too, for a precious solidarity reigned here. In spite of all the restrictions, we felt we were recognized as officers. This was because of the respect which our guards had for us. But our lack of freedom became more evident than at any other prison I had been in.

I observed my surroundings, an exercise which gave me not the slightest glimmer of hope of escaping. After a fortnight I felt ill with frustration. My sense of powerlessness so overwhelmed me, I was almost prepared to jump from one of the towers and was determined to attempt the impossible, even if it led nowhere. My examination of the walls and roofs remained disappointing as the castle was surrounded by steep precipices to the north and west. To the east, the slopes were gentler, but there were double rows of barbed wire along the guards' cat-walks.

The Germans in Colditz, respecting the Geneva Convention, let us out in the castle grounds from time to time to walk around in a wooded park surrounded on three sides by a fence of barbed wire and on one side by a wall. But it was such a nuisance to get ready for the park walk—assembling in the courtyard, being counted and re-counted—that many of the prisoners could not be bothered to go.

Apart from the wired-off section reserved for prisoners, the park was not particularly well guarded. On the other hand, the castle guards could survey the whole area including the path down to it.

For the walk, our guards counted us twice in the inner courtyard before we left. Then again after arrival in the park, and the same on the way back. This was done although the walk down took us only four minutes. In spite of these precautions, I felt that this was a weak spot in the castle's defences and made my plans accordingly.

Until the spring of 1941, no one had succeeded in escaping from the castle. The prisoners had tried tunnelling, hiding the spoil in the attics, and climbing the walls, but always in vain. They were caught and caught again to be punished and threatened, so I decided to do it alone. I planned to escape through the park, telling no one until the day of my attempt. In the meantime, I manu-factured a new civilian suit, much better than those I had made before and in due course I was ready. I chose Easter to execute my plan to escape on the park walk, for my observations of the route down from the castle showed that when we left the castle gate on the way to the park, we went down a small path past a big house known as the Terrace House. At the corner of this building, where there was a door, the path curved slightly. One day I noticed that the door was half-open. That was all.

Now the curve in the path by the corner of the Terrace House was of tremendous importance as I realized that if the marching column were to close in to the house, there was a moment, as a result of the curve, when the accompanying guards could not observe all the park-walkers at once.

Friday, 11 April was a glorious day. The hills showed the return of spring and the light blue sky was like a promise of joy. The river Mulde was brown and almost in flood as it raced through its wind-ing course. I looked at the forest and beyond to the horizon, but as I was still looking from behind the iron bars of my prison window, I hoped that this look would be the very last from my captivity.

It was half-past two; in about ten minutes we should be assembling for the park walk. I wore my uniform, but only for appearances as my white stockings were covered by blue trousers which reached to my shoes and my light cardigan was hidden under a thick chestnut-brown pullover. On top, I wore a wide khaki greatcoat to cover my small parcel of baggage, which, though concealed, made me look a little fatter than usual. Three of my friends had been let into my secret, together with our doctor.

Now the Germans had opened the wicket gate and we began to pass through, one at a time, while we were counted twice. As I went through the wicket, my luggage was not noticed by the guard commander in charge of the walk, a sergeant with a scarred face who counted us automatically. As with all professional jailers, he could count prisoners and be quite certain his figures were correct, even though his mind could be on other things.

On the other side of the gate, we were counted for the second time. These mechanical precautions did not alarm me in the least, as I knew it would not be too difficult to confuse such an arbitrary count, should there be a prisoner short.

At last, the column of park walkers started to move. Our steps echoed under the first vault, through to the sunlit German yard where a squad of guards took positions around our column.

As it was Good Friday, no one was about except for the guards and the prisoners. At 3 p.m. we passed the Terrace House and I noticed that the little door in the basement was still open. This looked good.

But no, I could not escape today as the guards along the sides of the column would be too dangerous. I weighed this consideration like an athlete who has signed a contract for a contest in an arena. So far, I had hardly started the game, but already I sought excuses to drop out. Do such excuses cause discouragement? I do not know. But the day was not over yet. I again contemplated success, even if today should begin only the first of a series of escape attempts. Perhaps I am like one of those musicians who refuse to play because the air is damp or because the position of the piano is not exactly right. Sometimes I felt like this on the sports field when competing in the long jump—imagining I had started on the wrong foot, I would stop and begin the run again.

Soon we reached the barbed-wire enclosure in the park, where we spent the next hour or so walking around. When it was time to go, we formed a column, we counted and began the march back. I was resolved to make my attempt before we reached the castle, if I possibly could.

I threw my coat over my back and marched on the left side of the column with my friend Tournon beside me. As we walked up the path, Tournon whispered, 'Now?'

'Impossible! No chance yet.'

I was in the third rank behind the colonels and other senior officers. Behind me were some Jews. None of them had the slightest idea of my intentions. One of my friends was in the front rank; the other, who was near the German sergeant, had agreed to start a diversion if need be and in the case of any shooting, to turn aside the sergeant's gun.

We crossed the bridge over a brook and started to climb the steep path. Tournon had whispered to the senior French officer, Colonel Le Brigant, 'Slowly'. The colonel, cunning as a fox, at once slowed the pace of the march. He did not know why, but he was anxious to co-operate as much as he could with any conspiracy his comrades had planned.

Now we had only about a hundred metres to go before we reached the Terrace House again. Tournon whispered once more, 'Now?'

'No!' I repeated furiously. I trembled with excitement. The guard at the head of the column was still looking ahead. I watched the guard on our flank. We were now close to the house. Another guard was ten metres behind me. I should have five seconds to act.

'This is it!' I whispered to Tournon, who, without turning, warned those around him to take no notice of anything, but to keep marching normally.

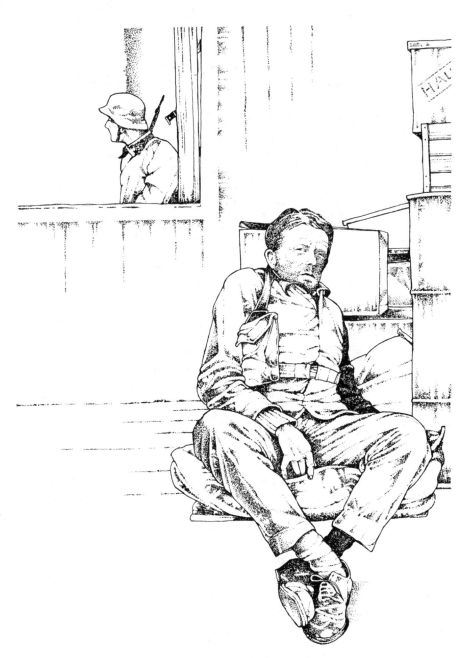

There followed twenty days of solitary confinement.

My heart was beating as if it would break. Tournon grabbed my coat; then with a single jump I reached the grass slope and fell. Was all lost? Would I be shot? I was on all fours and almost in despair, but I got up again and with two more jumps I reached the darkness beyond the little door.

For some seconds my universe was upside down. Little by little my awareness returned.

Where was I? In a vaulted cellar stored with beds and straw mattresses. I had scarcely time to grasp where I was, before I knew I had to get out and get away before the next count would reveal my absence. Then it would take only two minutes before the guards would be on my heels.

Still trembling with shock, I turned up the lower parts of my false blue trousers, so that they looked like plus-fours, revealing at the same time my white stockings with their decorative garters. I took off my pullover and my linen waistcoat. This changed my appearance in such a way that it would be improbable that I should be recognized. Indeed I looked elegant enough, with the collar of my open blue shirt falling down on my cardigan; my cap with buckle and flap and a small suitcase, completed the picture of a German traveller. This change took me about one minute. Now I had to get out to the walls of the park. I had already planned what to do. I worked like clockwork. On the tips of my toes I crossed the flagstones of the cellar, out through the door and up the grass slope in a single jump. I felt weightless as I reached the path. There was no one to be seen. Quickly, quickly. But no, I must not show haste. Somebody may be looking down from the castle. I went back down the path, with nerves strained to the utmost. There in the park were three Germans playing football inside the barbed wire enclosure. There was nothing for me to do but return to my cellar hiding place. This time, my excitement had gone. I knew that within moments an armed group of German soldiers might break in and catch me. If I should try to escape they would undoubtedly shoot.

I was becoming desperate, but my reason calmed my fears. I realized I must have enough patience to wait until dawn, when the park would be empty. My faith in doing this lay in my friend Tournon, who I believed would succeed in causing a diversion at the count. The German guards trusted their own counting efficiency and disliked having to report any irregularity for which they were responsible. If the count could be fixed, I should win some hours of respite, at least until the evening *Appell* at 6 p.m.

Time passed without any alarm being raised, so Tournon had succeeded after all. Then I saw three German officers pass the cellar with an Alsatian dog. Time was going and I felt I had to get out of the cellar at any price. All was clear outside, so I departed; my rubber-soled shoes made no noise.

For the second time I went quietly down to the park. There was no one there now, but eyes might be watching me from the windows of the Terrace House where a watcher could have followed my every step. I went to the small bridge over the brook and hid for a while in some bushes and ferns. Should anyone see me there, it would be quite clear what I was up to, so I hurried to a fallen tree lying across the brook; a few more steps and I had reached the other bank and was near the barbed wire fence which surrounded the ground of the park walk, near where the soldiers had played football about twenty minutes before.

Everything I did now I had already planned in detail days before. I felt like a guide to a party of mountaineers, leading them up a dangerous route which led only to the summit.

The whole park was like an immense eye watching me as I went along the barbed wire fence, to where it joined the wall, and grasped the upper strands of wire, putting my foot on the end of one of the wooden wire supports fastened to the wall. I stretched out my hands despairingly, until they felt the round top of the wall to which I clung tightly, whilst my crepe rubber shoes groped the wall to find a foothold somewhere. With a tremendous effort I succeeded in swinging myself to the top of the wall and down the other side, out of the castle grounds.

I had only a little money, yet I managed to travel by train as far as Nuremberg.

From now on, my voyage became a pleasure trip. I went through Stuttgart—Tuttlingen—Singen. On the evening of the Easter Monday, I was only ten kilometres from the Swiss frontier, near Schaffhausen. During the Monday night, I made my way through woodland paths to Gottmadingen, the last station before the frontier and customs-control, where I waited hidden in the bushes. A train passed at about 11 p.m. and the locomotive stopped five metres in front of me for the train to be searched. When the doors were shut again, I crept up to the engine, and when the engine driver gave the whistle signal to start, I sprang up onto the front of the locomotive between its headlights, where I hid. The driver opened the throttle and the train roared through the fresh air of the spring night. Five minutes later we passed the red lights of the enemy guard post; on under a bridge, and then into Switzerland. I had reconquered for myself the right to freedom.

MYSTERY OF THE DRIFTING DERELICT

Rupert Furneaux

'**B**rig Ahoy.' The traditional call from one ship to another echoed across the stormy Atlantic wastes. 'Ahoy, Ahoy,' hailed the seamen standing in the bows of the *Dei Gratia*. No answering call came from the brig bowling past on the opposite tack. No helmsman stood at her wheel and her decks were silent and empty. She was sailing under short canvas and steering very wild and evidently in distress; every few minutes she yawed and fell off into the wind. Captain Morehouse had spotted her at 1 p.m. about 4 to 6 miles distant on the port bow. The strange ship was making about 1½ to 2 knots, heading westward, in the opposite direction to the *Dei Gratia*. The wind was north and the sea was running high. It had been blowing hard all morning with rain and squalls but was now abating. Something he observed through his spy-glass struck Captain Morehouse as strange. Whereas the brig was sailing on the port tack, her jib and fore-topmast stay-sail were set on the starboard tack.

Now, two hours later, Morehouse leant on the rail watching the brig careering along on her erratic course 300 yards away. 'Brace the yards and haul for that vessel,' he ordered Chief Mate Deveau, who had come on deck from his watch below. 'Look out for her name,' he shouted to his crew. All hands strained their eyes as the brig came plunging by. As she fell off in the wind, her stern came into view. 'It's the *Mary Celeste*,' cried Helmsman John Johnson incredulously.

Astonished, Captain Morehouse echoed the name. The *Mary Celeste* was well known to him; her captain, Benjamin Briggs, his friend. Twenty-nine days before, they had dined together in New York. The *Mary Celeste*, an American-owned brig of 282 tons, bound for Genoa with a cargo of crude alcohol, sailed on 7 November 1872, followed eight days later by the *Dei Gratia*, a Nova Scotian brigantine of 295 tons, bound for Gibraltar, where she was to await orders, with a cargo of petroleum.

Now the paths of the two ships had crossed at Latitude 38.20N. by Longitude 17.15W., due east of the Azores, 591 miles from Gibraltar, on Wednesday, 5 December 1872, a date memorable in the history of the sea.

'Lower a boat and board her,' Morehouse ordered Deveau.

Oliver Deveau, accompanied by two men from the *Dei Gratia*, Second Mate John Wright and Seaman John Johnson, rowed across the choppy sea to the *Mary Celeste*. On reaching her, Deveau and Wright clambered aboard leaving Johnson in the boat. What exactly Deveau and Wright found, or did not find, on the *Mary Celeste* was told by them at the Court of Inquiry at Gibraltar some weeks later. From what they then stated, we learn that when they hoisted themselves over the derelict's rail they came upon an eerie scene. No face or voice greeted them; no sound was to be heard save the creaking of the rigging, the slap of sails and the swish of the waves as the *Mary Celeste* careered on her headlong way. Unlashed and unmanned, the wheel turned and spun as the sea twisted the rudder. Two sails, the foresail and the upper fore-topsail, had been blown away and the lower fore-topsail hung by its four corners. The main staysail lay loose on the forward-house. All the other sails were furled. Some of the rigging was gone.

Cautiously Deveau and Wright stepped on to the deserted deck. Slowly and carefully they examined the ship from stem to stern. They searched the main cabin, looked down the forward hatch, which was open, peered into the forecastle and inspected the galley. No one was aboard, that was certain. Yet their quick survey showed that the *Mary Celeste* was perfectly sound, her hull, masts, rigging and sails in good condition, her cargo well stowed and intact, plenty of food and water aboard, and no sign of damage, disorder or confusion, and no reason why she might have been suddenly abandoned. Fit to 'got round the world' as Seaman Anderson was later to put it. A complete and baffling mystery.

True there was $3\frac{1}{2}$ feet of water in the hold, and the cabin, forecastle and galley were a foot deep in water. But for a wooden ship of her size that was no more than normal leakage. The only sign of damage was that the binnacle had been knocked down, its glass broken, its compass destroyed. On the bunks in the forecastle lay the seamen's pipes, tobacco and clothes. In the cabin stood a harmonium, under the sofa lay a sewing machine. In the cabin was a clock which had stopped. On the bed was an impression of a body, one so small that it could have been made only by a child. The imprint of a tiny head was still visible on the pillow. The ship's crew and passengers had left in a great hurry.

On the cabin table the searchers found a chart showing the track of the vessel up to 24 November and a slate on which notes had been made for entry into the ship's log, showing that the last observation had been made at 8 a.m. on 25 November. The *Mary Celeste* had then been at Latitude 37.01N. by Longitude 25.01W., 6 miles distant from the north-easterly point of the island of St

Mary, the most easterly island of the Azores group. Now, ten days later, Deveau observed she was 378 miles to the north-eastwards, *still on her exact course to Gibraltar*, her first port of call. On the slate had been scribbled the words 'Fanny my dear wife. Frances M.R.' The writer had apparently been interrupted suddenly. The ship's navigational instruments and papers, with the exception of the log book, were missing, and the last entry, on 24 November, showed that she had been then 110 miles westward of St Mary.

It was all very puzzling. A perplexing mystery. If the *Mary Celeste* had been abandoned or her crew had been lost in some way on 25 November, to which the entry on the slate seemed to point as the fatal day, how had she held her exact course for ten days unmanned and unsteered? And in that time she had sailed 378 miles. And sailed for ten days apparently with no one on board.

His cursory examination of the derelict finished, Deveau returned to the *Dei Gratia*, where he reported to Captain Morehouse. He asked to be allowed to take two men and sail the *Mary Celeste* to Gibraltar. Morehouse, while he did not wish to reject the opportunity of earning for himself, his crew and his owners a considerable award for salvage, was at first doubtful of the feasibility of the plan. To spare three men out of his small crew of eight might endanger the safety of his own vessel and cargo, and three men would be hard put to it to sail the derelict the near 600 miles to Gibraltar, a journey of unpredictable perils in mid-December. For a minute Morehouse strode up and down pondering the problem. Then he turned and told Deveau, whom he knew to be an experienced seaman and who had been Master of a brig, 'You can have your men.' In a moment all was bustle and activity. Collecting the food the Steward had prepared for their evening meal, a compass, a barometer, a watch and his own navigational instruments, Deveau stepped into the boat with Seamen Charles Lund and Augustus Anderson, who had agreed to go with him on the *Mary Celeste*. By 4 p.m. they were on board, and by 9 p.m. they had pumped her dry, set her sails and got her under way. But it took them two or three days to 'set her to rights' and 'make any headway'.

They rowed across the choppy sea to the Mary Celeste.

For several days the *Mary Celeste* and the *Dei Gratia* sailed towards Gibraltar in company, speaking to each other each night and morning.

The day before reaching Gibraltar, the *Mary Celeste* and the *Dei Gratia* became separated in a storm and the official record shows that the *Dei Gratia* entered the Straits on the evening of 12 December and the *Mary Celeste* early in the following morning, appropriately on Friday the Thirteenth.

The bringing into port of a derelict, yet staunch, vessel whose captain, Benjamin Briggs, was well known and respected in Gibraltar caused a sensation, and speculation became rife as to the reason why she might have been abandoned in mid-ocean, and what might have happened to her captain and crew; excitement which was brought to fever pitch by the discovery in her cabin of a sword, the blade of which appeared to be blood-stained.

The *Mary Celeste* was taken into custody by T. J. Vecchio, the Master of the British Vice-Admiralty Court, a guard was placed on board and on 18 December the Court began the hearing of the claims of 'David Reed Morehouse, Master of the British brigantine *Dei Gratia* and for the owners, officers and crew of the said brigantine, claiming as salvors against the *Mary Celeste* and her cargo, proceeded against as derelict'. Sir James Cockrane, Knight and commissary of the Vice-Admiralty Court of Gibraltar presided. The evidence taken was not then published and its details remained unknown to the world for seventy years. Sufficient is it to remark that testimony was given by the captain and crew of the *Dei Gratia*, and Captain James Winchester, part owner of the *Mary Celeste* who came from New York, supplied the names of the lost captain and crew.

Meanwhile, the world was informed of the strange occurrence, the finding in mid-ocean of a staunch vessel fully provisioned and in a seaworthy condition apparently abandoned by her captain and crew. 'A marine tragedy,' as Mr Charles Edey Fay calls it, 'destined to become the most widely known of all the mysteries of the sea.'

The Liverpool *Mercury*, quoting the *Globe*'s correspondent at

Gibraltar, gave more details. It related that the *Mary Celeste* had been found abandoned under foremast staysail and jib; she had been pursuing her way for ten days without a soul on board; every document which could throw light on the mystery was gone; there was not the slightest clue to account for the desertion of the vessel and 'every conjecture is at fault'; the vessel had sustained no injury; a little phial of oil had been found standing by a sewing machine and a reel of cotton and a thimble 'not yet rolled off the table' in the cabin; the contents of the cabin indicated the one-time presence of a lady and child; a sword had been found and on it marks of blood; there were sharp cuts on the vessel's bulwarks. The whole thing was an absolute mystery. There was no trace of lady, child, captain or crew.

SURVIVOR

John Wingate DSC

The young man stood motionless for a moment outside the
bustling entrance to Dover station. His gas-mask was slung
over his right shoulder and from his left hand drooped the grip
which contained his emergency personal gear. 'Sub-Lieutenant
W. Bruce, RN' was stencilled in black upon the khaki canvas of
his holdall, but apart from this identification, there was little to
distinguish him from any of the scurrying figures dispersing into
the gloom of this wartime twilight. The wail of the all clear from
the siren was dying away and, for an instant, there was peace save
for the crying of the gulls as they flew lazily inland for the night.

Walter Bruce took off his cap to feel the wind in his thick fair
hair; he was weary from the long journey from Glasgow where he

had left his ship. With only half an hour's warning, he had been ordered south to report to Headquarters at Dover. He had been informed that, because he had gained his watch-keeping certificate, he could be useful in the Dover command, but otherwise he was told nothing. Yet, during the long journey southwards, the rumours of disaster multiplied: the Belgians were surrendering to the Germans, now that Holland was overrun; the French armies were in full retreat; with its back to the sea, the British Expeditionary Force had been cut off and was fighting for its life while Hitler's Panzers closed in from all sides.

Wally Bruce's eyes, as blue and clear as the waters of the Moray Firth whence his forbears came, looked upwards to the castle which towered, proud and defiant, high above Dover town. The battlements were silhouetted against the lowering clouds, a sky which reflected the last blood-red streaks of another sunset. In this silence, Wally felt an intense foreboding, a realization that events of gigantic proportions were about to unfold. This awareness emphasized the atmosphere of crisis that seemed to be Dover. He shook himself, smoothed his hair and replaced his cap.

'D'you want the castle, sir?' a husky voice asked quietly. 'There's a truck leaving now.' The Chief Petty Officer, part of the Rail Transport Officer's team, indicated a 15-cwt Bedford which, jammed with personnel, was waiting at the kerb, its darkened lights casting an oval pool of dim, blue light upon the road.

'Thanks, Chief.'

Wally scrambled into the front seat. The CPO saluted and banged shut the door of the truck. Wally was alone with his thoughts as the Bedford whined its way up to the castle. Things will never be the same again for me, he thought. All my training during these long years will soon be put to the test.

'Who are you?'

The questioner was the skipper of the drifter *Comfort*, a sturdy boat who had spent her peace-time days fishing off the banks of the Thames estuary. A rugged, unshaven seaman looked up with bleary eyes through the wheelhouse window at the young Lieutenant standing on the quay, a group of sailors at his back in the darkness.

'Sub-Lieutenant Bruce, sir. We've come to help with the boat-work.'

The skipper shrugged his shoulders, grunted, and then came the sound of the wheelhouse door opening.

'Ye better come aboard.'

The two men shook hands in the darkness. The skipper pointed towards the for'd hatch.

'Ye'd better kip down below for a wee bit. Ye'll be needing your sleep.'

Ten minutes later the little drifter, *Comfort*, slipped unnoticed from Dover south-west quay. She moved across the black waters of the harbour, then, to the throb of her heavy Gardiner diesel, she chugged between the breakwaters to set course for the open sea. The swell suddenly took her as she slid into the cross tide.

'What course do I want?' the skipper grunted.

Wally was still crouched over the chart which, cocoa-stained and crumpled, was spread out in the diminutive cubby-hole on the port side of the wheelhouse. A pool of blue light illuminated the ancient chart.

'Is the chart up to date, Skipper?'

'Up to last Friday, yes. I can't keep up with the corrections,' the old man grumbled, 'now that there's a new swept channel every other day.'

Wally smiled in the darkness. This independent Scotsman was, for once, adhering to the swept channels. The thumping diesel would certainly detonate any acoustic mines within reach.

'I'll take route Z,' the skipper growled. 'It's only thirty-nine miles compared with route Y.'

'You're ordered to use route Y, Skipper,' Wally said quietly. 'The Calais batteries have made Z pretty hot.'

The skipper spun the wheel to port as he sighted the South Foreland buoy flashing on his port bow.

'It's just as hot this side, Subbie. The Luftwaffe even shoots up our lightships now. The South Foreland has been replaced by that buoy. Can ye see it?'

'Yes, Skipper.'

'Take your departure from there, then. I'll use route Z: they won't see us in this darkness and we'll be there before dawn.'

'Aye, aye, Skipper.' Wally ran his parallel ruler over the chart, his stomach heaving with the combination of fear and the drifter's uneasy motion. Like all seamen, he detested the magnetic mine. The sudden, blinding flash in the darkness, the roar, and then the deluge of water: he hadn't experienced this new warfare yet. Scapa Flow and the relative safety of a cruiser in the North Sea off Norway had been comparatively peaceful, in spite of the vicissitudes of that heartrending campaign.

'Course for Calais buoy, route Z, South seventy East,' Wally reported.

The skipper grunted. The wheel spun again, the drifter heeled, then settled down on her new course.

'Another fine night,' Skipper Craig said. 'This'll be your first trip, then?'

'To Dunkirk?'

'Yes,' Craig growled. '*Dunkirk.*'

Wally resented the contemptuous note in the man's voice.

'It's a ruddy shambles, getting those bomb-happy troops off.'

In the silence, Wally heard only the swish of the water as *Comfort* dipped into the cross swell. He watched the granite features of the Scottish skipper, the craggy face that gleamed in the glow of the binnacle.

'Angus, ye take her. Course, South seventy East.'

A cadaverous figure detached itself from the corner of the wheelhouse and, without a word, took over the steering. Skipper Craig moved alongside Wally. The old Scot removed his cap and extracted from it his foul pipe. He filled the bowl with some evil-smelling tobacco, then applied the slow-match which hung from below the chart table. Clouds of smoke filled the tiny wheelhouse.

Wally suppressed the choking cough which threatened to over-whelm him: he wanted the dour Scot to continue the conversation. The frequency of the pipe-sucking decreased and then, peering through the open windows of the dog-house, at 2330 during the night of Monday, 28 May 1940, the old Scot began to talk in the darkness, as is the custom of seamen during the long watches of the night. 'The weather's been like this since the evacuation started,' growled Craig. 'Ruddy miracle if you ask me. A mill pond off the beaches, except for once or twice; ruddy miracle, Subbie, that's what it is.'

'What's it like, Skipper? Off the beaches?'

Craig did not speak at first. Wally logged the South Foreland light, then returned to the binnacle. A running fix had put them half a mile south of the line.

'Could you come round to South seventy-five East, sir, please?'

'Bring her round, as the subbie says, Angus. Course, South seventy-five East.'

'South seventy-five East, Skipper. Aye, aye.' Wally heard the soft voice of the Western Islander. Angus and Craig had worked together, it seemed, for many years.

'If the weather had been bad, Subbie, we wouldn't have got off more than a few thousand. We move into the shallows as far as we dare, load up and ferry them off to the destroyers. When they're full up, I take on as many as I can and return to Dover.'

'Easy as kiss-your-hand,' Angus said. 'Except for them Stukas.'

No one spoke for a long time. Wally had not yet been dive-bombed: the Junkers 87s Stukas, as they were being called, could not reach Scapa or the Norwegian fiords.

'What's my ETA,[1] Dyck Buoy, Subbie?'

'0320, at ten knots, Skipper.'

Craig nodded. The skipper broke the long silence, but he expressed the thoughts in all their minds as they passed three sweepers, inward bound, their dimmed mine-sweeping lights just visible in the darkness.

[1] Expected Time of Arrival.

'They've got guts,' Craig said, 'them sweeper boys.'

'Don't much like these magnetics,' Angus murmured. 'Ye never know.'

'D'you think we'll beat this menace, Subbie?' the skipper asked, almost childlike. 'The Hun has got us by the throat this time: most of the ports are closed.'

Wally hesitated: he had heard only yesterday that stocks of food were down to ten days throughout the country. All the ports were mined and the casualty rate of ships and sweepers was terrifying.

'We'll *have* to master this magnetic mine, Skipper, or we'll ruddy well starve.'

'What about this chap they're all talking about, then?' Craig asked. 'Bloomin' 'ero, I call 'im.'

'Ouvry, you mean? Lieutenant-Commander Ouvry?'

'Yes, that's the one. He's the chap who took a magnetic mine to bits in the mud off Shoeburyness. An aircraft had dropped it.'

'Didn't he describe every move he made to his mate on the other end of the telephone? In case he was blown up, like.'

'Yes,' Wally said quietly. 'I met Ouvry at *Vernon*, the Torpedo and Mining School. He was a quiet man.'

Craig was silent as, in the darkness, every man's imagination conjured up Ouvry's heroism.[1] Wally peered ahead into the blackness, but the sheen of the drifter's bow wave was the only glimmer of light. Drowsiness was beginning to engulf him, his eyelids aching from the strain of trying to keep awake.

A yellow flash of light leaped suddenly on their port bow. There was a rumble, a violent crack and then an intense violet and orange flame.

'Not far off,' Craig snapped. 'Port ten, full ahead.' He picked up his binoculars and swept the horizon line where, in the darkness, the source of the flames must be.

'E-boats[2] or some lurking U-boat,' Craig growled. 'Some poor blighter's bought it.'

---

[1] Lieutenant-Commander Ouvry was awarded the DSO.
[2] A German boat; the equivalent of our MTB.

Comfort's diesels were thumping at full speed, her hull quivering from the added power as she lifted to the swell.

'My God, Skipper,' Angus whispered, 'look at yon ship.' He was pointing with outstretched arm through the wheel-house window which the skipper had lowered. Wally tried to drag his eyes away but the horror of the scene riveted his gaze upon the sea where, sticking up like two sore thumbs, were the fore and after ends of a destroyer, her back broken. From amidships bubbled up globs of black smoke where her boiler rooms were still exploding. Above the rending of the tortured metal, wailed the shouts of trapped and drowning men. The bows and stern of the ship hung there, slowly dipping up and down in the swell like macabre marionettes.

'Look, sir . . .' Angus was pointing to where a wedge of black heads bobbed in the oily sea which gleamed fitfully from the flames of the burning ship.

The skipper took over the wheel and nursed his little drifter alongside the group of bedraggled swimmers. All hands had appeared from below and soon the dazed survivors were being hauled over the drifter's bulwarks; blankets were wrapped around the shivering men who, cigarettes now thrust between their lips, were gently escorted below into the saloon. Wally was hauling the last, an older man, from the water when Craig went full ahead to pick up the next knot of men struggling in the sea.

'I'm the captain,' the man gasped as, covered in slimy black oil fuel, he stumbled for'd on the slippery deck.

'What ship, sir?' Wally asked.

'Sorry, you wouldn't know, of course. I'm Commander Fisher,' the Captain said quietly. '*Wakeful*, an old "V" and "W".[1] Torpedoed on the port side, amidships. U-boat probably, or could have been an E-boat—never saw the swine.'

Commander Fisher choked with emotion, shock overcoming his self-control. Wally put his arm around him and turned him gently round to retrace his steps.

---

[1] Classes of destroyers built in the Great War. They were sturdy and well built.

Wally braced himself to meet the shock.

'Come with me, sir, to meet Skipper Craig. You'll be warm in the wheelhouse.'

By the glow of the binnacle, Wally watched Craig, his skill tested to the utmost as he coaxed the little drifter to the next survivor, a man screaming and waving off the port bow.

'Captain of *Wakeful*, Skipper,' Wally said.

'Glad to have you aboard, sir,' replied Craig, not taking his eyes from the water. 'Sit ye down and Angus'll give ye a cuppa.'

'Thanks, Skipper. You arrived just in time,' Fisher said quietly.

'Och, all in the day's work. How long have you been doing the Dunkirk run?'

'Must be four days.' The Captain scratched his hair, matted by the oil. 'What day is it now? I've lost all count of time.'

'Twenty-ninth May, Tuesday,' Wally said. 'How long will we be able to keep this up, sir?'

'Till we run out of destroyers.'

The door of the wheelhouse opened. Angus's face was silhouetted against the glare of the burning oil, which was already being extinguished by the long swell.

Wakeful's bow jutted into the sky, her pendant number, H.88, showing plainly as her fore-end dipped slowly up and down in the Channel. The shouts of the trapped men and the screams of the dying floated across the water through the scuttles, which were too small to allow men to escape. Her stern, hinged amidships, cocked upwards to form the second arm of a large 'V'.

Commander Fisher stared up at Wally, agony in his dark eyes. Wally felt sick as he stumbled from the wheelhouse for air.

'There's a ship coming up on the other side of her,' Angus was saying. 'She's flashing a blue light.'

Wally snatched up the signalling torch from the wheelhouse seat. He identified a *Halcyon* class minesweeper by the dark shape that had loomed up in the darkness which, mercifully, was beginning to envelop them as the flames died down.

'*Gossamer*, Skipper. She's picking up survivors.'

Angus poked his head through the door.

'We're awfu' full, Skipper. They'll have to stay on the upper deck now.'

Craig grunted. 'We'll go on until her gunwales are awash, man. Carry on getting 'em aboard.'

Wally had discarded his reefer; it was warm work hauling these pathetic remains aboard. He slung his Mae West life jacket to one side, regarded it for a moment, then donned it again. Commander Fisher had now joined him and was patching up, as best he could, his torn and bleeding men.

'Look you, sir,' Angus shouted. 'Two more ships.'

To starboard of *Gossamer*, the sleek lines of a destroyer loomed in the darkness. She was flashing to another but smaller outline.

'That's *Grafton*,' Fisher shouted. '*She'll* get my men out if anyone can.'

Though visibility had begun to shut down, Wally could distinguish also the unmistakable outline of one of the old coal-burners; with her single funnel and unbroken upper deck, this latest arrival must be one of the ancient *Hunt* minesweepers.

'*Grafton*'s stopped to lower a boat,' Fisher said. 'Wish she'd keep moving. She's asking for it with these U-boats and E-boats lurking about.' He had picked up the wheelhouse binoculars and was concentrating on the sweeper.

'I'm sure that's *Lydd*, the old minesweeper. I passed her less than an hour ago.' He looked across at Craig. 'Could we close *Grafton*, please, Skipper?' he asked. 'I'd like to hail her Captain to see if he could put a party aboard *Wakeful* to break into the messdecks through the upper deck.'

Craig waited for another man to be hauled inboard before going ahead. 'I'm going for'd, Skipper,' Wally said, 'to keep a lookout, now that visibility's shutting right down.'

He wove his way through the packed upper deck, the smell of smoke and oil sour in his nostrils. He looked across to where *Grafton* and *Lydd* had been. He strained his eyes, peering into the thickness of the night. There was the ghostly outline of *Wakeful*, the cries of the trapped men still a terrible accompaniment to the screeching of the rending metal. There, right ahead, loomed the trim outline of the destroyer *Grafton*. Wally's eyes swept across her silhouette, searching for *Lydd*.

A vivid light leaped suddenly, the horizon a sheet of flame, the night erupting into awful sound. Wally stood rooted to the deck, horror sweeping over him. *Grafton* wallowed there, a gigantic void gaping beneath her bridge, steam roaring from her boiler rooms as her safety valves lifted, white plumes drifting to leeward as the southerly wind freshened.

'God,' a man gasped, 'poor bastards . . .' his blackened face twitching as he wept unashamedly. Wally turned as he heard Commander Fisher shouting from the drifter's wheelhouse: 'For God's sake, all of you, keep your eyes skinned for E-boats. *They can't be . . .*'

A hail of bullets and shell splinters suddenly crashed into the upper works of the little drifter. Craig's horrified face appeared for an instant at the door of the wheelhouse as he peered upwards at the silhouette of *Lydd* who was now within a hundred yards, her guns flashing as fingers of green tracer curled towards the defenceless drifter.

Wally threw himself flat across the heaped bodies that had streamed up from the saloon below. He tried to clamber aft as *Grafton*'s 4.7s joined in, but the wounded and the dying, the decks slippery with blood, the little ship disintegrating beneath the murderous fire, made his progress impossible. He glanced aft to see Commander Fisher leaping from the wheelhouse. Disregarding the exploding world about him, he was holding up his hands as if to ward off some invisible blow, his face working grotesquely as he shouted towards *Lydd* who was already committed to the final phase of the tragedy.

Wally spun round. There, less than thirty yards distant, towered the bows of *Lydd* as she bore down upon her supposed adversary. Her bow wave gleamed at her stem. Her seamen could be seen pointing from her fo'c'sle. They turned suddenly towards their bridge as they saw and heard Fisher shouting:

'We're British . . . We're British, you ruddy fools. We're NOT E-boats . . .!'

The destroyer Captain's words were drowned by the crash as *Lydd*'s bows sliced through the drifter's wooden hull. Wally braced himself to meet the shock, felt his body go rigid as, paralysed by terror, he watched the bow of the sweeper towering above them for an instant. He held his breath, felt the drifter lurch, then roll over under them as the water came up to meet him.

He gasped from the sudden cold of the sea. He saw a black mass sweeping past him, white foam threshing in the darkness. *The propellers*, he thought. *Get away, for God's sake, get clear . . .* He kicked with all his might, his arms flailing as he strove feverishly to swim clear. An excruciating pain stabbed his head, there was a blinding light and he knew no more.

Wally's first recollection of consciousness was the intense cold and the suffocation against which he was struggling convulsively. Then, with a jerk, he came to himself: he was alone in the water and was choking from the seas which had increased with the breeze.

'Thank God for my Mae West,' he muttered to himself. He turned his head round the full horizon and there, to his astonishment, the macabre remains of *Wakeful* still jutted from the water, less than half a mile distant.

Though his head ached from the blow which he had suffered when *Lydd* rammed them, he must have been unconscious for only a short time: the other ships had disappeared but *Wakeful* was close and making the same leeway in this breeze as he was. The screams from the trapped men were less audible now, though an occasional cry of despair reached him where he floated in the chill of the early morning.

'My God, I'm lucky,' Wally muttered as he offered up a silent prayer of thankfulness. 'I must be *Comfort*'s only survivor.'[1]

---

[1] Commander Fisher was picked up: there were only two survivors.

APPOINTMENT WITH AN OCTOPUS

Arthur Grimble

The old navigators of the Gilberts used to talk with fear of a gigantic octopus that inhabited the seas between Samoa and the Ellice Islands. They said its tentacles were three arm-spans long and thicker at the base than the body of a full-grown man—a scale of measurements not out of keeping with what is known of the atrocious monster called *Octopus apollyon*. There were some who stated that this foul fiend of the ocean was also to be found in the waters between Onotoa, Tamana and Arorae in the Southern Gilberts. But I never came across a man who had seen one, and the biggest of the octopus breed I ever saw with my own eyes had tentacles only a little over six feet long. It was a member of the clan *Octopus vulgaris*, which swarms in all the lagoons. An average specimen of this variety is a dwarf beside *Octopus apollyon*: laid out flat, it has a total spread of no more than nine or ten feet; but it is a wicked-looking piece of work, even in death, with those disgusting suckers studding its arms and those bulging, filmed eyes staring out of the mottled gorgon face.

Possibly, if you can watch objectively, the sight of *Octopus vulgaris* searching for crabs and crayfish on the floor of the lagoon may move you to something like admiration. You cannot usually see the dreadful eyes from a water-glass straight above its feeding-ground, and your feeling for crustacea is too impersonal for horror at their fate between pouncing suckers and jaws. There is real beauty in the rich change of its colours as it moves from shadow to sunlight, and the gliding ease of its arms as they reach and flicker over the rough rocks fascinates the eye with its deadly grace. You feel that if only the creature would stick to its grubbing on the bottom, the shocking ugliness of its shape might even win your sympathy, as for some poor Caliban in the enchanted garden of the lagoon. But it is no honest grubber in the open. For every one of its kind that you see crawling below you, there are a dozen skulking in recesses of the reef that falls away like a cliff from the edge where you stand watching. When *Octopus vulgaris* has eaten its fill of the teeming crabs and crayfish, it seeks a dark cleft in the coral face and anchors itself there with a few of the large suckers nearest to its body. Thus shielded from attack in the rear, with tentacles gathered to pounce, it squats glaring from the shadows, alert for anything alive to swim within striking distance. It can hurl one or all of those whiplashes forward with the speed of dark lightning, and once its scores of suckers, rimmed with hooks for grip on slippery skins, are clamped about their prey, nothing but the brute's death will break their awful hold.

But that very quality of the octopus that most horrifies the imagination, its relentless tenacity, becomes its undoing when hungary man steps into the picture. The Gilbertese happened to value certain parts of it as food, and their method of fighting it is coolly based upon the one fact that its arms never change their grip.

They hunt for it in pairs. One man acts as the bait, his partner as the killer. First, they swim eyes-under at low tide just off the reef, and search the crannies of the submarine cliff for sight of any tentacle that may flicker out for a catch. When they have placed their quarry, they land on the reef for the next stage. The human bait starts the real game. He dives and tempts the lurking brute by swimming a few strokes in front of its cranny, at first a little beyond striking range. Then he turns and makes straight for the cranny, to give himself into the embrace of those waiting arms. Sometimes nothing happens. The beast will not always respond to the lure. But usually it strikes.

The partner on the reef above stares down through the pellucid water, waiting for his moment. His teeth are his only weapon. His killing efficiency depends on his avoiding every one of those strangling arms. He must wait until his partner's body has been drawn right up to the entrance of the cleft. The monster inside is groping then with its horny mouth against the victim's flesh, and sees nothing beyond it. That point is reached in a matter of no more than 30 seconds after the decoy has plunged. The killer dives, lays hold of his pinioned friend at arm's length, and jerks him away from the cleft; the octopus is torn adrift from the anchorage of its proximal suckers, and clamps itself the more fiercely to its prey. In the same second, the human bait gives a kick which brings him, with quarry annexed, to the surface. He turns on his back, still holding his breath for better buoyancy, and this exposes the body of the beast for the kill. The killer closes in, grasps the evil head from behind, and wrenches it away from its meal. Turning the face up towards himself, he plunges his teeth between the bulging eyes and bites down and in with all his strength. That is the end of it. It dies on the instant; the suckers release their hold; the arms fall away; the two fishers paddle with whoops of delighted laughter to the reef, where they string the catch to a pole before going to rout out the next one.

Any two boys of seventeen, any day of the week, will go out and get you half a dozen octopuses like that for the mere fun of it. Here

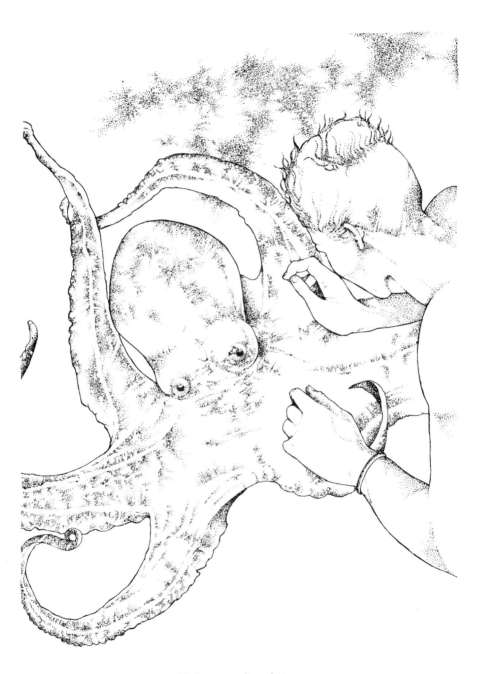

The brutes eyes burned at me.

lies the whole point of this story. The hunt is, in the most literal sense, nothing but child's play to the Gilbertese.

As I was standing one day at the end of a jetty in Tarawa lagoon, I saw two boys from the village shouldering a string of octopuses slung on a pole between them. I started to wade out in their direction, but before I hailed them they had stopped, planted the carrying-pole upright in a fissure and, leaving it there, swum off the edge for a while with faces submerged, evidently searching for something under water. I had been only a few months at Tarawa, and that was my first near view of an octopus-hunt. I watched every stage of it from the dive of the human bait to the landing of the dead catch. When it was over, I went up to them. I could hardly believe that in those few seconds, with no more than a frivolous-looking splash or two on the surface, they could have found, caught and killed the creature they were now stringing up before my eyes. They explained the amusing simplicity of the thing.

'There's only one trick the decoy-man must never forget,' they said, 'and that's not difficult to remember. If he is not wearing water-spectacles, he must cover his eyes with a hand as he comes close to the *kika* (octopus), or the suckers might blind him.' It appeared that the ultimate fate of the eyes was not the thing to worry about; the immediate point was that the sudden pain of a sucker clamping itself to an eyeball might cause the bait to expel his breath and inhale sea-water; that would spoil his buoyancy, and he would fail then to give his friend the best chance of a kill.

Then they began whispering together. I knew in a curdling flash what they were saying to each other. Before they turned to speak to me again, a horrified conviction was upon me. My damnable curiosity had led me into a trap from which there was no escape. They were going to propose that I should take a turn at being the bait myself, just to see how delightfully easy it was; and that is what they did. It did not even occur to them that I might not leap at the offer. I was already known as a young man who liked swimming and fishing and laughing with the villagers; I had just shown an interest in this particular form of hunting; naturally, I should enjoy the fun of it as much as they did. Without even waiting for my answer, they gleefully ducked off the edge of the reef to look for another octopus—a fine fat one—*mine*. Left standing there alone, I had one of those visions . . .

It was dusk in the village. The fishers were home; I saw the cooking-fires glowing orange-red between the brown lodges. There was laughter and shouted talk as the women prepared the evening meal. But the laughter was hard with scorn. 'What?' they were saying. 'Afraid of a *kika*? Why, even our boys are not afraid of a *kika*!' A curtain went down and rose again on the Residency; the Old Man was talking: 'A leader? You? The man who funked a schoolboy game? We don't leave your sort in charge of Districts.' The scene flashed to my uncles: 'Returned empty,' they said. 'We always knew you hadn't got it in you. Returned empty . . .'

Of course it was all overdrawn, but one fact was beyond doubt: the Gilbertese reserved all their most ribald humour for physical cowardice. No man gets passed for a leader by becoming the butt of that kind of wit. I decided I would rather face the octopus.

I was dressed in khaki slacks, canvas shoes and a short-sleeved singlet. I took off the shoes and made up my mind to shed the singlet if told to do so; but I was wildly determined to stick to my trousers throughout. Dead or alive, said a voice within me, an official minus his pants is a preposterous object, and I felt I could not face that extra horror. However, nobody asked me to remove anything.

I hope I did not look as yellow as I felt when I stood ready to take the plunge; I have never been so sick with fear before or since. 'Remember, one hand for your eyes,' said someone from a thousand miles off, and I dived.

I do not suppose it is really true that the eyes of an octopus shine in the dark; besides, it was clear daylight only six feet down in the water; but I could have sworn the brute's eyes burned at me as I turned in towards his cranny. That dark glow—whatever may have been its origin—was the last thing I saw as I blacked out with my left hand and rose into his clutches. Then, I remember chiefly a dreadful sliminess with a Herculean power behind it. Something whipped round my left forearm and the back of my neck, binding the two together. In the same flash, another something slapped itself high on my forehead, and I felt it crawling down inside the back of my singlet. My impulse was to tear at it with my right hand, but I felt the whole of that arm pinioned to my ribs. In most emergencies the mind works with crystal-clear impersonality. This was not even an emergency, for I knew myself perfectly safe. But my boyhood's nightmare was upon me. When I felt the swift constriction of those disgusting arms jerk my head and shoulders in towards the reef, my mind went blank of every thought save the beastliness of contact with that squat head. A mouth began to nuzzle below my throat, at the junction of the collarbones. I forgot there was anyone to save me. Yet something still directed me to hold my breath.

I was awakened from my cowardly trance by a quick, strong pull on my shoulders, back from the cranny. The cables round me tightened painfully, but I knew I was adrift from the reef. I gave a kick, rose to the surface and turned on my back with the brute sticking out of my chest like a tumour. My mouth was smothered by some flabby moving horror. The suckers felt like hot rings pulling at my skin. It was only two seconds, I suppose, from then to the attack of my delivery, but it seemed like a century of nausea.

My friend came up between me and the reef. He pounced, pulled, bit down, and the thing was over—for everyone but me. At the sudden relaxation of the tentacles, I let out a great breath, sank, and drew in the next under water. It took the united help of both boys to get me, coughing, heaving and pretending to join in their delighted laughter, back to the reef. I had to submit there to a kind of war-dance round me, in which the dead beast was slung whizzing past my head from one to the other. I had a chance to observe then that it was not by any stretch of fancy a giant, but just plain average. That took the bulge out of my budding self-esteem. I left hurriedly for the cover of the jetty, and was sick.

PERILOUS JOURNEY

John Simpson

A spume of hissing steam erupted a thousand feet into the air from the fiery belly of Mount Erebus. Conspicuous in the Antarctic wilderness, this single active volcano challenged the bleak dictatorship of the ice-gods. Moments later, as a northerly wind fanned away the gathering steam-cloud, three tiny figures were revealed on the blizzard-worn summit. It was 10 March 1908 . . .

Nearly four years later, one of these three men—the Yorkshire born Douglas Mawson—was, like Erebus, to stand alone against the hostile polar elements.

During January 1912, the oak ship *Aurora* bearing the Australasian Polar Expedition had ploughed its way through perilous masses of heaving pack ice, and dropped anchor in a bleak harbour off Cape Denison. By the end of January *Aurora* had steamed back to Australia. It left dogs, supplies, and a handful of men led by the 30-year-old Mawson to explore over 1,300 miles of ice-age desolation.

A month later the harbour at Cape Denison was frozen solid and effectively sealed off from the civilized world.

The expedition immediately began building their base-camp hut, often working in the teeth of skin-grazing blizzards. Later they hewed a second camp out of solid ice five miles away upon a frost-whitened escarpment. Preparations then followed for their forthcoming spring journeys—equipment was tested, supplies were sorted and teams of men and dogs practised sledge-hauling. But the long hard winter was to stretch from February to October before the reappearance of penguin and seal heralded the return of milder weather.

The men split into two teams. One party was to search out and mark the Southern Magnetic Pole. While Mawson, now an Australian citizen, along with his two companions, Dr Xavier Mertz, a Swiss ski-champion, and Lieutenant B. E. S. Ninnis of the British Royal Fusiliers, hoped to journey deep in an easterly direction to explore and survey regions inaccessible to all but the arctic birds.

On occasions during the blizzard-ravaged winter the expedition saw the mesmerizing magnetic curtain of the Southern Lights; and often stood beneath the scintillating star-diamonds which illuminated the boundless ether. Finally, as late as November, the two parties embarked on their marathon journeys. But they were considerably chastened; for the unrelenting gales had taken even Mawson by surprise. And with their deadline fixed at 15 January 1913—the date when *Aurora* was expected to return to take them home again—their strict schedule allowed for no margin of error.

With 17 dogs and three sledges packed with supplies and equipment, Mawsons team pushed on past the five-mile ice-cave camp. If at any time the weather proved too rough they decided they would lie low in their single tent. Their unwritten law was 'No distance covered—no "hoosh" '. Hoosh being the arctic explorers' nickname for pemmican—a heat giving, flesh building concoction of dried beef and fats to combat the sub-zero temperatures.

From the very start they encountered a succession of razor-sharp winds. These wild rampaging gales soon piled drifts of snow around sledges and tent, and when at times they managed short journeys they had to cross stretches of 'sastrugi', or wind-furrowed snow, forcing them to push and heave at the heavy sledges; for on terrain such as this, the dogs' pulling power was rendered virtually negligible.

By 13 November they'd moved less than 20 miles as one 100 mph hurricane buffeted them non-stop for 60 hours, as if determined to wipe their tent clean from the face of the earth.

After a day's hike their sleeping bags would be frozen solid, and putting up the tent in deep-freeze conditions with a wind rising was a bone-chilling experience. A glove taken off for 30 seconds meant severe frostbite. On top of that, saliva and breath froze around the base of their balaclavas and the wearer had to cope with a mask of ice clinging around his cheeks.

Once the tent was finally erected, and the primus lighted, they would begin the long thaw. Snow was melted for water; pemmican thrown into the cooking pot, and numbed bodies and aching stomachs would look forward to 'hoosh' washed down with powder-milk cocoa. There followed a shivering kind of sleep in the now damp sleeping bags.

In the middle of November they passed an eminence of brown rock called a 'nunatak' which rose out of the frozen wastes. Later, the ground dipped away and for a time they found themselves out of the wind. That evening they discovered that they had set up camp on the floor of an extinct volcano. It reminded Mawson of the sole surviving Antarctic volcano Mount Erebus where he had stood—four long years ago when a member of Sir Ernest Shackleton's Expedition.

Following a restful night they climbed out of the crater, and Ninnis noticed that one of the dogs, 'Ginger', had gone missing. A continuous drift of snow was now blowing diagonally across their path. Mawson, standing at the rear of his sledge, could not see the six husky dogs ahead feverishly pawing above a river of yawning space. Only when their terrified howls floated to him did he dig his heels deep into the snow. He had stopped on the very edge of an abyss.

In anguish he called out to Ninnis to anchor a rope in the snow. Then slowly, inch by inch, they dragged sledge and dogs out of the yawning pit to safety. Soon after, the dog 'Ginger' returned to share their meal.

Twenty-four hours later the three explorers entered a huge glacier where honey-combing on a gigantic scale had taken place with holes 70 feet deep and snow bridges and columns up to 50 feet high. Beyond the distant glacier rim stood mountains, amongst them Aurora Peak. They marked it as a beacon to lead them to safety on their homeward journey.

On that glacier, winds rallied to torment them, and it took a week of solid toil to trudge beyond. They were now 2,500 feet above sea level and into December, but there were to be no doubts about a white Christmas—*if* they survived . . .

The twelfth month greeted them with an above freezing temperature which brought sticky soft snow in its wake. The dogs got bogged down. Sweat ran freely and turned cold on their backs as, heads bowed, they slogged on. At times a midnight sun glimmered over the southern polar plateau, gliding the snowscape with cheerless gold.

Ninnis was now sleeping badly, suffering in secret dread from an almost gangrenous finger. All men were feeling the terrible strain. Their faces cracked and grey—for by now they had travelled over 300 lung-heaving miles.

December 14; and after striking camp, Mertz led on his skis. He veered off to the east in an attempt to select a suitable trail.

Ninnis, holding onto the dog reins of one sledge, saw the narrow snow bridge ahead. He aimed for it.

Suddenly the track beneath his feet gave way in an explosion of blinding freezing dust. Before he could cry out, gravity was dragging him, sucking him, sledge and dogs, down, down into the black bowels of the earth . . .

After one blood curdling minute all Mawson and Mertz could hear was the howl of one dying dog—alone on a ledge 150 feet down in the Antarctic depths. Beyond that was an unspeakable tomb—and a cold, cold silence.

Both Mertz and Mawson were stupified by the accident. But after searching and calling for many hours it became all too clear. Ninnis was gone: forever. And so was the sledge with all the dog food and most of their supplies. If they turned back immediately they might just have enough provisions to reach base camp . . . *if* they ate the remaining dogs. But those dogs were tired and thin.

That night one ravenous dog chewed through his harness and devoured some more of their precious food.

After marking Ninnis's grave they turned for home, utterly down-hearted. Mocking winds howled derisively as they slogged on through the eerie sunlit night. Their evening meal consisted of tasteless pieces of dog meat with the luxury of dog liver. As they ate they never dreamt that the liver was poisonous.

Three weeks after Ninnis died, both men were in a debilitated condition, still hiking towards the dream of a warm hut and companionship. But to Xavier Mertz, that dream was fast becoming hallucination. For grief, hunger, food poisoning, snow-blindness and exhaustion had taken their toll. His energy stock was bankrupt. Even in his imagination he could scarcely walk.

Mawson nursed him, and became tent bound with his sick companion. All the while his own hope of survival faded. Mertz grew frenzied, feverish—unconscious. One bleak morning Mawson found him dead in the tent; he was now terrifyingly alone . . .

This second tragedy found Douglas Mawson starved, exhausted, and with few provisions. His flesh was raw, his skin rotten and peppered with boils caused by poisoning and malnutrition. He had lost over four and a half stone in body weight and he was still one hundred miles from the base camp hut. Death began stalking him like a shadow.

Only the faintly beneficient sunlight, and a feeling of God within kept him going against all odds:

> 'Hope, like the glimmering taper's light
> Adorns and cheers the way,
> And still as darker grows the night
> Emits a brighter ray.'

And yet it would have been so easy to lie down in a blanket of snow, and die. Three days on and Mawson's senses were awry; his head ached continuously. Each footstep was an agony of relentless determination against the bleak elements which haunted the white immensity. Most of the dogs were now dead and he was hauling the sledge himself.

January 15 arrived. It was the day they should all be back at hut camp ready to sail home with the *Aurora*. But Mawson knew that wishful thinking was a waste of time and energy. Instead, he slept and woke to a breakfast of refrigerated dog meat, with its liver riddled with vitamin 'A' poisoning. There was no real sustenance to be gained from it . . . Each mouthful took him one step nearer the precipice of physical and mental collapse.

The following afternoon saw him, head bowed, plodding on. Snow drifted across his vision, obscuring the glacier ahead. He was recalling a winter's day in London 1910, when he'd turned down Captain Robert Falcon Scott's offer to join the British Antarctic Expedition with a guaranteed place on the Pole March. He wondered how Scott was getting on; not dreaming that at that moment he lay dead with two companions, Wilson and Bowers, in a tent almost obscured by drifting snow, over a thousand miles away. Mawson was at one with his memories and almost sleep-walking when the ground suddenly opened. A midnight grave rushed up to greet him . . . Was this how Ninnis had felt? As if in

Each footstep was an agony of relentless determination against the elements.

reply the sledge harness around his chest snapped tight, smashing into his ribs—expelling the last particle of air from his lungs. With pain-glazed eyes he looked up. Above, the sledge had ground to a halt, leaving him hanging like a puppet on a string, 15 feet down a bottomless shaft. If the sledge moved—he was done for.

Breath returned and with it came the gruesome thoughts. How was he to climb out? There was no strength left in his arms.

He climbed and fell—struggled and fell back. Then the temptation came to him to unbuckle the harness and end it all. But that inner presence bade him try again. With the last of his strength he heaved himself upwards . . .

Five minutes later he was lying in a pitiful heap by the side of the sledge—unconscious.

Mawson was at the end of his tether. If he once more fell down a snow covered crevasse—it would be his grave. But undaunted he limped on into unmapped regions. That evening, inspiration came. He would construct a ladder; attach it to the sledge and loop it over his shoulder as he marched. Should he then fall down an abyss . . . and the sledge held his weight—he would climb out using the ladder.

The following day he built his ladder, laboriously knotting ropes with swollen, frost-bitten fingers. He'd done less than two miles the next day when down he plunged into another gully. The sledge held and he slowly ascended the ladder to safety.

An eternity later he entered one of the earlier glaciers (now known as the Mertz Glacier), to be greeted by noises like cannon fire as subterranean pressures caused zig-zagging splits in the ice surface.

Hour followed minute and passed into days. The merciless winds never ceased, and death moved closer to the trudging skeleton of the survivor. At the end of January the song in his heart seemed to beat time to a funeral march.

In a last desperated gamble, Mawson fixed a sail to his sledge, thus enlisting the blizzards aid. The ploy eased his burden, but the wind still moaned and clawed at his back.

He was almost beyond caring when a dark blob partially submerged in the snowscape caught his eye. A rock? He veered towards it, without sensation. But when it proved to be a cairn, built by three of his men from base camp, Mawson felt old emotions return. Was it possible? In the buried cache was food, fresh oranges and a note. It said that the ship was awaiting 'their' return. But Mawson knew he'd never make the harbour in time.

He sucked at an orange and scoured the horizon. Nothing!— just the acid white wastes. There he read the note again and saw with a heart-numbing shock that it had been written TODAY! So the ship could still be there if he hurried!

He felt a sudden overwhelming desire to catch sight of his three hut companions—to see old friends back in Australia where he now had his home . . .

In one crazy moment he threw away his crampons and other essentials in an effort to lighten his load. Then he began ploughing a lone furrow towards the coast. But he was heading in the wrong direction!

By the time he realized his mistake his feet were bringing him torment. Each step had become a movement of agony. Now he needed those cast-off crampons more than ever.

With his spirits at zero, he pitched camp. That night the snow blizzards howled and a piece of tent canvas flapped like a demented bat above his head. When he woke he found he could hardly walk and had to spend twenty-four precious hours fashioning himself a new pair of crampons out of wood and nails. Now the ship must surely have sailed . . .

February dawned. In the huge ice arena the tiny figure limped on, while the ice-gods shook their frosted heads at the man who refused to die.

At all costs, ship or no ship, it was imperative that Mawson get back to the hut before winter returned with its plague of white death.

There were acres of sastrugi ahead, and the improvised crampons tortured his ruined feet. But though his mind was pain-crazed, he still held true to that inner spirit which God alone can extinguish. Mile followed mile—along a freezing corridor; across frozen plains, and through the valley of the white shadow.

Finally he reached the ice cave five miles from hut camp. Once inside he was like a broken butterfly beating against the translucent walls. Five miles—It could have been five hundred.

Beyond the cave entrance the most fearsome blizzard raged and ominous clouds circled in a treacherous sky. His heart sank . . .

Winter was back with a vengeance.

Wrestling with anguished thoughts, Douglas Mawson lay huddled on the ice cave floor. It was as if his body was being devoured by a plague of locusts. Some had entered his mouth and were crawling about in his stomach.

For a week he suffered in prison silence while the hurricane force winds re-arranged the snow scene beyond the cave. Then he heard the wind moderate and peered outside. It was as if a storm sea had petrified. Green-blue breakers were topped with glistening hoar frost, while jagged ice particles littered the cobalt-blue troughs.

With hardly the strength of a new-born kitten, Mawson entered the 40 mph swirling snow inferno and attempted the last torturous lap. Each single footfall became an endurance test.

He dropped down 1,000 feet in altitude before a mile dragged unwillingly by. Gazing in hope for a sign of the ship he saw nothing but the drifting snow.

The wind lessened as he descended towards the silent bay. Staggering forward he reached half-way to safety and stopped on a mound of powdery snow. Then he lifted his snow-goggles to scan the harbour . . .

The ship had gone. The bay was deserted.

Two hours on, and half a mile from the hut he glimpsed three figures standing down by the harbour. Late penguins? He lifted the goggles once more. They were men . . .

The blood drained from his head. Stifling a sob he waved and called, but could find no voice. No one saw him standing there; for one interminable minute. Then friendly shouts of excitement reached out to him. Running figures converged. Eager arms grasped him, helped him to safety.

Back in the fire-warmed hut the tragic tale poured out. Three silent companions shared his grief—and gazed at the pathetic figure with a mixture of horror and wonder. Later they told him he had missed the boat by only *seven* hours and that they had volunteered to stay behind to wait for him.

Now it would be a year before any of them would see *Aurora*, home and friends again. But they could wait. Mawson was alive . . .

He had survived!

HIGH-WIRE

Hayden McAllister

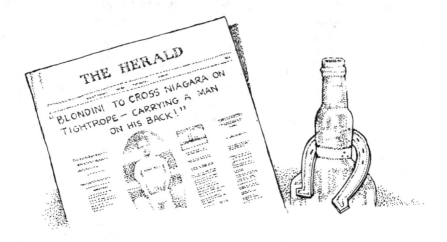

THE HERALD

"BLONDINI TO CROSS NIAGARA ON TIGHTROPE — CARRYING A MAN ON HIS BACK!"

The dust track which passed for a New York street was deserted except for an ill-fed horse which stood tethered outside the 'Yellow Lantern' saloon bar.

Inside the wooden building the gaming tables were unoccupied and the oil lamps turned low, for it was well past midnight. The only two inmates sat at the bar.

'Big' George Paducci, the owner, lit his cigar and re-arranged his massive body on the bar stool. 'Well?' he inquired of his companion. 'What d'you say Eli boy. Are you game?'

The other man, small and bleary eyed, stared at the newspaper spread-eagled between them on the bar top. The bold headlines ran:

'BLONDIN TO CROSS NIAGARA ON TIGHT-ROPE —CARRYING A MAN ON HIS BACK!'

Eli Tucker dragged his eyes away from the newsprint, but did not return Paducci's fevered gaze. Instead he peered into his empty whisky glass and whined: 'Gee I don't know George. I mean what you're suggestin' ain't strictly legal—but it sure bears some thinkin' about . . .'

'Bears some thinking about!' roared Paducci like a bull elephant. 'I'm offering you two thousand dollars to unfasten a guy-line and you've only got to the stage of *thinking* about it!' The blood rose in the big man's neck and his eyes narrowed dangerously. 'There's thousands of dollars at stake here boy—and I've been giving odds of 3 to 1 against Blondin ever getting across that high-wire. So I reckon you'd better make up your mind pretty darn quick!'

The small man ground his teeth reflectively, then edged his glass along the bar counter. 'Big' George topped it up . . . After a few moments, a lop-sided grin spread across Tucker's features. 'Suddenly I'm beginnin' to feel real neighbourly towards your idea George,' he said.

Paducci gave a brotherly leer. 'Now all I want you to do Eli, is to roll over—as if you've slipped—and fall on that guy-line support. But you've got to time it when Blondin and his pal are half-way across the Niagara. Got it?' He laid an affectionate paw on the small man's shoulder. 'There's nothing to it—the main rope starts swinging—the two darn fools fall a couple of hundred feet into the river and get picked up by the riverboat. And we fill our pockets with greenbacks. Right? Uh?' 'Besides,' Paducci blew some expensive cigar smoke in the other man's face, 'it's what most of the crowd secretly want. They won't admit it to your face—but ah reckon it's a fact. So the way I see it—we'll really be doing them a kinda favour.'

Eli Tucker tossed back his whisky in one huge gulp and smacked his lips. 'This sure is fine whisky there George,' he drawled.

Paducci's face now took on an angelic expression. 'Eli,' he said, 'I think it's best for you to work from the Canadian side of the Niagara. 'Cos I reckon most of the spectators—'specially the gamblers'll be on the New York side—in the finishing straight so to speak. Anyway. They won't be watching *you*, that's for sure. They'll only have eyes for the Frenchman and his passenger . . . until you pull out their support line. It should be a pushover,' he added, then guffawed at his unintentional pun. '*Push—over!* Like it Eli?'

'Like I said George,' grinned Tucker, commandeering the whisky bottle. 'Now we're *really* communicatin'!'

Charles Blondin was the stage name of Jean Francois Gravelet, and from a very early age the French born acrobat showed a remarkable propensity for climbing and balancing with no fear of heights. As early as 1830 at the precocious age of six, he appeared in a circus tight-rope act, billed as 'The Little Wonder'.

In 1857 Blondin decided to promote himself in a succession of high-wire spectaculars. The first of these big events which caught the public's imagination took place (the year before our story), in 1859 when he walked alone across the Niagara Falls on a tight-rope stretched 250 feet above the foaming waters.

It took him twenty breath-taking minutes to cross from Canada into America. Half-way across he stopped and let down a line to the crew of a boat which was waiting below in case of accident.

The crew tied a small bottle of champagne and a glass to the cord, and Blondin slowly hauled it up. Then he untied bottle and glass and poured himself a drink. With his glass primed with champagne, he dramatically let the bottle fall into the dark waters of the Niagara. Then—standing on one leg he drank the health of the terrified spectators who watched from the banks below.

'Carry a man across the Niagara on your back!' cried Mr Harry Colchard. 'Impossible!'

Blondin smiled. 'A thing is always "impossible" until it is done.'

'But surely you'd never bear the strain *and* balance properly?' cried the other incredulously.

'Please to remember that balance is the corner-stone of my profession . . . So kindly let me be the judge of the matter,' returned Blondin. 'You see, if it could not be done—I would not suggest it. Here! Climb upon my back. Come!—That's it! Put your weight on my shoulders, but with your arms only. Now. Clasp my body with your legs. But keep your feet away from *my* legs otherwise we are finished. Bon! See how I walk across the pattern on your carpet with the greatest of ease. Impossible did I hear you say?'

'Well I . . .'

Colchard climbed down. 'But think of the distance Mr Blondin.'

'I already have Mr Colchard. The rope will be exactly two thousand feet long, and three inches in diameter. It should, under the closest supervision, take approximately four months to assemble. And of course it must be secured by the necessary guy-lines, with every arrangement for safety.' Blondin scrutinized his fingernails. 'Naturally the crowds will flock to see such a spectacular event— and I will, as an honourable man, give them full value for their money.' Then the master tight-rope walker gazed imperturbably at Harry Colchard. 'So. Will you come?—'

'Of course I'll come and watch!' declared Colchard.

Blondin held up a hand. 'No! Will you accompany me across Niagara Falls perched on my back? *That* is what I am asking you . . .'

On 17 July 1860 a great cheer rose up from the crowd of spectators assembled on the Canadian side of the Niagara. They watched, enraptured, as Mr Harry Colchard carefully climbed on Mr Charles Blondin's back. Blondin was handed his long balancing pole, and the two men moved delicately out into space . . . By this time, Eli Tucker had been drinking heavily all day and was lying dazedly beside one of the guy-line moorings. A green-bottle fly was circuiting his nose with droning menace.

High above the crowds—Harry Colchard's arms were already beginning to ache. Those arms were his only means of direct support on Blondin's shoulders.

With a hoarse shout he told Blondin he needed to rest. The acrobat stopped, and Colchard stepped carefully down onto the rope, waiting there he balanced against Blondin until his arm muscles recovered sufficiently for him to continue.

It was an inappropriate moment to halt, for 250 feet below was a great forest of stunted pines, thrusting up their spear-head tops as if to impale the sun. Further out, lay the drumming, surging waters of the Niagara.

To Eli Tucker's befuddled vision the two small silhouettes above seemed to merge and become one creeping hunchback shadow. This dark apparition carrying its broom shank pole gradually edged out over the roaring falls apparently on thin air! The pole pointing one way, then that; as if it had a life of its own. It was like the magic stick of the 'sorcerer's apprentice' dictating the thunder music of the waterfall below.

Even above the sound of the rumbling cataract, Tucker could hear the dratted buzz buzz buzz of the green-bottle fly. He made another clumsy lunge at the insect, missed—then heard a hiss of excitement from the crowd.

Blondin and Colchard were parting company again—the latter's muscles were aching mercilessly now. For although the two men had practised the discipline regularly—the extra tension caused by the occasion was an unforeseen development . . . They took a long rest this time before Colchard sprang once more upon Blondin's back. The two men had almost reached half-way point . . .

Across on the American shore, conspicuous even in the huge crowd, 'Big' George Paducci was secretly relishing every single moment of high-wire drama. If the duo faltered, or swayed, he felt like bellowing out a roar of approval. Twenty thousand dollars worth of approval! For that was the sum he'd taken in bets.

But even *his* heart began to tighten as the two high-wire men passed *beyond* the safety vessel anchored midstream in the river.

'This sure is fine whisky there George,' he drawled.

Paducci chewed vigorously on his cigar as the acrobats came slowly, but surely, towards him. In a spasm of irritation he spat out his cigar and stood with his hands upon his hips. 'What the hell in tarnation does that Jack ass Tucker think he's playing at?' he muttered to himself. 'Why doesn't the darn fool pull out the guy line?'

If only he could have observed his accomplice back on the Canadian bank he'd have saved his breath . . . There the sozzled Eli Tucker lay flat on his back, mouth agape and snoring in the sun—while perched on the tip of his nose stood the triumphant green-bottle fly.

It was now obvious to Paducci that Blondin and Colchard were making their way painstakingly towards safety. And he couldn't have *that*! With a snort of rage he shouldered his way through the seething crowd. As the transfixed spectators gazed overhead he made his way towards the peg of the outer guy-line support and dragged it clear from its mooring . . . The effect was electric.

Blondin was twenty feet out over the middle span when it happened. He stopped instantly. His pole flicked from side to side as he made a desperate effort to regain balance. Poor Harry Colchard could do nothing but hang on, shut his eyes and pray. The crowd went deathly silent—then Blondin began to run like a swaying antelope across the gaping, teetering abyss.

With panther-like steps he reached the point where the guy-line joined the main rope and in an effort to steady himself he placed the ball of his right foot on the spliced joint. It snapped! Then the main rope began see-sawing thirty, some say forty, feet from side to side. The sweat broke out in great beads on Blondin's neck.

The vista below—the white foaming shore currents and the sea of upturned faces—lurched sickeningly from side to side. Colchard's stomach turned for it was like the view from the crows-nest of a storm-tossed schooner. But instead of a mast beneath him there was only Blondin—balanced on a three-inch precipice.

The Frenchman, with intense concentration, moved rapidly

along the veritable knife edge as it veered agonizingly from side to side on an ocean of yawning space. Hearts seemed to stop. Time wound down. The whole audience hardly dared to draw breath. But Blondin kept his rhythm, moving with the tight-rope—letting the pole counter-balance the sickening sway. All the while he took lynx-like steps to the next reinforcement of guy-lines. There he stopped, and Colchard climbed down.

After both men had regained their composure and rested sufficiently, Blondin braced himself for the final effort. But before he set out he looked back along the stretch of rope over which they'd just run a hair-raising aerial gauntlet. Then he gave a grim smile of satisfaction, for he knew that they'd survived the storm; safe harbour and a welcoming crowd lay directly ahead . . .

Down below, in America, 'Big' George Paducci was trying to bribe an incorruptible Marshal, and effectively lengthening his forthcoming jail sentence. While in Canada, Eli Tucker, having temporarily got rid of the green-bottle, was fumbling purposefully for the whisky-bottle.

Much later, Mr Harry Colchard was to write:
'It was not until we landed that I appreciated what we had done. Then it occurred to me that the man who pulled the guy-line must have been one of those who had bet that the feat could never be accomplished, and my indignation mastered all other feelings. You see, many thousands of pounds were bet upon the ability of Blondin to carry a man over, and human cupidity stops at no sacrifice.

'I shall never forget the wonderful tableau which the hundred thousand people presented as they stood gazing up at us as we approached the shore. The crowd became very much excited and surged towards us. Blondin stopped, fearing they would push each other over the bank. When the crowd was still again, Blondin started once more and with a quick run we soon came to the end of the rope and sprang to the ground.

'Cheer after cheer went up, and I was seized in the arms of a man who lifted me in the air, saying, "Thank God this terrible feat is over!"'

FLIGHT OF FEAR

Hammond Innes

Could I be at Khormaksar airfield at 0700 hours?

I was staying in the RAF Mess at Tarshyne Fort, and with no transport of my own, getting to the airfield at such an early hour was in itself a problem. In fact, I didn't make it until well after seven, but as I drew up at the HQ of the APL Support Flight, the old Avro Anson was still standing on the apron. There was a lot of low cloud and it looked like rain.

Inside the office there was a depressing air of inertia; everybody sitting around and no sign of activity. The radio operator shrugged his shoulders when I asked what time he expected to take off. 'It's bad up in the mountains,' he said. 'Looks like the monsoon is going to be early this year.'

And then the pilot came in, a big heavily-built man, whom they all called 'Pop'. He seemed nervous and worried. 'The weather? She is clampers already, I think.' He had a peculiar accent that I could not place. And the fact that he was over forty and still only a Flying Officer didn't give me any great confidence in him. I hung around there for an hour and a half in that debilitating atmosphere, and when I finally left with the assurance that they would contact me if the weather cleared, I felt that this was one of those back-water flights into which throw-out pilots were posted. And so, instead of flying into the trouble spot of Nisab, I went goggle-fishing in the warm, oil-saturated waters of Aden.

The following day I again hitched a ride up to the airfield. Again I was late, and again the old Anson was still on the apron. The sky was clear, no sign of rain, and yet the atmosphere in the Flight Office remained one of inertia. 'It looks all right, I agree,' the radio operator told me, 'but Pop's worried about the weather up at Am Ruseis.' It was Am Ruseis today, not Nisab. 'This damned milk-run of ours,' he added; 'you never can tell what will happen. It's always pretty dicey when the monsoon's due.'

But I was determined not to be baulked a second time. 'Haven't we got any sort of report on visibility up in the mountains?' I asked.

Pop came in at that moment. 'We wait for it now.' He shook his head with a worried frown. 'But I don't like it. The weather she change too dam' quick this time of the year.' And he went over to the window and stood gazing out at the blue sky.

Forty minutes later the report came through. Weather good, visibility 30 miles. Even then, Pop hesitated, muttering to himself. Then suddenly the decision was taken and we hurried out to the plane. A moment later we took off.

I cannot remember ever being more nervous about a flight. We were due to make three calls, the first at Am Ruseis. When I had told a senior RAF officer the previous night what my destination was, he had said, 'Rather you than me, old boy. That's a very tricky one, that is.' Apparently Am Ruseis airstrip was in the bottom

288

of a narrow ravine, requiring a tight descent inside the rock walls and a sudden turn onto the landing field. 'It's under attack, too, right at this moment,' he had added.

As we headed east, climbing steadily, I was wishing I had my old-Etonian daredevil of a pilot of the pirate-coast flight at the helm, instead of this over-aged and worried man. It was still clear overhead, but in front of us I could see great cotton-wool clouds of cumulus-nimbus standing up out of the desert as though we were headed into a dozen atomic explosions. And then, suddenly, above them I glimpsed the dark knife-edges of the mountain tops.

We crossed the escarpment at 9,500 feet, dodging between the mushroom growths of cumulus, and only a few hundred feet below us volcanic ridges, as bare and black and empty of life as the day they had been created by some huge re-adjustment of the earth's surface, stood like the gates of Paradise Lost.

I barely had time to take stock of this utter desolation before the plane gave a violent lurch and tipped over on to one wing. Imagination instantly pictured what it would be like to crash amongst those knife-edged ridges, so impossible of access on foot; and then we were in a side-slipping descent that left my heart in my mouth. Turning and twisting through long corridors between the clouds, we came suddenly out into the bright sunlight, and there below us, as we did a sharp banking turn, was a steep ravine—the airstrip of Am Ruseis.

We were below the level of the mountains then and almost immediately we seemed to be enclosed in walls of red rock, with barely room to turn. I had a brief glimpse of a vertical wall of rock sliding past my window and then we had done a tight turn and there was rock again, close beyond the opposite window, now high above me. We were side-slipping again now, sliding on one wing tip down the whole face of the ravineside, with the hard, flat sand-stretch of the airstrip rushing up to meet us. And straight ahead of us was another rock face, with the stone walls of a fort perched on the top of it.

I was convinced then that the pilot had left it too late. We were going to crash. And then, unbelievably, he skidded the aircraft round on its tail, pivoting on one wing tip, and in one side-slipping rush slammed it down onto the airstrip.

Before we had taxied to a stop two Land Rovers were driving pell-mell across the sand towards us. They were full of RAF Regiment officers, sun-reddened, tired and a little jumpy. Their three hundred Levy troops, scattered along the walls of the ravine and in the fort, had been in action all night. 'There's a shower of bastards called the Abhudi up in those hills,' one of them told me. 'They're firing on us all the time.' One Levy corporal had been killed during the night, they added.

We had mail for them. And there was more mail to go out, and despatches. As we waited for these, Pop paced up and down, constantly glancing at his wrist-watch. I could feel the nervous tension in him building up, and every now and then he stopped his pacing and glanced up at the sky. But there was no cloud there; only an eye-searing humid sun haze.

I doubt whether we were there more than five minutes, but Pop couldn't get out of the place fast enough, lifting the old Anson up the face of the ravine walls in tight turns, standing her on her tail at such a crazy angle that I clutched the arms of my seat, nerves taut with the fear that he was going to stall the plane and go into a tail spin. Up and up we climbed, and then back across those vile volcanic ridges until the scene changed back again and we were dropping down into another world. The mountains had vanished. Ahead was nothing but sand.

We came in to an easy, straightforward landing. No fort this time. No sign of habitation. Just a broad belt of sand and gravel, with a little camel thorn dotted about. We came to a standstill and Pop came aft and opened the fuselage door. He was sweating.

A camel was grazing close by, and seated beside it, cross-legged on a brightly coloured carpet, was an extremely fat Arab—a eunuch I was convinced—dressed in turban and flowing robes and smoking a water pipe. With him was his black servant, a brass-bound trunk, a carpet bed-roll and a chromium-plated pressure

The pilot was over forty and still only a Flying-Officer.

lamp. It was such an unbelievable sight, there in that lonely stretch of desert, that I would not have been in the least surprised if there had been a genie attached to that incongruous pressure lamp!

On the carpet, close beside him, lay a dirty bundle of clothes. Closer inspection revealed it as a child, its eyes dull with sickness. The sick child proved to be the reason for our landing. It was as though that pressure lamp really did have magic powers, for I never discovered how the fat Arab had managed to conjure an RAF plane out of the sky to take the wretched boy to hospital at Aden.

There now began an interminable argument, whilst Pop paced nervously up and down. It appeared that the Arab would not let the child make the journey alone. He must accompany him. Not only that, but he insisted that he must take with him the carpet, the bed-roll, the brass-bound trunk, and the pressure lamp. I felt that for two pins he would have insisted upon taking the camel and his servant as well!

In the end we achieved a compromise. He would accompany the child, and the pressure lamp would go with him. 'He can sell that at Crater,' the radio operator said. 'He hasn't any money, only goods.'

Once that was settled, we bundled them both in and took off in a hell of a hurry. As we climbed, I could see the mountains all round us again, rising up from the sand, which must once have been the bed of a great river. We kept fairly low this time, crossing a few small volcanic outcrops and then winding our way through the wadis of dry river beds until we came to a wide sand plain scattered with the dusty green of crops and a few villages. Each village was centred about a *dhar*, or fortified house, some of which were three stories high.

Baihan, our last stop, appeared suddenly through a gap in some bare hills, and we skimmed a dry river bed, made a tight, low turn and dropped onto an airstrip of soft sand close below the *dhar* walls.

Here we were to pick up an appendix case, a local Government Guard, due to be evacuated to hospital. We were met by a hook-nosed, effeminate-looking Arab, clad in an American shirt hanging loose outside a green skirt. His Land Rover announced that he was part of the Locust Control. With him was the Captain of the local Government Guard, an impressive, ramrod figure in black Arab headdress, the curved-bladed *jambia* knife of authority stuck in his belt.

Though both the Captain of the Guard and the officer of Locust Control had come out to meet us, they had not thought to bring the sick private with them. With many shrugs they intimated that he would be along in a few minutes and we knew that that might mean half an hour, an hour, maybe more. Time was of no object to them. Pop was livid. With one eye on the clouds that were now beginning to gather overhead, he told them that if the private wasn't there in five minutes, he would take off without him.

In the end, it was a quarter of an hour before we at last got him on board, a small dark man, dazed by the pain that had stricken him and moving like a sleep-walker, but still resolutely clutching his rifle, which at no time would he relinquish even for a moment.

We took off for Aden then, climbing steadily again to 9,500 feet. The clouds had built up considerably whilst we had waited at Bahrain. They stood in thick, piled-up masses over the escarpment, and as we headed south-west and they closed about us, the sun vanished and it became very dark.

Leaning forward I could see into the cockpit, with Pop seated at the controls and the radio operator's head bent as he held the earphones tight against his ears; their stillness and concentration suggested tension and an unpleasant sensation of uncertainty was communicated to me. We were turning and twisting through narrowing corridors in the cloud, and every now and then white wisps enveloped us so that we were flying momentarily in a void until we found the next corridor. And as we climbed up into the thicker clouds, these corridors became fewer and fewer, the blank white walls closing in on us faster. I kept on glancing at my watch, trying to work out in my mind the moment when we would cross the escarpment and those grim, eroded ridges would be behind us.

Unsure of my plot and completely helpless, I sat there with the Government Guard, the eunuch and the sick child. The eunuch began to complain in a high-pitched, frightened voice. He had never been in a plane before, but though he did not understand what was going on, he, too, had sensed the tension. I gripped the arms of my seat as the plane was tossed about in a violent eddy. And then suddenly we were in cloud again and it was dark.

It was at this moment that the radio operator turned round and caught my eye. He gave me the thumbs-down sign, using both thumbs in an urgent, stabbing movement, and I suddenly felt empty inside. I knew that we hadn't crossed the escarpment yet.

The plane lurched again, and then suddenly rolled over onto the port wing-tip. It was lighter then and looking down through my window, I found myself momentarily suspended over a long, funnelling gap in the clouds. It was like looking down a plastic tube, and at the bottom was a small, dark patch of volcanic mountain top, and right in the centre, looking very small, the silver shape of a crashed plane lay spreadeagled against the rock.

I only caught that one brief glimpse of it before we were back in the cloud and my body was thrust hard into my seat as we made a tight turn, side-slipping all the time, a sickening sideways plunge that seemed to go on and on, endlessly.

The light increased again as we came out of the cloud, but still we plunged down like a dead duck on one wing, with the ground and that crashed aircraft slamming up towards us at a fantastic rate. At the very last moment, just as it seemed inevitable that we should go on falling until we smashed ourselves into the ground, Pop dragged the plane round by its tail in a complete 180° turn, the nose lifted and the wheels slammed down onto a waterlogged airstrip. Sheets of mud flew up on either side as we bounced; down again in another back-breaking jolt, another bounce, and then we were on the deck and plunging forward through mud and water towards a little hut.

We stopped close beside it, and as the engines were cut, I sat back, dazed and exhausted. Pop came back down the fuselage. For the first time during the whole trip I saw him smile. 'Why am I so good to you boys, eh?' he said, and the smile spread into a broad grin.

I couldn't help it. I had to give vent to the tension that still gripped me. 'I thought we were going to crash,' I said. He patted my shoulder in a fatherly way. 'I tell you something,' he said, 'there was a moment when I think so, too.'

He went aft and opened the fuselage door. Outside, it was pouring with rain and bitterly cold. We were 7,000 feet up and wearing nothing but tropical kit. Dark clouds streamed low overhead, and from what looked like a little mud fort, a battered Land Rover came flying through the mud towards us. It drew up close beside us and an RAF Regiment officer got out. 'You've brought reinforcements, have you?' he said.

'Reinforcements?' Pop laughed. 'I haven't brought you any reinforcements.'

The Flight Lieutenant's face fell. 'Then why are you here?'

'I am here because I am a lucky chap. We are just coming up to the escarpment when we get a radio message from Khormaksar to say the monsoon has struck and we cannot land there.'

'There's a hell of a storm raging over Aden,' the radio operator put in. 'Visibility about a hundred yards, the cloud base right down onto the deck and raining buckets.'

And Pop added, 'I do not think we make it anyway, against those headwinds. Not enough petrol. And then I looked down, and there is the old Valetta and your airfield right below me, and I remember that I have stored two cans of petrol in this hut here against a rainy day. And this is a rainy day all right,' he added, sniffing at the mountain downpour from the open fuselage door like a dog unwilling to leave its kennel. 'I'm a dam' lucky chap to find this place, I think.'

But I knew now that it wasn't luck. It had been gradually dawning on me that this man Pop was no ordinary pilot. Any man who can side-slip an aircraft 3,000 feet down a funnel through storm clouds and land on a waterlogged airfield without tipping the plane up onto its nose must be good.

'Well, now that you're here, I hope you can all handle small arms. We're expecting to be attacked at any moment.

The place where we had landed was Mukeiras. It was only three miles from the Yemen border, a tiny airfield perched on the very lip of the escarpment. Until recently it had been a summer leave camp for the RAF, but now the grey little stone-walled Rest House was a sandbagged fortress with a Bren gun mounted on the roof, and scattered around it were the tents of the Levy troops, who were all busy erecting small circular redoubts of piled-up rock, ready to withstand the expected attack.

After the humid heat of Aden, it was unbelievably cold. The rock walls, the little patches of green grass, the sudden glimpses of country far below seen through ragged gaps in the clouds— incredibly it was like the English Lake District. We had barely reached the Rest House when cloud enveloped the whole area in a white mist. A startling clap of thunder reverberated round the hills, lightning stabbed the dark interior of the house. In shorts and sleeveless shirts we shivered from the dank chill of stone and concrete walls.

We borrowed pullovers and greatcoats and sat pretending to read magazines whilst listening and waiting for the expected attack. It was then that I was able to solve the mystery of Pop's lack of seniority when he was so obviously a first-rate pilot.

He was Polish, the son of an anti-espionage officer killed by the Russians in 1936. In his own country he had been a ski instructor to the Alpine Regiment. He had also flown for an Air Circus, which accounted for his ability to side-slip an Anson, a thing which I was told later is no ordinary feat. He had joined the Polish Air Force, and after the defeat in 1939 he was in no less than four prisoner-of-war and concentration camps, and one by one escaped from each of them. He eventually got out through Roumania and joined the Polish Air Force in Britain.

Now, all he seemed to worry about was the poor wretched Government Guard. He kept on staring out of the window, which showed visibility nil and the rocks streaming water. 'If we do not get out of here today,' he said, 'then maybe I have to operate myself. An ignorant man like me!' And he shook his head. 'I do not think that would be very good—either for me, or for that poor devil!'

But by now I was quite convinced he was capable of anything— even to removing an appendix under radio instruction from Aden.

THE LONELY SEA
AND THE SKY
Francis Chichester

In 1929, having only just got his pilot's licence, Francis Chichester was all set to try and break the world record flying-time between London and Darwin.

We accompany him for the first tiring 1,900 miles of his hazardous journey . . .

The total inventory of difficulties was immense, but had this advantage, that it took my mind off the chief worry which was whether I had the flying skill to make the flight. I wanted to beat Hinkler's record. He had achieved the flight from London to Darwin, Australia, in fifteen and a half days. It was 12,000 miles by the route flown, so that he averaged 750 miles a day. It was not much use trying to beat his time by only a few hours, so I divided the distance as nearly as possible into 500-mile stages, and decided to attempt two stages a day. This would require twelve and a half hours' flying every day, with a halt for refuelling, probably in a fresh, strange country, in the middle of the day. In order to make the final landing of the day in daylight, I should have to start in the dark in the morning at about 2 o'clock. So I had to enlist the help of the Air Ministry to obtain permission from the various countries to fly over them at night without navigation lights, for to fit a Moth with the only navigation lights then available would be like fitting out a five-ton yacht with a steamer's anchor.

On 19 December I worked hard all day. I flew over to De Haviland's at Stag Lane to have a cover fitted to the front cockpit, which was both streamlined and easy to open, so that I could get out my rubber boat in a hurry. Also, I had a hole cut in the back of the front cockpit seat, so that I could extract food from where I sat at the controls. I collected and stowed all my food and gear. I made telephone calls about last minute permits. Not until after dark did I take off from Brooklands to fly to Croydon Aerodrome, where I had to clear Customs, etc., before leaving the country. At Croydon an Air Ministry official immediately pounced on me to know why I was flying without navigation lights.

After refuelling with petrol and oil I cleared the Customs and collected my journey log-book, *carnet de passage*, licence, and my passport with endorsements for seventeen countries, and was ready to leave. Walking near a hangar I asked a stranger for some information. When we came under a light he said, 'Aren't you Chichester? Don't you know me? I'm Waller of Hooton. I shall always remember your turning up at Liverpool in a new machine without a compass and with that ridiculous map of yours.' He had just flown down himself in his own aeroplane. Had I been for any more flights since then? 'Yes, I made a flight round Europe.'

'Great heavens! But you've only just got your licence, haven't you? Perhaps you're going to fly home now,' he added, jokingly.

'Yes, as a matter of fact I am.'

I had not talked about my proposed trip for fear of failure and being laughed at.

'You're not really!' he said. 'When are you starting?'

'In six hours.'

He was silent for some time.

I ate dinner in a panic. When the porter told me I was wanted on the telephone I got hot and cold with fear that it was something which would stop me. I gasped with relief when it turned out to be the Meteorological Office, telling me that I must not land at Grogak, Rembang, Bima, Reo or Larantoeka in the Dutch East Indies because they were flooded. I could not worry about that.

I was up at 1.30 and ate bacon and eggs.

At 3.15 I took off across the grass field. This was the first time I had taken off with a full load up. The aeroplane was carrying its own weight in payload. I thought this was the reason for the long and horribly bumpy take-off, but actually the ground, frozen hard, had ripped open a tyre and tube. As soon as I left the ground I felt the tremendous thrill of being off to Australia. The four exhaust stubs belched bluish flames against the night sky. I wobbled about at first both in yaw and pitch, for this was the first time I had steered a course at night. Luckily, I had moonlight at the start, and began to pick out the fields below. I could see the broad bands of hoar frost along the lee of the hedges. I kept on trying to fly steady and level. I had no blind-flying instruments, and the horizon was vague and indefinite. I set about trying to read the drift, another thing I had not had time to practise. Leaving the coast and flying off into the murky darkness was another exciting moment. The moonlight was cut off by a layer of cloud, and now the horizon had completely vanished. All I could see was a glint on a small patch of water directly beneath the aeroplane. I hoped to keep roughly level by means of the altimeter, and when I looked at it, the dial was rotating without stopping. I had nothing to judge the height by except the patch of sea underneath. If the waves were small I might be only a few feet above them; if large, I might be thousands of feet up.

I had expected to cross the Channel in about fifteen minutes, and when I was still over water after three-quarters of an hour I began to feel lost. The truth was that I was making a hash of my first night navigation. I had over-estimated the drift, and thought I had crossed the south coast at Folkestone. When France did not show up as expected, I wondered if I was heading into the North

Sea. If I had been able to study my map, and use a ruler and protractor, I would have seen quickly what was happening, but there was no light in the cockpit, and I did not like to stop looking out while I worked a torch with the map and instruments. Gradually, I reasoned that the North Sea was an impossibility and that I was headed south towards Dieppe.

At last, an hour after leaving England, a high, whitish cliff loomed up just ahead. I flew along beside the dim, ghostly white face for some five miles, determining the compass bearing of its direction. There was only one five-mile piece of coast running in this direction—I must be north-east of Dieppe. I worked out a fresh course for Paris from that spot, allowing ten degrees for drift; but the wind had dropped altogether, so I was set to the west of Paris. As a bleak, dismal, November grey crept into the sky, I was cold and cramped and attacked by an overpowering desire to sleep. I got a map fix, and worked out a fresh course for Lyons. Dawn broke, the earth was white with frost, the canals and patches of water covered with ice. Smoke drifted lazily above the chimney tops. After seven and a half hours in the air I landed at Lyons. It was a good landing, but the machine tried to slew round at the end of its run because of its flat tyre. I ran 300 yards in my big sheepskin boots, then had an enormous omelet with a bottle of red wine. The tyre was mended for me, and I got away after one and three-quarter hours on the ground.

Climbing with full load to 10,000 feet in order to cross the Alps seemed to take an age. I kept on looking at my watch, and wondering whether I could reach Pisa before dark. I flew over the Cenis Col with 3,000 feet to spare and it was a great relief to have crossed the Alps in smooth air; also to be flying faster on the long descent to Turin after the slow, tedious climb with full load. Everything went well until I ran into rough air at Genoa. Whizz! Whop! Bump! Each bump sent a shower of petrol into my face from the vent of the cockpit tank in front. I tried flying over the sea, but it was worse there. I was scared stiff that the wings would fold up. I bolted back to the mainland again, and was hurled this way and that as I climbed with throttle wide open at the steepest possible angle against the down-draught coming through a col in the hills. The slots clanked each time an extra strong bump stalled the aeroplane. I only just managed to clear the col. Then I flew down a valley parallel with the coast. At first I tried to climb in the hope of escaping the bumps, but each time I gained a few hundred feet a violent downwash of air forced me down again. I felt as hot as if I had just run a mile race.

Night fell, and at last the air became calm again. I plodded on to Pisa, where I could see the aerodrome a long way ahead splendidly lit with a searchlight signalling me. I flew up to it, and cut my motor three times to let them know on the ground that I had arrived, and then shut off to land. Close to the ground I found that it was not an airfield, but bright lights illuminating a long, L-shaped hoarding, half a mile long at the corner of two streets. The search-light was a powerful beam from a motor-car.

I soon recognized the airfield as a big black space, but there was not a single light showing except from some barracks at one end. My first shot at landing in the dark was a dud; I bumped and went round again. However, at my next shot I landed well and started to taxi in, but the wheels got bogged in the mud. A swarm of soldiers seemed to spring out of the ground and pushed the Gipsy Moth out of the mud, breaking one or two of the ribs in the leading edge.

I asked in French about the lights, and they said that they had expected me to circle for half an hour while they went to find the light operator. The Italians were extremely kind and helpful, but everything had to be discussed at great length. It took four and a half hours of solid talk and argument before I had refuelled, checked over the motor and satisfied the Air Force, Customs and police authorities. They lent me a camp-bed and I tried to sleep at 10 o'clock, but I was too tired. I had started tired, had put in a strenuous 20 hours, of which 12 had been spent flying 780 miles. I only had two and a half hours sleep before getting into the air again at 1.45 a.m. I took off in the dark with no lights on the air-field, so that I had landed and taken off from an airfield which I

I flew down a valley parallel with the coast.

had never seen. It was a lovely, fine night when I reached Naples. The sky became overcast, and I was flitting along under the ceiling of a low, wide-roofed cavern. Vesuvius was a magnificent sight with dark, billowy smoke rolling slowly from the cone, and a million sparkling, twinkling lights clustering round the bay at the foot of the volcano. I flew over the Gulf of Salerno into pitch darkness. I could see nothing ahead or below. Presently, flashes of lightning from a black storm-cloud lit up the whole area. I was able to dodge this, but later flew into a rain-cloud. I could not see six feet ahead, and glided down until I could distinguish land by its utter blackness in comparison with the less black sea.

I was now flying beside a barren, mountainous country, apparently uninhabited, because there was not a single light visible anywhere. Daybreak was approaching, and as the tatty grey storm-clouds began to outline the mountains, sleepiness became an agony. I moved anything I could, waved my arms, jumped up and down in the seat, stamped my feet. If I jumped up I was asleep before I landed in the seat. I was primitive man looking at a stark, primeval scene, the black masses of towering mountains, the rugged grey precipices of rock dropping sheer into the sea and the full surface of the sea flitting out of sight under threatening cloud. Each time I slept I heard separate motor explosions, usually about four, with an increasing interval of silence between them. Then silence, and I woke with a jolt, petrified with fear that the motor had stopped. The first few times this happened I felt certain the motor *had* stopped; it was worse when I realized that the motor was still firing steadily at 3,600 times a minute. I no longer had the fright which kept me awake for a few seconds. I took off my flying-helmet and stuck my head into the slip-stream. I tried watching the cliffs, but my eyes would not align properly; I saw double. At last day came; I had been flying for six hours. I was tempted to look for one of the three emergency landing-strips on the beach where it widened, for the desire for the aeroplane to roll to a standstill so that I could loll my head against the cockpit edge and go to sleep was overpowering. I had already passed the first of these landing-strips; when I came to the second it was half washed away. Then, at the toe of Italy, sleepiness abated, and I flew on for another age across the straits and on to Mount Etna, looking enormous and solid in her snow cap. I landed at Catania and was stuck there for three hours. Petrol and a Customs officer had to be fetched from the town. When I had everything ready I found my journey log-book was still in the town and I had to wait another hour for it to turn up.

I managed to get in fifteen minutes sleep, which was a godsend. It was obvious now that I could not reach Africa before dark, so I asked carefully about night-landing facilities at Homs. I was assured that the airfield there had everything that could be desired in night-landing facilities. Then I flew over Malta. I thought of stopping there, but I had made up my mind to reach Africa in two days. I flew through a curtain of stinging hail, and a terrific flash of lightning near by made the aeroplane rock. After that, most of the 285-mile sea crossing was in fine weather. The sun set magnificently.

I was thrilled by my first sight of Africa, but surprised to see by the twinkling lights that the terrain sloped steeply up from the sea, whereas I had expected a broad, level sand desert. When I reached Homs it looked small, no more than a village, and there was no sign of an airfield. I thought I had made a mistake, and flew on for six to eight miles to the next promontory of the coast. Looking back, I saw a large reddish light, stronger than any other. When I reached the headland there was not a light in sight ahead, so I returned to investigate the red light. I was disgusted to find that it was a big bonfire in a deserted area of the country. I did not realize that it was lit to indicate a landing-place. I decided to head for Tripoli, seventy miles to the west. If I did not find a landing-ground before that, I knew that Tripoli was an Italian air force base.

There were no lights visible along the coast. Presently I flew into cloud, and could see nothing. I did not like it, with no blind-flying instruments, and no altimeter. Later, I spotted a searchlight ahead, flashing at regular intervals. I thought it was an airfield signalling to me, and it cheered me up. After flying on another twenty miles I could see a magnificent cordon of light, and thought that the airfield was really well lighted up. I began to sing. Later the light appeared to be just as far away. When at last I arrived I found that the airfield was the harbour, and the searchlight was the lighthouse, on the Mole. I circled the town in the dark, but could not see any airfield. Then a starry light flashed ten miles to the west of the town, and I flew over to that. I could see no airfield boundary lights, and glided down close to the ground, when I found that a motor-car was switching its lights on and off, trying to overtake another one.

Then an unmistakable searchlight appeared in the sky to the east of the town. There were no boundary lights, just the one search-light, which was lowered to the ground as I approached. It was pointing right at the hangars. If I landed along the beam, I should be heading right for the hangars, and I judged that there was only 200 yards between the light and the hangars. I could not be sure of a good landing in the dark after so long in the air. I circled the field, and could see a fine square of flat ground, surrounded by trees. I decided to land on this, short of the searchlight. I glided in steadily until suddenly, wonk! I was jolted forward and found myself held into the cockpit by my harness. The Gipsy Moth had tipped on to its nose. I had an empty feeling of utter failure; it was the end of my flight and my foolish dreams. I was aware of the dead silence which succeeded the motor roar, yet the rhythmic engine beat continued, not only in my brain but in every part of my body. I scrambled out of the cockpit, stepped onto one of the inter-wing struts and from there jumped to the ground. To my amazement I landed with a splash. 'Good God! I'm in the sea.' I listened but could hear no waves. The water only came to my ankles. I started towards the searchlight; a few steps and I floundered on to my knees. Then, stumbling forward, I touched a bank, and climbed up it (it was only a foot high). I felt like Puss in Boots in my long sheepskin boots. I stopped there, filled my pipe, but could not get the cigarette lighter to light.

The searchlight beam started moving, flickered round and

settled on the aeroplane. I could see waves in the fabric of the top and bottom wings, and a tear in the wing with the strut sticking through. 'Complete write-off,' I thought, and looked the other way. I tried to light my pipe. I was astonished to see the silhouette of a war dance on the wings of the Moth. Dozens of people dancing hard with their legs lifting like marionettes. Presently I heard the thumping of many feet. Then thirty soldiers came running to the ditch separating them from my bank. They rushed off to the side, found a crossing, then rushed up to me all talking to me at once, and pawing me as if unable to believe I was alive. I borrowed a match and set off with them for the searchlight. The commandant took me to a room in the empty mess and produced some wine. I kept on falling asleep as I drank. An orderly took me off to sleep in the room of a pilot away in the desert. Later I woke up and found myself groping along the wall, dreaming that I was flying, and suddenly all visibility vanished and I could do nothing but wait to crash.

Next morning I went out to find the Moth being wheeled in by a number of soldiers. The NCO in charge, Marzocchi, spoke French, and told me that the aeroplane was undamaged except for a front inter-wing strut and a broken propeller. I just did not believe him; but he was right. My amazement was only exceeded by my joy. I had landed in a dead flat salt pan, covered with four inches of water. It was so flat that coming in steadily I had not known I was down. The wheelmarks could be seen for thirty-five yards before the plane nosed over. This was due to my keeping the tail up in gliding trim.

IN THE
GOBI DESERT

Luigi Barzini

Prince Borghese the Roman Prince, Ettore Guizzardi the mechanical genius and Luigi Barzini the great writer are the occupants of the 40 hp Itala motor car which is ultimately to win the 1907 Peking to Paris automobile race.

Here Barzini describes their adventure as they cross The Gobi Desert . . .

The road we followed sloped perceptibly downwards. About eight o'clock we came to a kind of ledge. The meadows had again disappeared. The thick, grey, sparse blades of grass came back, timidly gathering in larger patches, between which were vast zones, sterile and bare. We were now upon the threshold of the real Desert.

Gobi, in Mongolian, means a cavity. The desert is an immense depression in the centre of Mongolia—it is the cavity, the *gobi*, which once held a sea. We now stood upon the bank of that departed sea. It was a regular shore, steep, with a sudden falling made by the breaking of the waves. We were now to enter on a lower plane: the bottom of the ancient sea. It had its inlets, its promontories, its little peninsulas clearly visible. Before us the sterile plain stretched to the uttermost distance, undulating, seeming to rise again on the horizon, because of the same optical delusion by which a sea horizon always looks higher than the shore.

A steep descent of about twenty or thirty yards launched us on these hard, flat sands which had once known sea-storms. We began a fantastic race across the strangest and most desolate landscape, a race which was both an assault and a flight.

Gradually, as we advanced, the earth became more barren, more squalid, more sad; now flat and even, now irregular on the surface, broken up by sudden uprisings; now made up of crystalline sand that sparkled in the sun; now viscous, the colour of trodden mud. There was no form of life on it, except certain little lizards of a colour so like that of the earth that they became invisible the moment they stopped. You could almost have taken them for tiny bits of the ground, suddenly grown alive and splashing away here and there from under the wheels of the motor-car.

The hours succeeded one another with a deadly monotony. The heat with the advancing day became more burning. The air seemed motionless, and we took in with great joy the freshening breath which the speed of the car brought against our faces. We were passing from the coolness of the morning to a tropical temperature, without intermediate zones. We noticed a curious phenomenon: the sun was absolutely burning, yet the shade was still cold; and we had the sensation of one who warms himself before a big fire in the heart of the winter, when he feels himself tingling with heat on the side of the flame, and numb with cold on the other. The sky was of an inexorable limpidity. So limpid was it, that our eye could not measure the distances. We saw everything quite close to us. The horizon seemed always a few miles away, yet we had to run for hours before we could reach any landmark seen clearly at great distances on the brow of some hillock.

This terrible transparency was due to the entire absence of moisture in the atmosphere. The dryness of the air began to cause us a suffering which increased every moment. Our skin was parched as with fever, and the sun beat so hotly on our hands and faces that it was as if there was centred upon us the most powerful light of an immeasurable lens. We had been conscious of the same feeling the day before; indeed, it was upon the road to Pong-kiong that there first came to our minds the simile of a lens, by which to express our sensations; but we had not then guessed that in the real desert the power of the lens would increase by so many degrees. We now understood why caravans never travelled during the day. But as for ourselves, by this time we neither would nor could stop. The only relief we could get we got by speed.

We only found one well. About ten o'clock we went down a further step, onto a lower sea-level. This second 'shore' probably represents some halt in that long retreat of the sea which was to end in its annihilation, and which lasts perhaps thousands of centuries. The ground was white with saltness. In certain places it reminded me of the area round the Dead Sea near Jericho, but here there were no green banks of Jordan. We were running over a dead land, over a part of the earth which lived too soon for the human race. Who knows but that the sight around us was an exact prophetic vision of what our own world will be in some millions of years?—dried up, dead, lying under an unalterable blue which will give it a moonlike aspect in the infinite spaces of the firmament.

The most cruel part of the desert is about forty miles long. Caravans always try to cross it on a single march. They fill their barrels and skins with water at the last wells, and they start by the light of the stars. The road they follow is now marked by whitening bones. Bones of camels, of mules, of oxen and horses are scattered here and there over the whole of the caravan road we were following. But in the desert those traces of slaughter are almost continuous. Often a storm will overtake convoys, isolate them in the denseness of its whirling sand, oblige them to stop, and then destroy them. All old or tired or footsore animals fall there. It is a place of agonies. There is breathing about it an indescribable spirit of death, and I don't know where it comes from—perhaps from the lugubrious aspect of the landscape, from the oppressive strangeness of its bare

The horizon seemed always a few miles away.

outline, from its changeless absence of colour, or from its heavy stillness full of anguish. It emanates from all things around, and impresses with a sense of some unknown and imminent danger, of a continual threat, of an ambush; of some inconceivable sorrow, for which you prepare with passive resignation. One thought alone survives in your heart, one desire rather, a shapeless, vague, unheeded but still persistent desire: that of escaping, of treading no longer over that dead body of a world—of being freed. You look to the horizon as to a place of salvation and rest. Beyond every gap you expect to find the object of some vague aspiration of your soul. However slight a hill may be, you imagine it must hide something unexpected and good waiting for you beyond it. But you pass hills and gaps, the horizon which was before you becomes the horizon which you leave behind, and the desolation seems endless. Your mind becomes inert, your soul is drowned and lost in an unconquerable sadness. The time of your departure from the last halt lies dim in your memory among the mists of the past; to your stunned intelligence all grows dark, all seems immeasurably far and dim. Your departure and your arrival seem equally distant. You know this only, that you *must* arrive, that you *will* arrive—and from this idea comes the only strength remaining with you: the great power called Patience. You gather your patience, and so, *On!* All the resisting faculties of your mind and body are disciplined in the service of patience . . .

We had ended by becoming silent, almost as though by an instinct desiring to hoard all our energies. Besides, a word means a thought; and there are moments when thought itself costs too much labour.

About ten o'clock we were in the heart of the worst zone of the Gobi. The two caravan halting-places at either end of this zone are marked by an enormous quantity of *obos*, that is, of the peculiar altars of the nomadic Mongolian. The *obo* is perhaps the first kind of altar that humanity ever erected. In consists of a heap of stones. In order to implore the protection of the gods before crossing the desert, and to thank the same gods for granted safety after the desert is crossed, the pious caravan-driver takes a stone, lays it upon an *obo*, kneels down and prays. From our first entrance into Mongolia, while the Great Wall was still within sight, we found *obos* upon the summit of hills; those were not like the *obos* of the desert. Perhaps they had been abandoned; they were damaged by the storms and reduced to shapeless little masses.

The *obos* which we found here upon the threshold of the most desolate region of the desert often bore a terrible likeness to the figure of a man. These too were erected upon little heights like the first ones we had seen. But these were shaped, cunningly, and were crowned by the skull of an ox or a horse. They truly seemed altars erected in honour of Death. More than once from a distance those little piles outlined against the limpid sky really seemed to our saddened eyes like the figures of men, and in the whitened skulls which crowned them we thought we saw men's faces. There were so many that they made a crowd, and the presence of human beings, no matter of what kind, would have been for us a source of joy—it would have broken the monotony and the long solitude of our journey. In the desert, all men become dear to a man, not so much perhaps because of a sense of human brotherhood, or through a solidarity against the common dangers, as because they offer the comforting spectacle of *life*. We would look at all those upright 'men' scrutinizingly, then wonder at their stillness, but think that perhaps they had seen us and had stopped out of wonder . . . and then suddenly the unbroken solitude would stand again all round us, more heavy and more painful than before, as the imagined crown turned into stone, and its faces were changed into skulls as though by some dismal power of magic.

At the foot of every *obo* were little strips of paper with prayers written in Tibetan characters, or little flags discoloured by time also bearing traces of sacred writings. The Monogolian people have a poetical superstition, by which they believe that the wind in waving that paper and those flags shakes the written prayer out of them and bears it up to Buddha. In passing over this place the air would therefore be filled with prayers as it is filled with perfume when it passes over flowers. Does not the use of incense in our own religious ceremonies bear some analogy to this thought?

We owed also a practical kind of gratitude to those *obos*, for by the process of building them the road had been freed from all stones. And who knows whether the origin of this strange religious usage may not lie in the need to improve the stony road? So the charitable act of clearing a way for other men may gradually have turned into a religious rite amid a people for whom every action and every event immediately acquire a mystical significance.

Suddenly we noticed that the radiator, the lung of the motor-car, was not breathing freely. In the great heat of the desert the current of air produced by our speed alone was no longer sufficient to refresh the water of the engine's cooling-jacket; and this water was evaporating with a violent and continuous rush from the vent of the radiator. For a long time (or at least for what seemed to us a long time) we had been looking for a well, to change the water in the engine. We did not want to use that of our reservoir unless we were obliged to do so by extreme need. The reservoir held scarcely fifteen litres, and it would be wiser to keep them for a last emergency. Any accident to the motor-car might leave us suddenly stranded, and that water would then be our only hope of salvation.

From time to time one of us would exclaim, looking intently towards the horizon, 'A well! Down there I see some vegetation—there is a dark patch.'

'Yes, yes,' would reply the others eagerly.

Illusions are easily communicated. But the dark patches either did not exist or turned out to have been shadows. We were at last obliged to have recourse to the water in our tank, and we stopped in order to transfer it to the radiator. The earth seemed to burn under our feet. There came up from it a heavy sultriness and a blinding reverberation of light. We were tormented by almost unbearable thirst. When we saw the water gushing out of the reservoir and sparkling in the sunshine, we could not resist the temptation, and drank it greedily, with our eyes half shut to enjoy it better, our mouth scaled on to the siphon—the same siphon, by the way, which was used for transferring the petrol. The water was hot and smelt of petrol and of varnish—at any other time it would have seemed nauseating; but all is relative in this world. The Prince was the most moderate of us three; he scarcely moistened his lips, and soon he begged us not to exhaust that precious store. Our monotonous flight over the desert recommenced.

At midday we began to see a few blades of grass in some slight depressions where a little moisture had evidently collected. Soon after we were surprised by the flight of some wild birds, and it was not long before we saw a little stagnant pool in a large cavity. Along its banks were solemnly stalking some cranes and other birds of the same order. We stopped to take water, and Ettore went to fetch it with the cooking-pan. The water was absolutely undrinkable—foetid, yellowish, slightly salted. We gave it to the motor, which has no palate. Still, that water signified by its presence that we were already out of the sinister range of absolute aridity, and now it was not long before we found wells surrounded by some encamped caravans.

OPERATION BONEBREAKER

Eric Hosking & Frank W. Lane

Eric Hosking, a famous bird photographer, tells of one of his most dangerous assignments . . .

Lammergeier, flying dragon, ossifrage, golden-headed eagle, bearded vulture, bone-breaker; such are the names which have been applied to this magnificent bird—half vulture, half eagle. Having studied and photographed it in the air and at the nest in the high sierras of southern Spain, watched it at close range in Pakistan and East Africa, and observed it dropping bones in Jordan, I can only echo the words of that veteran ornithologist, the late Dick Meinertzhagen: 'Seen at close quarters I know no bird so impressive.'

The lammergeier is primarily a gliding bird—an albatross of the land. With its huge angled wings spreading nine feet, the great bird glides effortlessly for mile after mile, sometimes sweeping a few

316

yards above the ground, sometimes soaring until it is invisible. Just how high it soars no one knows, but it has been seen at about 25,000 feet on Mount Everest.

However like an eagle in appearance, the lammergeier is more like a vulture in character. It rarely makes an overt attack on any mammal or bird capable of defending itself, although it occasionally attacks a wounded one. It is a scavenger, living largely on carrion, offal and bones. If it finds other vultures at a feast it stands by until the carcass is picked clean, making no attempt to join the squabbling. Only when the others have departed does the lammergeier descend upon the skeleton.

But it is a master of the sneak attack, when it can do the maximum of damage with the minimum of risk. One habit, according to Dick Meinertzhagen, is to swoop on an animal—such as chamois or wild goat—when it is in a precarious position on a cliff-face, strike it with the tip of a powerful wing or with its talons, and send it hurtling to its death. There are even a few records of attacks on humans, but they are decidedly exceptions to its general behaviour.

The lammergeier is a bone-breaker. Bones and even skulls of carcasses are taken aloft and dropped on rocks. Heaps of splintered bones are sometimes found near outcrops of rock, the bone-breaker's anvil. Writing of such an ossuary in Kenya, R. E. Moreau says: 'Over an area of some forty yards each way the bare rock was littered with white splinters of bone. In hollows they lay in drifts. I could have collected a dozen pailfuls.' The purpose of this exercise is to get at the marrow and brains from the bones and skull. The lammergeier's stiff, gouge-shaped tongue is adapted for extracting such succulent fare.

While in Wadi Rum with Guy Mountfort and John Wightman in 1963 we watched a lammergeier dropping an object onto the top of Jebel Um Ishrin. One of the best-known natural history legends tells how the Greek dramatist, Aeschylus, died when an 'eagle' (almost certainly a lammergeier) dropped a tortoise, mistaking his bald pate for a rock.

Lammergeiers nest in mountains, usually in a cave or a recess in a cliff, the foundation of the nests being sticks and branches, but various adornments are added. E. H. N. Lowther says of a nest built on a crag 6,000 feet high in the Himalayas near Simla:

'My first impression was that the lammergeier must be the King of the Rag and Bone merchants, for the nest was a huge collection of soiled sticks and dirty old rags and pieces of wool, with a large piece of sacking billowing in the breeze; this the bird must have had considerable difficulty in carrying. On these reposed pieces of green bottles, old bones—real veterans these—and horns. The far wall was white with droppings, possibly of years.'

One to three eggs are laid, but generally only one young is reared. Incubation lasts for an average of fifty-three days, and after hatching the fledgling remains in the nest for between 105 and 117 days.

Such is a brief account of the lammergeier, the bird that lured me to Spain in the early summer of 1959. But to photograph this magnificent bird at the nest is no light undertaking, so I decided to lead an expedition of my own, 'Operation Bone-breaker'.

For months I read every word I could find about it, wrote scores of letters and planned everything down to the last detail. The other members of the expedition were Dr John Ash, a professional ornithologist; James Ferguson-Lees, John Parrinder and George Shannon (all of whom had been in the Cota Doñana and Finland with me); Mrs Eileen Parrinder, who came as botanist; Johnnie and Gwen Johnson, who not only took out all our equipment and brought it back, but also did all the sound recording; Bob Spencer, an excellent field ornithologist who wished to do some ringing, especially of young lammergeiers; and Dr John Stafford, medical officer and naturalist.

The Spanish ornithologists, Antonio Cano and Antonio Valverde, joined us in the high sierras of south-eastern Spain. During the spring of 1958 they had found a lammergier's nest but it was not, unfortunately, occupied in 1959. Like many other birds of prey, the lammergeier often has several nesting sites, sometimes using one for two or three years in succession, then abandoning it for another, only to return to it later.

We were probably the first party of Englishmen to visit the area for many years, because we were received by the Mayor and the whole town came to greet us. We were interviewed by the local newspaper men and I had to give an impromptu radio talk.

Unfortunately a landslide had completely blocked the mountain road so, to while away the time, we went for a walk accompanied by at least forty of the local children, who, by their chatter and laughter, made certain that we saw few birds. We were amused to see a boy goat-herd carrying an umbrella—it seemed so completely out of place—until without much warning the heavens opened and we realized how sensible he was. Later we discovered that it was the general practice, not only to keep off the rain but also to shelter from the blistering sun.

Bulldozers were unknown in this part of Spain and the landslide had to be cleared by an army of men with shovels and wheelbarrows. Next morning we got through and were soon admiring the spectacular scenery.

Once settled in, our first task was to find a lammergeier and hope that it would lead us to a nest. Each day we went to different parts of the sierra, watching with binoculars and telescope. Sections of cliff-face were carefully examined for white droppings, hours were spent in positions that had commanding views, in the hope that a lammergeier would show up. Sometimes the weather was gorgeous, sometimes it poured with rain, and on at least one occasion it snowed and was freezing cold.

Then suddenly one day a huge bird flew overhead. It looked like an outsize falcon with long diamond-shaped tail and long narrow wings. My first sight of a lammergeier. What a view, what a bird! Breast and throat were bright orange, head cream, the back was brown, eye a vivid orange-red. We watched it for an hour or more, hardly daring to lower our binoculars lest we lost sight of it. Eventually it flew into a small cave on the side of a steep limestone cliff, 1,500 feet above the valley floor.

The next day we set out to examine the cave. As we climbed, the scenery became more and more fantastic; jagged limestone peaks towered above us, streams in the distant valleys glinted in the sun, forests of pine trees threw long, cool shadows, and all around us the ground was carpeted with a variegated pattern of wild flowers, especially peonies and saxifrages.

We eventually reached a narrow grassy ledge about thirty feet below the cave. The two Spaniards were determined to get to the cave but when halfway Tono Valverde slipped and crashed back onto the ledge, narrowly missing the edge and a sheer fall of 150 to 200 feet. We feared he was badly hurt but he picked himself up as though he had just tripped over his bootlace. Eventually, with the aid of pitons and rope, Antonio Cano scaled the vertical cliff-face and disappeared inside the cave. He found a nest about three feet across, made of pine, oak and juniper branches with a thick lining of sheep's wool. Scattered about were two legs of sheep, several hooves and bones of sheep and goats, a dog's skull—and an old rope sandal! There was one huge chick.

Antonio let down a rope and Tono climbed up it followed by George. They put the youngster into a sack and lowered it to us. It was by far the largest chick I had ever seen, as big as a medium-sized turkey. Wearing leather gloves James made a careful examination—it had enormous talons, a three-inch hooked bill and a gape big enough to take a man's fist.

Never have I wanted to photograph anything more than those lammergeiers—but never have I seen a more difficult site. We had to erect a hide inside the cave no more than a couple of feet from the nest, or across a gully 150 ft. away. The first site was too close, the second too distant for successful photography.

We finally put up two hides, one for me at the 150 feet site, the other just over 200 feet for George to make the film. My hide was on a rock jutting out over a valley with a sheer drop of about 200 feet. When I entered the hide my companions roped me to a nearby rock, for fear I might fall into the valley.

Early on the morning of 2 June I left with two keepers for the first attempt at photography. As we approached the hide we saw a lammergeier circling overhead. Then it closed its wings and dived

This magnificent bird – half vulture, half eagle.

headlong, swinging up at the last moment before disappearing into the cave. It stayed for only a moment or two, then flew out of sight. We arrived at eight o'clock and the keepers saw me into the hide.

The young lammergeier was two months old and I had imagined that the adults would bring in food only once or twice every twenty-four hours. But within half an hour I saw an adult fly into the cave carrying what appeared to be a piece of wool a foot long. The parent stayed only forty seconds.

As the sun began to warm the air, thousands of flies appeared, and at times I wondered whether they would make photography impossible as there were clouds of them between the camera and the nest.

Soon after ten-thirty I heard the young bird chittering and a moment later an adult alighted by its side. It did not bring any food but picked up bits of fur and bone and offered these to the chick, which pecked at them but made no effort to swallow any. The adult stayed for twenty minutes and, after photographing it with the 600-mm lens, I studied it carefully through my × 8 Zeiss binoculars. Seeing it thus at only fifty yards range was a wonderful experience and its beauty left an indelible impression on my mind. As it left the cave it leaned forward, opened its great wings and, without a flap, sailed away.

Shortly before 1 p.m. I heard an adult call, and from the side peephole which overlooked the valley, saw the bird fly towards the hide. Closer and closer it came and sailed by with one wing no more than two feet away. It was the most incredible view imaginable— for seconds my eye seemed fixed on the lammergeier's and I am sure my heart missed a beat or two. I also realized why the lammergeier is so often called the bearded vulture: two black tufts of long stiff bristles stood out prominently from its chin. It turned and swept round towards the nest and I could see that it carried food in its talons. It flew well below the cave and then soared up to it. The chick nearly fell out of the cave as it dived for the food and swallowed great hunks of it. This was surprising, because I had watched the feeding process at the nest of a griffon vulture and there the adult had regurgitated all the food. Vultures do not, as a rule, carry food in their talons but this lammergeier certainly did.

The temperature inside the hide at 4 p.m. was 92°F and when the lammergeier again visited the nest so much perspiration dripped from my forehead I could not see clearly. I stayed in the hide till 7 p.m.—eleven hours of superb bird-watching.

After the first session we left the hide for two days. When we returned the whole outfit had disappeared. Three of the support poles were found in the valley but the fourth and the hide itself were never recovered. A tremendous gale had swept down the valley carrying all before it. I had a nightmare vision of a bird photographer dangling from a rope, buffeted by an angry wind, swinging to and fro over the deep valley!

Having photographed the lammergeier at the nest I now wanted to photograph it on its own. I bought a sick lamb, had it painlessly put to death, and then we pegged it down near the top of a mountain where we hoped the lammergeiers would see it. We erected two hides thirty feet away so that George could film from one while I took stills from the other.

Before long clouds of flies descended on the carcass. A raven tore at the entrails, carrying some away. An Egyptian vulture inspected it but after twenty minutes decided it was not ripe enough to be seasonable and went away. We stayed for eight hours in those hides, getting hotter and hotter, but no lammergeiers obliged.

The next day I decided to make another attempt. The smell from the carcass nearly knocked me over but, somehow, once settled in the hide I did not find the odour so offensive. I had not been waiting long when I realized that great shadows were sweeping across my hide—griffon vultures. Out of the corner of my eye I saw an Egyptian vulture alight and move towards the carcass, then a raven flew on to the lamb's head and pecked at its eyes. As the raven flew away, a black kite alighted but this was chased away by the Egyptian vulture. Some griffons came down in the distance but seemed in no hurry to start their feast. Was this because they were suspicious, not hungry, or the carcass was not ripe enough?

Four hours elapsed before things really started to happen but once they did it was a free-for-all with no holds barred. With its wings widespread a griffon waddled and, growling gruffly, jumped towards the carcass. Others alighted some yards away and bounded forward—let battle commence! For a time they seemed more intent on fighting each other than in feeding but there soon developed a 'pecking order'. One huge griffon sank its head into the carcass, tore a lump off, swallowed it and at the same time viciously struck out with its feet in an attempt to drive off competitors.

I made a quick count: there were thirty-four griffons at or near the lamb, four Egyptians, two black kites and two ravens, with another seventeen griffons waiting on rocks or pine trees.

But there was no sign of a lammergeier. Although we tried again and again we never saw one come down to take food. But to my dying day I shall never forget that view of the bone-breaker as it swept by my hide, our eyes fixed on each other.

RESCUE
EAST OF EVEREST

Edmund Hillary

For someone who has always enjoyed time at home I seem to have a flair for getting involved in things that take me away from it. I had agreed to lead a New Zealand Alpine Club expedition to the Barun Valley, east of Everest, and we had a dozen good mountains to climb and the Iswa and Choyang valleys to explore.

We gathered all our equipment in Dharan and trekked up the Arun river to the north. There was heavy snow on the pass into the Barun valley and while two teams pushed their way into the Iswa and Choyang valleys I organized the arduous lift of supplies over the pass and up to Base Camp at the foot of Makalu. I was elated to find the valley just as beautiful as I remembered it. High above us on both sides were tremendous rock precipices and jagged ice ridges, but the valley was green and the air gloriously fresh and scented with azaleas.

From Base Camp Wilkins, McFarlane and I set off up the Barun glacier with five Sherpas. Despite our lack of acclimatization we hacked our way up an ice peak of 20,370 feet and revealed in the superb views of Everest, Lhotse and Makalu. In *East of Everest* I tell the first-hand story of what happened to us over the next few days.

Next day we moved farther up the Barun glacier and camped near its head at a height of about 18,800 feet. From this camp McFarlane, Wilkins and I set off to climb an obviously easy peak to the north-east which we felt would give us an excellent idea of the whole of the Barun neve. It proved to be more of a mound of rubble than a peak, and after a long, dull plod up shingle slopes and an easy snow ridge we reached the top—20,300 feet. It was a very valuable viewpoint and Jim McFarlane regretted the fact that he had not brought his phototheodolite along. To the north-east were several easily accessible passes and McFarlane was eager to have a look over one of them into Tibet. His enthusiasm was infectious and Wilkins agreed to accompany him. I wanted to return to camp and get things organized, for we were planning to commence our return trip down the valley the same afternoon. They roped up and headed off towards the pass, and with a final word that they should not be too late I plunged off down the easy side of the mountain and back to camp.

The afternoon passed very slowly. At 4 p.m., I crawled out of the tent and searched the glacier for signs of Wilkins and McFarlane, but I could not see anything. I felt a surge of anger. What could they be doing? I had told them to get back early and now the afternoon was nearly gone. We could not possibly go down the valley today. Feeling somewhat disgruntled, I crawled back into the tent. Time passed and there was no sign of them. My anger had changed to worry. The clouds were down around the peaks and the weather was dull and gloomy. I decided to set a deadline. If they had not turned up by six o'clock I would go and look for them. It was getting cold now and I crawled inside my sleeping bag and was soon snug and warm. At about 5.30 p.m. I heard a faint shout. It was one of the boys! I wriggled out of my bag and struggled through the door of the tent. Staggering into camp was Wilkins. He was alone. With a tight feeling in the pit of my stomach, I saw that his face was covered with blood.

'Where's Jim?'

'We fell down a crevasse. I got out, but Jim is still down there.'

We got Wilkins into the tent and gave him a drink, and he told me the story.

After they left me they had crossed over the head of the glacier and up onto a little saddle on the main divide. From there, much to their excitement, they had been able to look far out onto the high plateau and peaks of Tibet. After enjoying the view to the full they had turned to come home. They were tired and suffering a little from the effects of altitude, but the glacier seemed to have no crevasses and they plugged dully downwards thinking of nothing but reaching the camp and resting. Wilkins was leading, with only a short stretch of rope, thirty or forty feet, separating him from McFarlane. They were reaching a crest on the glacier where it dropped off rather more steeply, when suddenly without warning Wilkins stepped on a thin crust of snow which concealed a great crevasse. He had no memory of falling, but found himself squatting in deep, loose snow sixty feet down at the narrow bottom of the crevasse. Beside him was McFarlane. Wilkins examined himself and found that despite his terrific fall he seemed comparatively unhurt, although his snowglasses had cut his forehead and he was having trouble in keeping the blood out of his eyes. He examined McFarlane and found that he was having some difficulty in moving at all. It was obvious that he was either badly bruised or had broken something.

Wilkins set to work to try to make a way out: it was quite impossible to get out of the hole down which they had fallen. The crevasse in places was very wide and narrowed at the top with over-hanging lips of ice. He started working his way along the crevasse to where it narrowed. Wriggling through small ice passages and scrambling along a snowy ledge which clung to the wall of the crevasse, he made considerable height. Above him the sky was cut off by a thin roof of snow. On every side great unstable-looking masses of snow and ice hung menacingly. It was a horrifying place, but he had to get out. Cutting steps in the walls of the crevasse he inched his way upwards, fearful that at any moment he might dislodge an avalanche that would sweep him to the bottom again. He was aiming for a point where there was a hole in the roof. After two hours of difficult and nerve-racking work he reached the hole and started dragging himself out. At the last moment he felt the snow giving way under him and frantically clawed his way to the surface, leaving his ice-axe sunk in the snow behind. He could do nothing for McFarlane, who was too injured to help himself. The only thing to do was to get help. Lying up on the edge of the crevasse was McFarlane's ice-axe, so Wilkins picked it up and then carefully and cautiously made his way across to the edge of the glacier. Tired and shocked as he was, his trip down the rough boulders beside the glacier must have been a nightmare. The climb up to the tents took the last of his strength.

I looked anxiously at the sky. The weather was still dull and night was not far off. I felt a great sense of urgency. We must get up and find the hole in the glacier before darkness fell. I shouted instructions at our five Sherpas and then quickly bundled together two sleeping bags, some ropes, food and water. I made sure the Sherpas had all their warm clothing, for I knew we could not be back until long after dark. We dropped down from the camp and started off up the rocks beside the glacier. The loose, rolling boulders made for tiring and exasperating travelling. To my worried mind they seemed to be deliberately hindering our progress. The light was already getting very dim and I raced on ahead of the Sherpas, impelled by the fear that we might not find the crevasse. I was searching anxiously now for some sign of tracks, and suddenly to my relief I saw Wilkins's hat on top of a boulder and a set of uneven tracks leading off into the dim whiteness of the glacier. I stifled my urge to follow them and waited impatiently for the Sherpas to catch up. We put on the rope and then I cautiously started along Wilkins's steps. They led far out across the glacier. The light now was very bad. It was almost dark and I berated myself for having arrived too late. 'Now we will never find him!' And then I noticed, fifty feet in front of us, a small, round, black hole in the snow. 'It must be the one!' I rushed over towards it, but the Sherpas were holding me firmly with a tight rope. Wilkins had warned me about the overhanging lips of the crevasse, so I lay down on my stomach and wriggled slowly over to the hole. I looked down into a black void.

'Hello, Jim!'

For one awful moment there was no reply and then, to my intense relief, a faint voice came from far below. I asked him how he was. His replies were strangely hesitant but seemed quite rational. He said he was quite comfortable, that he was not badly hurt at all, but he thought he had a broken finger. His main trouble was that he was feeling rather thirsty. I pulled my torch out of my pocket and shone it downwards. The cold, gleaming walls of the crevasse sprang into life, and with a shock I realized how deep it was. I could not see the bottom. McFarlane called up that he could see the light or the reflection of it. I told him I would lower a rope down. I crawled back to the Sherpas, got another rope and then returned to the hole. I was not very happy about my position, because with the torch I could see that I was lying on top of a thin corniced lip. If that broke off it would probably engulf McFarlane. I lowered the rope carefully down the crevasse. It disappeared out of the range of my light but still went on down. McFarlane did not seem to be able to get it. His voice sounded very weak now and at times rather aimless. I tried swinging the rope around desperately in the hope that it would strike him and he could get hold of it, but with no result.

I crept back from the hole and thought what to do. It was pitch-dark now. The wind was whistling over the glacier and it was bitterly cold. The Sherpas, despite all their clothes, were obviously un-happy and miserable. Their morale did not seem too high. I decided the only thing to do was to go down the crevasse myself. I explained this to them in detail in my faltering Hindustani. They would lower me on two ropes. When I reached the bottom I would tie McFarlane on one of the ropes and they were to pull him to the surface. Then they could pull me up. They obviously understood my instructions but tried to persuade me against going down. I ignored their pleas.

I tied the two ropes around me and wriggled once again over to the hole in the ice, and then with a hollow feeling of insecurity, I pushed myself over the edge and dropped into the hole. The ropes came tight and I hung free, unable to reach either wall of the crevasse. I immediately realized I had made a mistake. I had tied the ropes around my waist instead of taking most of the weight around my thighs or feet. Already the rope was cutting into me, crushing my chest and restricting my breathing, but I thought I could stick it out long enough to get down to the bottom of the crevasse. I yelled to the Sherpas to lower me, and slowly, in a series of great jerks, I dropped down. I seemed to go on for ever. The crevasse had narrowed now and I could touch one of the smooth hard walls. And then the Sherpas stopped lowering and I just hung there, gasping like a fish. With all my strength I yelled at them to lower me farther, but they would not move. I twisted frantically on the end of the rope to ease the strain. I knew I could not last for long and I started thinking, 'What a funny way to die.' The Sherpas still ignored my shouts to lower me farther so I called out for them to pull me up. At first there was no response. Then from below me McFarlane's voice joined in shouting, 'Uppa uppa,' and like an answer to a prayer I started moving upwards. I must have transmitted something of my urgency to the Sherpas, for they were pulling with all their strength and I gained height rapidly. Then I jammed under the overhanging lip of the crevasse. The rope was cutting into the edge and held me immovably. The Sherpas panicked once again. Tugging like madmen, they tried to wrench me free. Something had to give and I could feel my ribs bending under the fierce pressure of the rope and a sharp pain in

I wriggled over to the hole in the ice with a feeling of hollow insecurity.

my side. I yelled to them once again to ease off a little, and after some long moments they obeyed. The smooth, slippery ice gave no purchase to my flaying hands, but with a tremendous wriggle I managed to get an arm over the top of the crevasse and my eyes rose above the edge. In the blackness I could see dimly the straining figures of the Sherpas, but I could not move any further. Still suspended from the rope, I could feel all my strength draining out of me. With an impassioned plea that would have done credit to Romeo and Juliet, I tried to persuade one of the Sherpas to come over closer so that I could grasp him with my hand, but they all refused to move nearer the edge. I started wriggling again and somehow got my other elbow above the surface. And then they pulled me out like a cork from a bottle, I have had few better moments than that—lying exhausted on the ice at 19,500 feet, feeling the air flood into my released lungs, with the chattering Sherpas pouring water down my throat.

It was not long before some of my strength came back and I started racking my brains to decide what next to do. The Sherpas were tired and cold, and their morale could not be relied on. It seemed as if our chances of getting McFarlane out were very slim ones. I slid over to the hole once again and shouted down to McFarlane:

'We may have to leave you down there for the night, Jim. If we lower down a couple of sleeping bags, do you think you will be all right?'

There was the usual long pause and then Jim's weak but cheerful reply that he would be quite comfortable. I tied the rope around two sleeping bags and started lowering them carefully over the edge. They seemed to go on for ever and soon disappeared out of the range of my torch. The rope came slack and I knew that they had reached the bottom. McFarlane called out that he had managed to get hold of them and that he had got the rope too. Why not pull him out then? I called down and asked him to tie the rope around his waist. I knew it was taking a risk because he might not be capable of tying it properly, but it was worth a try. It was many minutes before McFarlane's voice told me he thought he was safely tied on. I signalled to the Sherpas to start pulling in the rope.

They took in the slack and next moment McFarlane was on his way up. With growing excitement I grabbed hold of the rope and added my weight to the Sherpas! And then the rope stopped, McFarlane must be jammed under the overhanging edge. I crawled to the edge and peered over. The rope was cutting in deeply and I could not see anything. I tried jerking it free, but to no avail, and then out of the darkness appeared McFarlane's questing hand. Stretching down, I just managed to touch it before it fell listlessly away again and some dreadful choking sounds came from under the ice. We must lower him down again! I shouted desperately at the Sherpas and, startled into life, they commenced lowering with a rush. In a minute the rope came slack and McFarlane was on the bottom again.

I crawled over to the edge and shouted down. It was a long time before he replied. His voice was weak, but seemed somehow indestructible and cheerful. He said he had had a few bad moments up top, but that now he was all right. He would have to spend the night down there. I told him to crawl into the sleeping bags and he said that he would. I waited a few moments and then asked him if he was getting into them; there was a pause and he said, 'Yes.' We anchored the end of McFarlane's rope solidly into the ice and then started slowly downwards. I felt bruised and weak and it was painful to breathe, but worse than this was the awful sense of shame in having to leave poor McFarlane sixty feet down in the ice. My only consolation was the two sleeping bags which should keep him safe and warm.

The trip back to the tents was a nightmare. The Sherpas were almost as tired as I was, and we slid and fell over the loose rocks. It took us a long time to get up to the tents. I crawled in beside Wilkins and got into the comfort and security of my sleeping bag. The thought of McFarlane dominated my mind and I felt sure I would never sleep. But Nature was kind and my head had barely touched my rough pillow before I had fallen into a deep sleep.

I woke with a start and looked at my watch. It was still dark and the wind was flapping vigorously at the tent. It was only about 4.30 a.m. I undid the zip and looked out—there was a swirling mist of light snow. My chest felt stiff and painful, but I knew we must get moving, for a heavy fall of snow could prove disastrous. I wakened the Sherpas and we started a cooker going. Wilkins was much refreshed. In the dim morning light we left the tent and started off into the driving snow. I was relieved to find it was fairly light, and did not think it would trouble us much. We were all travelling slowly and it was a long and bitter grind over the loose rocks, but as we went, it cleared, and when we reached the side of the glacier we could actually see the little black hole several hundred yards out.

Wilkins and I roped together. I think both of us had the same thought, but neither of us had uttered it. Would McFarlane still be alive? Wilkins carefully belayed me and I wriggled once again on my stomach over to the edge of the hole and looked down. In the morning light I could see the smooth hard shining walls of ice dropping down, but at the bottom it was still dark. I shouted a greeting. There was a long pause and then, to my intense relief, a faint reply—thank God, he was still alive! And then to my amazement McFarlane called out that he had had quite a good night, but he was feeling a little cold now and rather thirsty. 'It won't take us long to get you out, Jim.'

I conferred with Wilkins. We were still very much afraid of dislodging the corniced edge of the crevasse and engulfing McFarlane. Wilkins, with great courage, offered to descend by the very dangerous route by which he had made his escape and to try to get McFarlane through that way. On the end of the rope we made a sling to put under his thighs to take the weight and then, after arranging a code of signals, we watched him climb cautiously into the second jagged hole fifty feet to the right. He slowly disappeared from view. For an eternity we seemed to let the rope out, and well over a hundred feet had gone before he signalled that he had reached McFarlane. It was a long time before the signal came to pull in the rope, and we tugged and hauled with all our strength. But all that came to the surface was Wilkins himself. He had a depressing story to tell. He had managed to reach McFarlane, but only after great difficulty. The route was quite impossible for anyone not possessed of his full strength and agility. McFarlane was unable to help himself. Contrary to what he had told me, he had not got into his sleeping bags but had just draped them over his knees. He had taken his gloves off his hands and they were cold and stiff. It gave him a good deal of pain in the back to be moved and he was obviously suffering from concussion. This was bad news. Wilkins had tied a sling around McFarlane and he considered the only chance was to lower a rope straight down the other hole and hope that McFarlane could clip it onto the sling.

We moved to the other hole again and lowered the rope. McFarlane got it and called out that he had attached it. We started pulling him in. We were all much fresher and stronger now and the rope came in rapidly, and then it jammed. McFarlane was stuck under the overhang. Wilkins leaned alarmingly over the edge and tried frantically to release it, but it was useless, and we lowered McFarlane right down to the bottom again. We would just have to take the risk of cutting some of the edge away! Carefully held on two ropes Wilkins and Da Thondup chipped away the edge, trying to make the falling pieces of ice as small as possible. They cut it back about a foot without anything major falling off, so we decided to give it another go. Up McFarlane came. He reached the cornice and jammed once more. I leaned over the edge. There he was, only a short distance below me. Leaning hard out on the rope, I stretched down and managed to get a hand on the slings around his body. Exerting all my strength I pulled him outwards. He came loose and the next moment with a mighty tug he was pulled over the edge.

We carried him over to a bed we had made. His clothing was frozen and hard, so we dressed him in warm clothing of our own. His hands and feet were the greatest worry. His hands, which had been battered by the fall down the crevasse, were whitish-blue and frozen stiff like claws. When we removed his boots his feet were hard and lifeless, but in spirit he was as strong and cheerful as ever and he jokingly commented that he much preferred being carried down the glacier to walking. We knew we must get him down as quickly as possible—down into the denser air of lower altitudes and back to the ministrations of Dr Michael Ball. We tied three pack fames together with a rope into a rough stretcher. On this we placed an inflated air-mattress. Jim was by now inside a sleeping bag and we gently lifted him onto the stretcher.

We dragged him over the glacier to the edge of the rocks and started carrying him down. It was terribly hard work. Carrying a man at any time is a difficult business, but at over 19,000 feet it was most exhausting. The five Sherpas worked magnificently, and Wilkins and I took turns as a sixth man on the stretcher. We rarely made more than fifty feet, slipping and crashing over the boulders, before we would have to have a rest and stop, gasping for breath. My chest was hurting me abominably and Wilkins seemed at the end of his tether. It was obvious that we could never reach our camp, so when we finally gained a flat stretch of gravel with a small stream running through it we left McFarlane there with Wilkins to look after him and the Sherpas and I crossed over and climbed slowly up to our tents. The first necessity was to get medical aid.

Four of the Sherpas set to work packing up all the tents to move the camp back to McFarlane. The remaining Sherpa, Kancha, and I had a quick meal and then, carrying light packs, started off down the valley. Spurred on by my apprehension, I set a fast pace down the terraces above the Barun glacier. It was snowing again and there was a strong and bitter wind, but the going was fairly easy. Then we dropped down on to the moraine of the glacier and had to jump from boulder to shifting boulder. With every jump my chest seemed to burst with pain, and I started dropping behind. I knew I could not get down to camp that day—it was much too far. Kancha was waiting for me on a little flat stretch of gravel beside some ice cliffs in the centre of the glacier. I decided to camp. We pitched our little tent and crawled inside. I was too tired to eat, and fell immediately into a deep sleep—dead to the world.

It was still dark when we started again next morning. I wanted to reach Base Camp by breakfast time, before the others had started off on any trips. We stumbled downwards. I was stiff and sore, and seemed unable to go quickly. It was eight o'clock when we forded the river and started climbing up towards Base Camp. There were some shouted greetings and I saw, with great relief, that there was a big crowd in camp. George Lowe's strong, confident figure came towards me and I felt a lifting of my burden. Everyone was there, all looking fresh and strong. I told them the whole story and then left the rescue operations in their safe and capable hands.

It took the party four hard days to carry Jim down the glacier to Base Camp. I rested most of the time as I was still having difficulty with my breathing. Each time I coughed or took a deep breath I felt a stab of pain—an X-ray later showed I had three broken ribs. Jim arrived at Base Camp in pretty good condition but his feet were badly frost-bitten and his fingers had been nipped as well. We decided to rest him up and get him strong before he had to face the long carry out to India.

ON THE MOON

James B. Irwin & William A. Emerson

Astronaut Jim Irwin describes some of his experiences as the Lunar Module *Falcon* comes in to land on the moon . . .

The face of the moon is beautiful in a stark, awesome, barren way. It is all ochres, tans, golds, whites, greys, browns—no greens, no blues. We were hanging loose, coming to the burn itself. We were going down to land on the surface. Dave Scott was doing most of the hand-control action, but in the main we were telling the computer what to do.

The Lunar Module is almost as big inside at the Command Module. You need room for two guys to stand side by side and look out the window. The area to the rear of the crew is not very wide, perhaps two feet, but long enough for a man to sleep in. Together we were sharing a space a little smaller than a bedroom on a train. The consoles were forward of us, right next to the window.

We also had a console at our waist level, and we had switches and circuit breakers on the outboard side of both of us. We had redundancy in controls so that either of us could fly it. Actually, the Lunar Module flies very much like a helicopter; that's why we trained in choppers.

It was time for us to go into our Power Descent Initiation Burn, a twelve-minute power burn to the lunar surface. At the onset of this burn, the *Endeavour* would be about 350 nautical miles behind us; it would catch up and be approximately overhead at the time that we touched down. We started firing the engine, which has approximately the same thrust as the SPS engine of 30,000 pounds.

At 8,000 feet we pitched over, changing our altitude about 30 degrees. We had been coming in on our backs, looking up, feet first. Now we got our first good view of the landing site. After we pitched over it *was* like a helicopter. Dave looked at the left and saw a mountain up above us—it sort of misled him. In our simulations we had never seen a mountain above us. There we were at 7,000 or 8,000 feet, and Mount Hadley Delta was towering above us, soaring up 13,000 feet from its base. It gave the impression that we were a little short of our landing point.

Dave didn't want me looking at the surface at all; he wanted me to concentrate on the information on the computer and other instruments. He wanted to be certain that he had instant information relayed to him. He was going to pick out the landmarks. But Dave couldn't identify the landmarks; the features on the real surface didn't look like the ones we had trained with. We could see the great canyon, or Hadley Rille—so he played the landing point to be about the right relative distance from it. There were lots of craters out there, making it difficult to find a smooth place to land.

I kept telling myself, 'Jim, this is really a simulation. You are not really landing on the moon.' If I had believed I was landing on the moon, I would have been so excited I don't know if I could have made it. It was really hard not to look out. It was the smoothest 'simulation' we had ever run. Everything worked just perfectly.

When we pitched over, the computer knew exactly where it was going to land the vehicle. It displayed a number in a keyboard. I gave that number to Dave, and he looked at a grid imprinted on his window. He located that number on the grid, and he could sight the landing spot on the face of the moon. The spot didn't look familiar to him, so he made a couple of corrections, inputs for the computer. The primary concern was a smooth spot.

Now we were not moving forward, not moving laterally. We were coming down very positively, straight down. I thought we were going to have the smoothest, easiest touchdown that had ever been accomplished on the moon. Our engines began to stir up dust at about 100 feet, which completely obscured the surface. We were landing on instruments. Of course, we had a probe on the landing gear that was searching for the surface. When that probe touched the surface of the moon it would turn on a light in the cabin, telling us to turn off the engine.

The light came on. I called 'Contact!' Dave immediately pressed the button to shut the engine—and then we fell. We hit. We hit hard; I said, 'BAM!' but it was reported in some of the press accounts as 'damn.' It was the hardest landing I have ever been in. Then we pitched up and rolled off to the side. It was a tremendous impact with a pitching and rolling motion. Everything rocked around, and I thought all the gear was going to fall off. I was sure something was broken and we might have to go into one of those abort situations. If you pass 45 degrees and are still moving, you have to abort. If the Lunar Module turns over on its side, you can't get back from the moon . . .

We just froze in position as we waited for the ground to look at all our systems. They had to tell us whether we had a STAY condition.

As soon as we got the STAY, we started powering down. Evidently, we had landed right on the rim of a small crater. Dave and I pounded each other on the shoulder, feeling real relief and gratitude. We had made it . . .

'Okay, Houston. The *Falcon* is on the plain at Hadley.'

The excitement was overwhelming, but now I could let myself believe it. Dave and I were on the surface of the moon. We looked out across a beautiful little valley with high mountains on three sides of us and the deep gorge of Hadley Rille a mile to the west. The great Apennines were gold and brown in the early morning sunshine. It was like some beautiful little valley in the mountains of Colorado, high above the timberline.

There was the excitement of exploring a place where man had never been before, but the most exciting thing, what really moved me and touched my soul, was that I could feel God's presence there. In the three days of exploration, there were a couple of times when I actually looked up to see the earth—and it was a difficult manoeuvre in that bulky suit; you had to grab onto something to hold yourself steady and then lean back as far as you could. That beautiful, warm living object looked so fragile, so delicate, that if you touched it with a finger it would crumble and fall apart. Seeing this has to change a man, has to make a man appreciate the creation of God and the love of God.

There we are in the spacecraft, and even before the dust settles Dave is describing the surface of the moon through the windows of the *Falcon*. 'We're sure in a fine place here,' Dave tells Houston. 'We can see St George; it looks like it is right over a little rise. I'm sure it's much farther than that,' he corrects himself, looking more carefully. 'We see Bennett Hill . . .' But Houston brings us back to immediate business, after encouraging Dave by telling him that the Science Support Team in the back room is doing 'slow rolls'.

Dave and I have decided that we want to be in the best possible shape while we are working on the surface of the moon, and therefore we are going to sleep before we do any exploring. The doctors don't believe we can relax enough to do it. So, to take the edge off the excitement, we plan to get a good look around before we bed down for the night. We are going to depressurize, open the hatch, and Dave will stand on top of the engine cover. He is scheduled to take pictures and describe the lurain.

Finally, all our homework was done and we were ready to go. We depressurized, and Dave climbed up through the open hatch. As I watched him, I decided he was just a frustrated tank commander. He stood up in that hatch and looked around as if he were the Desert Fox. He described the whole panoramic view; then he began shooting with two Hasselblads, alternately using a 60-mm lens and a 500-mm telephoto lens. He offered me a chance to look out, but my umbilicals weren't long enough and I didn't want to take the time to rearrange them. (The umbilicals lock into your suit at your chest and into the console inside the spacecraft.)

Then we closed the hatch, repressurized the Lunar Module, and began to get ready for our night, though it was still early morning on the moon. We put up the window shades and powered down the *Falcon* as much as we could. The environmental control system and the communications were still operating, but the computers were down, and we turned many of the other instruments off to reduce the electrical load.

Dave was sleeping fore and aft and I was athwart ship, with my hammock slung under his. I noticed that my hammock was bowed out a little bit and my feet were sort of dangling off. It was noisy in the Lunar Module with the pumps and the fans running, something like sleeping in a boiler room. But, man, it was comfortable sleeping! Those hammocks felt like water beds, and we were light as a feather. That first night's sleep was the best I had the three nights we were there.

Houston had us up an hour early the next morning because of a slight oxygen leak. It turned out that we had left a urine dump valve open, and once that was corrected the problem was solved, and we hit the day about twenty-two minutes early.

We got all the helmets and visors aligned and adjusted, and we put each other's boots on and verified that each other's gloves were properly locked on. Dave and I had more conversation while dressing than we'd had altogether in the preceding several days. Then we checked out our backpacks and attached the emergency oxygen supply to the tops of our PLSSs (Portable Life Support

System). When I examined mine, I found a large-sized nick in the antenna. We reported it and ended up using that good grey tape to wrap and reinforce it at the weak point so that it wouldn't break off. Finally, when everything was GO, we depressurized the Lunar Module and opened the front hatch.

Dave climbed out first. I followed him, but I got hung up in the hatch. Dave talked me out. It's rather a tight squeeze and you are going out backwards, of course, on your belly, and you have to scrunch down to the right elevation and kinda ease the backpack underneath the hatch. As you could see on our lunar television coverage, Dave came down very confidently, but, having shorter legs, I had to reach for each step on the ladder. When my feet came to rest on the footpad of the module, I thought it was the surface of the moon. But as soon as I put all my weight down, the footpad rotated and I had to swing around, hanging onto the ladder, to keep from going on my back.

I could hear Dave's historic landing speech: 'As I stand out here in the wonders of the unknown at Hadley, I sort of realize there's a fundamental truth to our nature. Man must explore. And this is exploration at its greatest.'

My first thoughts were somewhat less rhetorical. Oh, my golly, I thought, I'm going to fall on my backside in front of all those millions of television viewers.

I just barely caught myself. Recovering my dignity, I heard Dave say, parenthetically, 'Well, I see why we are in a tilt . . . We are on a slope of about ten degrees, and the left rear footpad is probably two feet lower than the right rear footpad.' Houston would occasionally refer to our Lunar Module as the Leaning Tower of Pisa—which Dave showed no signs of appreciating.

I looked to the south. I remember saying, 'Oh, boy, it's beautiful out here! Reminds me of Sun Valley.' The Apennines were very familiar looking. They were rounded and treeless, and there were even mountains that looked like Half Dollar and Dollar Mountains in Sun Valley. They looked like excellent ski slopes.

All around us there was soft material on the surface about three inches deep, just like powder snow. We knew that underneath this dust there might be rocks that we could trip over. If we did, it wouldn't be a serious matter, because we wouldn't fall very hard. I only weighed 26 pounds on the moon, 50 pounds suited up with all my equipment. On the earth, I weighed 160 pounds, the suit weighed 60, and the backpack 80–300 pounds, so it was a real chore to walk. But on the moon, at 1/6 G, it was easy and exhilarating. However, the suit restricted movement. That's why we didn't walk with a natural gait. When you don't have the weight of your legs available to push against the suit, you are constrained as to how far you can move. Consequently, you just use the ball of your foot to push off. That's why we looked like kangaroos when we walked. We flexed the boot and that propelled us forward.

Walking on the moon feels just like walking on a trampoline—the same lightness, the same bouncy feeling. Falling down is the same too. If you fall down on a trampoline, you put your hands out and catch yourself and push yourself back up. You can do the same thing on the moon. The surface, of course, is very soft. The only danger is the possibility of tearing your suit, and that's remote. You'd have to have an extremely sharp object to penetrate the layers of the suit. If that happened, they say your blood would boil. You'd have ten to twenty seconds if the pressure immediately went to zero. If you could get back into the spacecraft and repressurize it before the suit got down from 4 psi to 2.5, you would probably be okay.

Dave and I both fell down twice while we were on the moon. When this happened, we'd help each other up to keep from getting any dustier than we had to; dirt on the suit absorbed heat from the sun and put a strain on our built-in cooling systems.

After a little reconnoitring, we were ready to off-load our lunar dune buggy, the Rover, the first surface transportation ever designed for another planet. We couldn't wait to take a spin.

The Rover was packed in an outside equipment bay in a container that was a little larger than a suitcase. When you look at the Rover it is hard to believe that it will fold up into such a compact package.

344

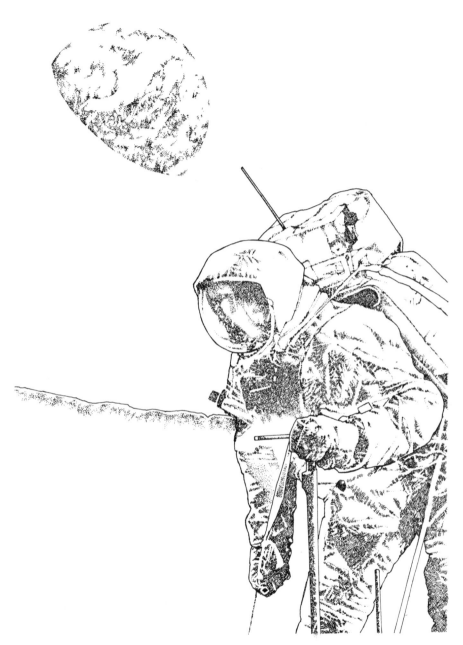

On the earth I weighed 160 pounds, on the moon 50 pounds suited up.

It is an amazing little vehicle, but then when you pay $8 million for a dune buggy, you expect something pretty good. Even the earth version that we trained in, designed for 1 G, cost $1 million.

With a little help from Houston, we pulled some pins and the Rover sprang out, and then we pulled on lanyards and straps and it assembled itself. The chassis folded into position, the wheels flopped out, and we secured everything with locking pins that slid into catches.

There is no air in the tyres; they are made out of woven piano wire stretched to provide a surface like an ordinary tyre. The tyres are faced with titanium chevrons designed to ride on top of the dust. When you go over a rock, they just bow up and absorb the impact and spring back again. Amazing. We drove over a lot of rocks on the surface of the moon and never broke one of those piano wires.

The Rover is powered by sealed electric motors in its wheel hubs, each one just about the size of the motor in a power drill. It runs on two 36-volt batteries and has a gyroscopic navigational system. It mounts a special communications package that kept us in radio and TV contact with the earth. The whole stripped-down buggy weighs about 455 pounds on earth but only 76 pounds on the moon and is built to carry $2\frac{1}{2}$ times its weight at a maximum speed of about 10 miles per hour. But the Rover felt faster than this. There is no atmosphere on the moon, so there isn't any wind in your face, but there is a great feeling of motion.

Of course, you are constantly dodging rocks and craters. You hit a rock and you are literally airborne. You just bounce into space, float for a while, and then come down. Rover is a flying machine. It is also a great little roadrunner with four-wheel steering—each wheel steers on a different radius. This means that, when you turn right, the right-hand wheel will steer on a smaller radius than the left-hand wheel. The Rover could make a circle within its own ten-foot length. I've never liked safety belts, but we couldn't have done without them on the Rover. It had a definite pitching motion that was a cross between a bucking bronco and an old rowboat on a rough lake—up and down, up and down. You could easily get sea-sick if you had any problem with motion.

Communications between us and Dr Joseph Allen, our Capsule Communicator during EVAs on the lunar surface, were so clear that it was hard to believe we were really on the moon. It was as if 'Little Joe' were sitting on one of those mountains talking to us. This seemed to bring us closer to home. Actually, the radio signal (S-Band) suffered minimal losses going through space. It was sent out from Honeysuckle Creek, Australia, our prime station. The sending antenna is a 210-foot dish.

Joe gave us minute instructions to cope with each hitch. 'Buckle up for safety,' he told Dave, for all the world like a parent talking to a child.

Dave drove off while I stayed back at the *Falcon* taking pictures of him with a movie camera, or trying to (the camera jammed). Then Dave's voice to Houston: 'I don't have any front steering, Joe.'

'Press on,' Houston answered.

Dave took a little spin in the Rover, and then he picked me up at the front door of the Lunar Module and we took off on Traverse 1, heading directly south. Dave did a remarkable job with rear-wheel steering only, dodging the craters and most of the rocks. We were heading for Hadley Rille and the front of the Apennine Mountains, an area that is most important from a geological point of view. This traverse would give us a sort of security; it would ensure the best possible use of our time in case we had to leave the moon after the first EVA. The traverse was planned to take us directly to the farthest point on the route so that we would have enough supplies in our backpacks and time to walk back to the Lunar Module if the Rover broke down. You always have to have 'walk back' capability.

My seat belt turned out to be too short. We didn't realize, when we made the adjustments on earth, that at 1/6 G the suit would balloon more and it would be difficult to compress it enough to fasten the seat belt. So every time we got out of the Rover, Dave had to come around and unfasten my seat belt, and he'd help me buckle up before we could take off. If that wasn't an aggravation. I felt like a baby.

Well, we were bouncing and skimming along, and to our amazement no dust was being thrown up. The big concern had been that we'd be surrounded by a cloud of dust that might keep us from seeing where we were going and prevent us from making any observations. Not so. The fenders worked like a dream in keeping the dust down.

At one point we came over a little rise and there was a crater about twenty feet deep right in front of us. Dave made a quick left turn that threw the vehicle up on the two right wheels. I felt sure we were going to flip. What if the thing did roll over and pin us underneath it? Could we ever release those seat belts so we could get out from under and turn the Rover back over? We never had to find out.

Suddenly Dave shouted, 'Hey, you can see the rille!' From the top of this ridge we could look down into and across Hadley Rille.

We were amazed at how huge Hadley Rille was. We could look down about 1,000 feet and across to the far wall at least a mile away. Both Dave and I suspected that Hadley Rille was a fracture in the moon's crust (most scientists had assumed that the sinuous rilles of the moon were in some way volcanic—formed by collapsed lava tubes or the result of flows of volcanic material). Looking to the south along the edge of the rille that faces to the northwest, I could see several large blocks that had rolled downslope three quarters of the way to the bottom. Soon I could see the bottom itself—very smooth, about 200 metres wide, and with two very large boulders right on the surface of the bottom.

'It looks like we could drive down to the bottom over here on this side, doesn't it?' Dave asked hopefully. And he actually wiggled over and found a smooth place that sloped from St George's Crater into a gully that dropped to the bottom of the rille. 'Let's drive down there and sample some rocks.'

'Dave, you are free to go ahead. I'll wait right here for you,' I told him. I reasoned that we might have made it down and back, but if we had driven to the bottom and something happened to the machine, we'd never have been able to get out. You wouldn't have either the energy or the time to walk up that incline. You'd be completely exhausted, and you'd run out of oxygen. As it happened, the next day, on the second traverse, we learned that the Rover had tremendous hill-climbing capabilities and could climb a 15-degree slope.

We drive up on the east rim of Elbow, moving easily up the 10-degree slope, and Houston confirms that we are to stop here and follow the checklist, as planned. This is our first stop. It turns out that we have gained back the twenty minutes we lost. It's a sporty driving course, and Dave has been going like gangbusters. Now we settle down to getting rock samples, with Dave wielding his hammer and me the bag man.

We find and identify basalt, breccia, olivine, and plagioclase. I dig a little trench and get some soil which is quite friable. Dave picks up a rock that looks something like a raindrop, and right behind him I discover one of those fresh craters with a lot of glassy-looking rocks in it. About then we get the signal from Houston to move on up to St George.

On the way, we produce a constant stream of information on every block, rock, and crater, and we are grading the ejecta from all craters along the way as to how fresh it appears to be. Houston breaks in to ask us if we can see our old tracks as we double back, and we can; the old Hansel and Gretel trick still works. When we crossed our old tracks, it gave me a curious feeling. I knew how Robinson Crusoe felt when he saw the footprints on the beach . . .

WORLDS
WITHOUT END

Anthony Buckley

It was not until we developed the high speed cine film that we realized we had made a sizeable chunk of the room disappear.

It was undetectable to the naked eye but the film clearly showed that, for a split second, we had made a ten foot diameter hole in the wall of the workshop.

If we had been scientists we would have followed up this phenomenon with a good deal of caution and Rolands would never have embarked on a journey which was to cost not only his life but which would wreak destruction on a scale unknown to mankind.

Rolands and I were two young marine engineers and partners in our own diving equipment company. We had just come to the end of twelve month's work building a six man research submarine. It was a jet propelled Submersible and its revolutionary design enabled it to be used at depths of 4 miles. It was now complete and ready for its sea trials. However, we were not entirely satisfied that the lights, used for filming in the total darkness of the sea's deepest levels, were the best that could be built. Rolands, who without doubt was a genius, had an idea for improving them.

Like most brilliant innovators, Rolands was convinced that there was always a better way of doing anything—one just had to find it. He would get an inkling that something could work and would follow up his idea until it came out right or wrong.

On the workbench we had set up a bank of gas lasers which Rolands had considerably modified in the hope that it could produce the intense illumination we were seeking.

'I have focused it to take in that filing cabinet and the wall behind' he said. I started the cine camera running so that we could later check the film for light intensity. We put on welding goggles and I switched off the workshop lights. In the darkness I heard Rolands flick on the switch of his machine. A burst of brilliant white light seared across the workshop. The next instant: 'Crack!' and the light snapped off.

Rolands muttered a curse. 'The circuit fuse has blown!'

We had worked well into the evening so, while Rolands repaired his machine, I decided to develop the film then call it a day. An hour later Rolands stumped into the darkroom. 'I've tried four times and the result's always the same—a beautiful flash of white light—then Bang! The circuit fuse melts.' 'Pity,' I said, holding the newly developed film to the light 'your machine seems a pretty efficient . . .' My words froze as I stared in disbelief at the film. It showed a clean-cut hole in the wall through which could be seen the road outside. We dashed from the darkroom through to the workshop. We ran our fingers over the brickwork and the filing cabinet. They looked and felt perfectly normal. The photograph made no sense.

'Can't be X-Ray,' muttered Rolands, his brow wrinkled in puzzlement.

Suddenly I was inspired; 'Invisibility,' I shouted. 'We've discovered the secret of Invisibility!'

Rolands' expression did not change. He had already discounted this possibility. ' 'Fraid not old chap. You see, even if we turned the wall to glass, the uneven structure of the brickwork would reflect most of the light which would make it quite impossible to see through.'

He paced the room for a minute. Then he stopped and stabbing the photograph with a forefinger said: 'It could be . . . that, just for an instant, we sent this section of wall and that filing cabinet into a Fourth Dimension.'

'You mean your machine actually removed them from this room!' I said, gasping at the enormity of the idea.

'Into a completely separate Universe which exists in parallel with our own,' returned Rolands. 'At least that's the Theory,' he added. He was clearly not fully satisfied with his explanation and his next words made me shudder with apprehension.

'I'm going to take a look for myself. Then we'll get nearer the answer.'

'That's crazy!' I grabbed him by the shoulders. 'God only knows what might happen to you.'

Calmly he removed himself from my frenzied grasp. 'The wall, the filing cabinet came back in perfect shape . . . why shouldn't I?' There was a letter on the cabinet which had lain there for days. He picked it up. 'Look! It's completely unscathed.'

He waved aside my protests and pointed to the Submersible. 'I shall lock myself inside that and use its Video camera to film whatever is on the other side. In the fraction of a second that I'm there, I might get a couple of photographs.'

We were both in a high state of excitement and I think I was swayed by his argument that if a piece of paper could survive, he would certainly be safe inside the Submersible which could withstand pressures of five tons per square inch.

Whilst Rolands busied himself with the gas lasers, I inspected the Submersible. Apart from a welding kit and some other tools which had been left inside, it was fully charged and ready to go: a totally enclosed, life-sustaining environment. Its maiden voyage would only last an instant but was to be the most momentous journey in the history of mankind.

The Submersible sat in front of the workshop doors, its stream-lined, compact form giving it the appearance of some futuristic space ship. Rolands was inside. His voice came over the intercom: 'I've got all four Video cameras and the sound tapes running so if there's anything around we should pick it up. Goodbye for the moment old friend . . . LET IT RIP!'

At his signal I switched on the gas lasers.

The intense beam flooded the Submersible for an instant then, as before, cut out. Simultaneously I was deafened by an explosion followed by the screech of tortured metal. The steel doors of the workshop were ripped apart as if they had been paper. Wedged sideways in the ragged hole, like an arrow, was the Submersible. Its surface was scorched and covered in solidified blobs of molten metal.

'Rolands!' I cried. I threw myself at the entry port. It radiated an almost unbearable heat but, using a crowbar for leverage, I had it open at last. Gingerly I lowered myself inside. It was as quiet and dark as the grave in there. The hot foetid air was stifling.

'Rolands?' I whispered. I fumbled for my matches and lit one. The first thing I saw was a large inscription which had been etched into the Submersible's steel wall with the welding torch. I read the words in horror and amazement:

'I AM A TRILLION YEARS OLD—I HAVE DESTROYED A BILLION WORLDS'

I turned away. My match illuminated a gleaming white object. I gasped. It was a bone! Broken pieces of skeleton glinted from every corner. A skull rolled at my feet. My brain reeled. The match went out and I screamed and screamed in an agony of terror and incomprehension.

Neighbours had heard the commotion and called the police and I spent the next 48 hours drugged in a hospital bed. Through my dreams stalked an unending vision of Rolands' skull uttering those baleful words carved in the Submersible.

On the third day I was visited by a Coroner and a Police Inspector.

They plainly disbelieved my story. The Coroner said that the bones in the Submersible had crumbled to dust and that they must have been at least a thousand years old. How could they possibly belong to Rolands? he argued. I was as mystified as he. He clearly believed that I had set the thing up in a fit of madness and, shaking his head sadly, left the room.

The policeman said that, although Rolands would be reported missing, no crime had been committed. He then took four steel plates from his briefcase and handed them to me. I recognized them as the eating dishes from the Submersible. The Inspector was about to speak but changed his mind. Instead he gave me a strange, quizzical look then departed.

I examined the plates. Each was covered with writing, carefully etched into the steel surfaces. One plate carried my name in capital letters. I began to read the words below. It was a description of Rolands's experience but his overwhelming message was a warning to me and all Mankind. As for his conclusions, at first I thought he must have gone crazy, but in the light of all that had happened I have no other explanation to offer.

He wanted his astonishing words to last millions of years and he had only a few hours in which to write them. He was afraid that paper, like his own flesh, might decompose in the atmosphere contained by the Submersible; he therefore chose to write on steel. His story began:

'Destroy the gas laser machine. It is an ABOMINATION.

'As you turned on the machine, the room seemed to explode about me. There was a rush of colour; white, grey, blue and finally black. And yet there was not the least motion or sound. Nothing but all-enveloping blackness showed on the Video screens. The Submersible was suspended in Space!

'I could not understand why I had not returned to the workshop. I should have been back in less than a second. I prayed that my

The submersible looked like some futuristic space ship.

36 hour supply of Oxygen would be enough. An hour passed and I was on the verge of panic when my eye caught a speck of light showing in the blackness of the forward scanner. It seemed a million miles away yet it was the only friendly thing in the vast emptiness outside. Without further thought, I fired the Submersible's jet drive and unwittingly turned my craft into a missile far deadlier than any Nuclear bomb.

'Had I remained stationary, perhaps the Submersible would have simply hung in empty space for an eternity eventually returning, like the wall and filing cabinet, to the spot from which it began its journey.

'The acceleration was unbearable and I blacked out immediately. When I recovered, the engines had already burnt out in one massive thrust against the nil-resistance of space. In amazement I gazed at the Starboard Video screen; suspended against a background of twinkling stars hung a vast planet, striated with beautiful pinks and greens, its Poles tipped blue-white with ice.

'I stared for several minutes in a rapture until it fell behind. With a heart full of wonder I turned to another screen. A Sun of blazing intensity swung into the screen. The glare was more than I could stand and I was thankful when it passed away out of sight to be replaced by a crater-pocked world similar to our Moon.

'Overcome with awe, I prayed I would be able to return and tell the World of this incredible Universe. The ecstasy of my experience is indescribable but now that I realize the unspeakable sacrifice that will continue to be made for timeless ages I beg you never to repeat it.

'Almost directly ahead was a sphere, marbled with blue and white. I estimated that the Submersible's trajectory would take me past well to Port. Instead, my craft seemed to heave round and point me directly at the planet. I watched with mounting anxiety as the world loomed enormous in the Video screen. Its colour began to deepen until it became a scintillating blue. Its shape seemed to be changing and, to my horror, massive pieces of matter began to tear from it. It was then that I realized that it was not the Submersible which had changed direction, but the planet! It had wrenched itself from its orbit and was hurtling towards me. Within seconds my craft would explode like an atom bomb when it hit the surface. I covered my face with my hands in a futile gesture of self protection.

'There came a sharp crack like a distant rifle shot. Then silence. I looked at the Video screen, my heart pounding with hope. The planet had entirely disappeared! Ahead was another world. As the distance closed it repeated the behaviour of my previous encounter, shedding great lobes of itself which followed in the planet's wake. Then came the same brilliant blue until finally, at the instant before impact, it vanished with a small detonation.

'I had no explanation and, in confusion, turned to the rear scanners. The awe-inspiring magnitude of the scene almost stopped my heart; the Submersible had a thousand starts in tow!

'Like a procession of gigantic ball bearings drawn after a magnet, they followed in my path. Some spinning and rolling directly behind, others drawn from a million miles away. Every few moments an incandescent light would erupt from the throng; doubtless caused by planets colliding or crashing into a sun.

'My feelings could not accept what the mind knew to be true: that it was my entry to this Universe that was the cause—I had become the Apocalyptic Beast of Destruction!

'My guilt has been compounded with the knowledge that I am responsible for the deaths of millions upon millions of people. There is no doubt that this place is peopled—I saw a thousand spaceships fleeing hopelessly before me. None could escape the immense gravitational pull of the Submersible. Who knows how many more must die before I—The Monster of Destruction—leave this Universe. I have heard that God can forgive any sin. May I be forgiven now and forever because my dead hand will continue to destroy for an eternity.

'As my last few hours of oxygen and, with it my own life, come to an end, I wish to set down my opinion. Maybe one day Science will prove me right.

'I am convinced that the gas laser ray has uniformly compressed every particle of the Submersible and myself. We have been miniaturized but have lost none of our original weight. Indeed by firing the Submersible's jets I caused a gigantic increase in weight because I am travelling close to the speed of light. It seems that Einstein was right! Earth time is stretched—The experiment which to you takes only a fraction of a second will last countless millions of years in this Universe.

'And now I come to the most amazing part of all—I am convinced that this Solar System is contained within an atom. An atom which is perhaps part of some speck of dust in the workshop!

'It is possible that every atom in this Sub-Atomic world contains yet more Universes? Where can it end?

'Death will be a blessed release from my torment of guilt but before then I must pose a question for the arrogant mind of Mankind to ponder—a question which shall shake Man's assurance to its roots for the very reason that this question is unanswerable! WHERE IN ALL OF GOD'S CREATION DOES YOUR WORLD LIE? WHAT SPECK OF DUST CONTAINS YOUR UNIVERSE?'

L IFEBOAT

Cyril Jolly

The first of a series of spectacular sea rescues which made the name of Coxswain Henry Blogg famous throughout the world was the service he and his Cromer lifeboat crew gave to the Swedish ship *Fernebo*. The winter of 1917 is well remembered, for it was one of the worst in the records. Tuesday, 9 January, the day on which the *Fernebo* struck, was the worst of that terrible winter. A fierce gale, blowing at 50 miles an hour from the northeast, was pushing the waters of the North Sea onto the North Norfolk coast, making a perilous lee shore for shipping. It was just such conditions as these that had earned this part of the coast the nickname 'Devil's Throat', and had for centuries littered its shores with the bones of many ships.

Blinding squalls of hail and sleet had added further horrors to the fury of the wind and the sea. Throughout the previous night the gale had torn limbs from trees and slates from roofs, and the hail had rattled like small shot on window-panes, as though challenging the inmates to leave their homes, while the dawn brought no relief.

Suddenly, above the noise of the storm, came the ominous burst of the rocket signal. No one was surprised, for this was 'lifeboat weather', and during the night both coastguard and Henry Blogg had been watching a small steamer, the Greek ship *Pyrin*, trying to ride out the gale in the roadstead off Cromer. Since daylight the coxswain had been to the top of the cliff two or three times, fearing, with good cause, that before long the ship would be in grave difficulty. Just after 11 a.m. the wind-buffeted watchers saw her run up the signal, 'Am drifting. Require assistance.'

As the townsfolk heard the rockets they shuddered at the thought of the crew of their lifeboat, the *Louisa Heartwell*, going out in such appalling conditions. A man did not have to be faint-hearted to flinch at those waves, which followed one another in fury to crash against the groynes with a violence that flung the tons of water skyward, only to fall back and add further to the confusion.

Before the sound of the second signal had died away some of the lifeboat-men were dashing towards the boathouse on the east gangway. They had to be off the mark as quickly as firemen, for a lost minute could mean a lost life. Some already wore their sea-boots; those who did not left it to their relatives to grab them up and bring them to the boathouse.

Before Henry Blogg reached the gangway he knew what a grim struggle lay ahead, for the tide was almost out, and there were more than a hundred yards of difficult beach between his lifeboat and the water, where a fierce fight in a boiling surf was inevitable.

The ship in trouble was just two miles off Cromer. Not far, perhaps, on a summer day, but in the teeth of that gale, pitting oars against such seas, two miles was a very long way.

The boat-house was a tangle of men and equipment as the crew struggled into lifebelts and oilskins. Outside, forty willing launchers, including many soldiers billeted in the town, had arrived and were running out the ropes with which they would drag the boat across the sands. Others were taking up positions against the shafts at the rear of the carriage, to push the heavy craft into the sea.

The thirty-eight-foot-long *Louisa Heartwell* was of the Liverpool type. She was as big a boat as could be got onto a carriage, but she was needed to work under sail to Haisborough Sands—twelve miles out. The lighter Norfolk-and-Suffolk type of boat, ideal where there was a rapidly shelving beach which enabled the boat to go straight into deep water, was no good at Cromer, where the violence of the surf on the flat beach made a light boat too dangerous to launch. The extra effort needed to get the big, heavier boat launched can easily be imagined. The *Louisa Heartwell* was, however, a fine boat, and had done yeoman service at this danger point to navigators. This was to be her great day—a day which would always couple her name with the *Fernebo* in what Commander Basil Hall, RNLI Inspector, called 'one of the most gallant rescues in the annals of the Lifeboat Service'.

Big as she looked in her house, the *Louisa Heartwell* seemed a puny thing against the breakers that were thundering on the shore. Her clinker-built hull looked wonderfully stout, yet those seas could crush her like an eggshell if they caught her unprepared. But she was game for the service—game as her crew and her launchers.

Led by the head launcher, Tom ('Bussey') Allen, the strong, eager men pushed and pulled at shafts and ropes and heaved at the wheel-spokes as the boat was set in motion. Shouting, laughing, and swearing, Tom encouraged them as, helped by her own weight, the boat ran down the slope and onto the sands, where the launchers hauled and heaved like madmen in their effort to keep up her momentum.

There was not one launcher too many, for the wind checked

the heavy boat, and the wide iron wheel-plates of the laden carriage sank into the wet sand, demanding every ounce of strength the men could exert. It was a gruelling test, as there was a low bank of sand to be crossed, and it looked as formidable as a range of hills. It was the first obstacle the sea had provided against the rescue of the men on board the *Pyrin*. Heaving and pushing with all their might, these stout-hearted launchers got the boat to the surf, and the leading man on each rope was into the water, first to his knees and then to his waist. But before she could be got afloat a great wave caught and pushed her back, flinging the men on the ropes.

As the launchers again went deep into the water, with the salt spray half blinding them, they were pushed back once more and knocked sideways. They rallied and struggled on. Then, when the boat was at last deep enough to pull the launching-ropes and shoot her into the water, and the crew were ready with oars poised, a huge wave flung her back again, scattering the launchers. Only by clinging to the ropes did many save themselves from drowning. Three times this happened, but suddenly the coxswain saw a chance, and, taking their cue from him with skill gained by many a battle with the sea, the launchers snatched it, and the *Louisa Heartwell* was afloat. The time was then about 11.40 a.m.

The second phase of the struggle was left to the crew of seventeen. Pulling with all their might, two men to each oar, they gained yard by yard, but could not prevent the wind and current from dragging them sideways towards a new danger.

Henry Blogg exhorted and instructed his crew, trying with every trick of seamanship he knew to counter that crabwise drift. But to the onlookers it seemed certain that the boat, so courageously launched, was doomed to be smashed against her own pier.

In groups on the cliffs, the promenade, and the beach hundreds of shivering, rain-soaked men and women breathlessly watched the struggle. Then, when it looked as though only a miracle could save her, the *Louisa Heartwell* cleared the pier by a few yards. One could almost feel the release of tension as the townsfolk saw that another danger had been averted.

A smother of hail and spray hid the lifeboat for minutes on end, and when the watchers, protecting their strained eyes with cupped hands, again saw the *Louisa Heartwell* she had hoisted a sail and was beating up towards the *Pyrin*.

The crew were barely conscious of the stinging hail, for the icy spray whipped up by the gale was flung continuously over the open boat. They pulled and pushed the heavy oars, jarred by each blow of the sea and thrown about by the steep pitching of their boat. At one moment they were climbing a great wall of water at an angle that threatened to shoot every man backward into the sea; the next, the boat had tipped into the trough of the seas, almost standing on her bows.

Progress was slow, but at 2 p.m., after three hours of back- and spirit-breaking effort, they had reached the *Pyrin*. The fine effort had its reward, for sixteen men were taken into the *Louisa Heartwell*, and the stricken ship was left for the sea to toss contemptuously on the beach the next day.

The journey back to Cromer was much less strenuous, for with the roaring gale behind them they had to have the drogue out to steady them. Half an hour later they had landed the *Pyrin*'s crew.

The relief of the rescued at getting ashore was almost equalled by the relief the rescuers felt to be safely back after that gruelling contest. With their oilskins flapping in the gale, they clasped the hands of their friends as they ran into the surf to help in the landing. Then they made their way through the excited crowd to the boat-house, to shed their wet clothes, while Tom Allen, soaked to the neck, was organizing the launchers to get the boat on skeats and then onto its carriage.

The crew were in an exhausted state, for the average age exceeded fifty, and some of the members were nearly seventy years of age. Two and a half years of war had drawn away the younger men to the Navy and merchant fleet, leaving only the older men to man the boat.

But it had been a good day's work, and now it was over they could relax and enjoy cups of steaming cocoa.

Their relief was short-lived, however, for hardly had they got into their dry clothes ready for the return home when a message came that the storm had put another ship in jeopardy. The Swedish ship *Fernebo* was in great difficulty three to four miles out.

The immediate reaction was that the Cromer crew could not aid her. They were too exhausted, and some other lifeboat must go. Then came the news that the only other boats within reach could not be launched owing to the appalling conditions. Every effort had been made, but all attempts had been unavailing. That meant that if help was to reach the *Fernebo* it must come from Cromer, or the crew would perish.

When he received the message Henry Blogg looked at his crew, and knew that he must put it to them. In a few blunt sentences he told them how things stood. He was ready to go, he said, and he believed his crew would want to go with him. The exhausted men saw the need, and, tired as they were, battered as some of them had been, they were prepared to face that howling gale again. Even as they nodded or growled their readiness they knew that conditions were even worse than in the morning, for the tide was higher. But, having already achieved the seemingly impossible that day under Blogg, there was fire in their hearts. They would follow if Henry Blogg would lead.

They struggled back into their wet oilskins and cork lifebelts, tied their cold sou'westers under their chins, and started the grim battle all over again.

The spirit of Cromer's lifeboat-men is shown in a dozen magnificent rescues while Henry Blogg was coxwain, but at no time did a crew show a finer spirit of sacrifice and duty than when those exhausted, ageing men faced that wild sea for the second time in a few hours.

On board the *Fernebo* two of the crew were attending to their thirty-two-year-old chief engineer, Johan Anderson, of Gothenburg, who had been injured when the steamer first got into difficulties. They brought him up from the engine-room to his cabin, and were attending to his wounds when a heavy explosion threw them across the cabin. As, bruised and shocked, they scrambled up on deck to see what had happened there was a terrifying sound of rending iron and wood as the ship broke her back. The injured man was never seen alive again.

Entirely out of control and at the mercy of the storm, the Swedish ship had struck a mine. The explosion amidships split the ship in halves, and as the onlookers watched they saw the two halves drift apart in a swirl of smoke and steam. Big seas tossed and hit them, but they neither listed nor sank, for the *Fernebo* was stacked with timber, which kept them buoyant.

Again there was no lack of launchers, for news that another vessel was in distress had spread through the town, and the shore and cliffs were soon lined with crowds of excited people, ready to face hail and wind to see what they sensed would be a magnificent struggle. Warm homes and shelter from that Arctic wind were forgotten as they stood, soaked and shivering, looking down on Henry Blogg and his crew as they grappled with one of the worst seas they had ever known off Cromer. Even to this day old and middle-aged men proudly claim, 'I was there. I saw the *Fernebo*.'

As expected, the launching was worse than before, and every effort seemed to be useless. The seas were so mountainous that even when the lifeboat was afloat the tired crew, with three fresh members, could not get her clear of the breakers. She was driven relentlessly back onto the shore, and wave following wave overpowered the oarsmen. One rearing sea caught the heavy boat as if she were a toy and hurled her right onto the beach. The sea had won the first round, and the bruised crew sprawled half collapsed over their oars as the breakers continued their relentless pounding of the foreshore.

The men were helped by willing hands to the boathouse, while the *Louisa Heartwell* was dragged up the beach. The sense of defeat weighed upon them all, but they had done as much as human beings could do: the wild North Sea had proved too much for their strength.

While the coxswain and crew were making their second launching six men of the crippled *Fernebo* decided to risk getting ashore in a small boat. Their plight was desperate, for they did not realize the turbulence created by the huge waves which crashed unceasingly upon the beach. They could see that the *Louisa Hartwell* was fighting a losing battle, and decided that their only hope of survival was to take the desperate chance of reaching safety in their own small boat.

With bated breath the crowd watched the little craft leave the wreck and begin to move towards them. Such a suicidal attempt seemed sheer madness, but that tiny boat kept afloat as she crept slowly shoreward, aided by the force of water and the following wind. It was incredible! A miracle was happening before their eyes, for the boat had nearly reached the beach and had only a hundred, eighty, fifty yards to go to safety. Then, like a piece of driftwood, she was picked up and capsized, and the six men were thrown into the seething water.

A cry of horror went up from the onlookers, but in an instant a dozen watchers on the water's edge, opposite the spot where the boat had overturned, linked hands and went into the surf. The leader, Private Stewart Holmes, was soon up to his waist, his armpits, his neck, and was grabbing a struggling seaman. Another chain of men had formed to complete the rescue, and between them they got the half-drowned man ashore. Even as they were doing this Holmes had reached and was pulling another man towards shallow water. A third, a fourth, a fifth, and the last man was saved. Above the noise of the storm there arose cheer after cheer, for this was really something to shout about. A grim tragedy had been averted by the initiative and courage of ordinary folk who had acted without thought of their own safety. It was not known until later that the last seaman to be rescued had nearly drowned Private Holmes by his struggling, and the soldier had to be hurried to hospital.

But the drama had not ended.

Through the spindrift and gloom of that wild day the rolling shapes of the two portions of the *Fernebo* could be seen as the storm drove them closer and closer to the shore. Then, about 5 p.m., they grounded, with the grinding roar of iron on stones. The afterpart struck the shore near the groyne, which runs four hundred feet into the sea below the 'Doctor's Steps'. The fore-half was some hundred and fifty yards away against the next breakwater, opposite Cromer lighthouse. Fortunately the remaining crew were all on the afterpart of the ship.

The Cromer Rocket Life-saving Company set up their line-throwing gun opposite the wreck, but although this was only a short way out, the wind was too strong and the lines were blown wide or short of the objective.

The Sheringham Company also arrived and tried their skill, but with no better result.

By 9 p.m. the two companies had to admit defeat. Twelve rockets had been fired, and not one had been near enough to be secured.

Two very powerful Army searchlights had been brought up from a near-by AA unit and positioned on the cliffs, and their beams directed downward clearly showed the plight of the remaining members of the *Fernebo*'s crew.

Here was drama indeed. The brilliant beams cut through the dark night and, illuminating the scene of the struggle, showed how near that broken hulk was to the shore, and yet how far. The turbulent sea filled that narrow gulf, making it almost impassable for men and boats.

The rockets having failed, the only hope of rescue now lay with Henry Blogg and his men. He had seen his exhausted crew rested a little from their six-hour battering, and he realized that the sailors on the wreck would lose their lives unless he could do something quickly. He hurried to Commander Hall, who was in charge of operations.

The Commander was at first opposed to exposing the lifeboat and her crew to a further attempt under the prevailing conditions.

'It's impossible,' he said.

'No, it isn't sir,' Blogg replied.

'But you won't get anybody to go out with you in this weather.'

'Oh, yes, I shall, sir.'

'Your men are worn out, Blogg.'

'It's not a question of my men, sir: it's the others—those who are in danger out there.'

'All right, Blogg,' the Commander assented, 'if you think so. And may God be with you.'

Blogg put it to his crew, and although every man was feeling the strain, not one hung back or made excuses. Bruised and battered as they were by their previous attempt, they would try again to get those despairing figures off the wreck in the face of one of the fiercest gales Cromer had ever known. Compassion is a great driving force, but here it was being helped by confidence in a great and fearless leader. Wherever Henry Blogg led they would follow —even into the 'Devil's Throat'.

On board the afterpart of the *Fernebo* Captain Evald Palmgren and the men with him could not see much of Cromer's lights, for the fear of Zeppelins had enforced a blackout, but they could see the dancing lights of many lanterns winking through the rain-swept darkness. Hope was almost dead, for again and again they had seen the flash of the rocket-gun, and knew the wind was too strong for the projectile. The sea was now in its worst mood, and showed no sign of abating. Everything seemed against them.

On shore, the news had gone round among the chilled watchers that their boat was going to try again, and cheer after cheer of encouragement rang out across the water, bringing new hope to the wrecked men and voicing the challenge of the *Louisa Heartwell's* crew flung in the teeth of that north-easter. The cheering could mean only one thing to the *Fernebo*'s men: a new attempt was to be made to save them.

Hope broke through the hardening crust of despair, and they strengthened their grip on ropes and rails as the seas tried harder than ever to dislodge them.

So for the third time that day the boat was dragged on its carriage into the sea, this time in darkness, with the help only of swinging lamps, the light of which made the wet oilskins glisten and reflected

Willing hands helped the men ashore.

back from the slanting, stinging sleet. For half an hour they struggled to get clear of the surf. Each time they tried they were swept
back into the shallows, but each time they managed to keep the
boat's head to the seas and start pulling again to get into deeper
water. When half-way between shore and wreck the searchlights
held the *Louisa Heartwell* as, for a moment, she rode the crest of a
huge wave and, the next, was completely lost to view in the trough
of the waves.

Some witnesses say five thousand people were gathered on the
shore to watch that fight. Not one who saw it will ever forget it, and
many a man not used to praying did so now for that little boat
fighting those mountainous seas. Wet through and shivering, they
watched spellbound. Had that crew of twenty men all been in their
thirties and fresh to the task they could not have pulled harder. It
was magnificent. Henry Blogg was getting more out of them than
they knew they had in them.

Suddenly a tremendous sea hit the *Louisa Heartwell*, smashing
five oars and washing three more overboard, and the boat began
drifting almost helpless towards a groyne. Then, and only then,
did they have to give up and Henry Blogg let the boat come ashore.
Another round had been won by the sea!

A period of comparative inaction followed, during which the
spectators stamped their feet and beat their arms to restore
circulation. Some dashed indoors for a quick cup of tea or to snatch
some food, but they were soon back on the shore, for what was
happening in Cromer that night was something they might never
see again, something they would have to talk about when stories of
sea rescue were being told in the years to come. A county that
boasted the greatness of its seamen was watching a trial of strength
between some of its ablest lifeboat-men and the North Sea in a
roaring fury. Neither the slashing hail nor the onshore gale that
tried to push people from their vantage-points above this arena
could make them leave. They must see this thing through.

Rockets were still being fired, as though in a forlorn hope of
reaching the wreck, and it was planned to wait until the tide ran

out a little, then move the apparatus farther down the beach towards the ship. But Henry Blogg had seen a chance. The tide had reached a point where an 'outset', or seaward flow from a breakwater, was sweeping almost out to the wreck. If he could get the lifeboat in that it would help them to reach the ship.

'Tom Bussey,' said the coxswain to his head launcher, who had been wet through since morning, 'go and get them spare oars. We're going to have another go.'

That was the Blogg spirit—an invincible determination that would not let him see that he was beaten. For sheer courage Henry Blogg had no peer.

The men had had a breather. The new oars were shipped, and scores of launchers ran the boat into the water for the fourth launch that day. Then, with searchlights focused on their target, they pulled with all their skill and strength.

Watched with agonized anxiety from wreck and shore, the lifeboat slowly approached the wreck, and time and again it looked as though the stout boat must be flung against the barnacled sides of the broken *Fernebo*. One moment the *Louisa Heartwell* could be seen, vividly clear against the ship, and the next she had slid into the trough of the waves and disappeared from view. No one could remember how long it took to get the exhausted survivors into the boat, but it seemed an age, fraught with anxious suspense, before the lifeboat began to draw away from the wreck.

Then, to the spectators' unspeakable relief, the victory rocket 'Green burns white' went up from the lifeboat, and the searchlights followed her as she came quickly to the shore, where willing hands helped the eleven rescued men and the rescuers to safety.

It was nearly 1 a.m., and Henry Blogg and his crew had battled on and off for fourteen hours, risking their lives to save total strangers—Greeks and Swedes—from the fury of the sea.

It was over! Blogg had won the last round and beaten the North Sea in its worst mood. Overcome with joy after long hours of suspense and anxiety, the crowd shouted and cheered in wild excitement.

371

One Cromer man, looking back over nearly forty years to that scene, recalled how he had stood as a lad of nine watching the drama, and although soaked to the skin had stayed far into the night to see the excited crowd drag the lifeboat ashore with her rescued men, her crew, and her wonderful coxswain. He too had yelled himself hoarse acclaiming the lifeboat-men, and there and then had placed Henry Blogg alongside Horatio Nelson and Robert Falcon Scott as his boyhood heroes.

WING AND A PRAYER

Neil Williams

For the first time since the inception of the World Aerobatic Championships ten years before, it was decided to hold this event in the United Kingdom in 1970. The British Team from quite modest beginnings, had grown over this period to a point where we stood a good chance of being highly placed, equipped as we were with two modern aircraft, a two seater Zlin Trener, and a 160 hp single seater Zlin 526 Akrobat. This latter machine was owned by a group of dedicated aerobatic pilots, and we had set ourselves a difficult target in forming the spearhead of the team which was to represent the UK. The airfield chosen for the 6th World Aerobatic Championships was RAF Hullavington, in Wiltshire, and at last we had one of the advantages of the home team, namely the ability to fly over the contest airfield for several months, so as to familiarize ourselves with the local topography. Because Hullavington is in the Lyneham Zone, we had to maintain telephone communication with Lyneham at all times, and this meant that some of the aerobatic team had to man the otherwise disused control tower when flying was taking place. This suited us very well, because of the need to have somebody on the ground to criticize our performances, since errors of as little as two degrees in pitch or roll could lose valuable marks in the contest.

So it was, that on a fine June morning, I took off in the Zlin Akrobat to practise my freestyle sequence. The wind was very light and so did not pose any problem, but I was not quite satisfied with my first two rehearsals. I decided to try once again. This time things were progressing a little better, and I settled down to fly steadily. The aircraft was going beautifully, and I determined to finish the sequence and then land, but as I pulled out of my fifth manoeuvre I ran into trouble. As the aircraft levelled out of the dive there was a loud bang and a severe jolt shook the machine: I was thrown sideways in the cockpit, and at the same instant there was a very loud and peculiar change in the slipstream noise. The problem seemed to be on the left of the aircraft, but when I looked left, everything seemed normal, except that I was being forced against the left side of the cockpit.

I throttled back instinctively and looked around, to find that although the left wing was flying straight and level, the rest of the aeroplane was rolling to the left, around the failure point in the left wing root. By this stage the aircraft was beginning to lose height, although I still had some degree of control remaining. I throttled back to reduce air loads but this caused the nose to drop further, and *dihedral*[1] was by now noticeably increasing, and the roll and yaw to the left were becoming steadily more determined. I then tried full power in an attempt to get the nose up, but to no avail. By now I was outside the airfield and losing height fast. It was my intention to try and keep the wings as level as possible and to try

[1] Angle of tilt of aircraft's wings.

and hit the ground at as shallow an angle as possible, hopefully in an open space. It was soon apparent, however, that due to rapid loss of control which I was experiencing, I was not going to make it, and for the first time, the certainty that I was about to be killed came home to me. Control was finally lost at about 300 feet, when the aircraft had turned left through 90° from the original heading, and was banked about 90° to the left (at least the fuselage was). The left wing by now had folded to about 45° and I was treated to the interesting spectacle of the rivets along the top of the main spar opening up like a zip fastener as dihedral increased. When the nose finally dropped I was holding full right aileron, full right rudder, and full power, with a large amount of sideslip. The natural tendency to pull back on the stick only made the situation worse.

In spite of being badly frightened I was still able to think clearly at this stage and I remembered a report I had heard many years ago about a Bulgarian pilot who had had a top wing bolt fail on an early mark of Zlin whilst under negative 'g' and that the aircraft had involuntarily flickrolled the right way up, whereupon the wing came back into position, and the aircraft was landed by a very frightened, but alive, pilot. I had guessed by this time that a lower wing bolt had failed and that I was faced with a similar situation, albeit inverted.

It seemed that if positive 'g' had saved the Bulgarian, negative 'g' might work for me, though at this stage I was so low that I did not have much hope of success. Two things helped me: taking some positive action, no matter how hopeless, was preventing panic, and if it went wrong, at least it would be quick. Anyway there was no time left, and I couldn't think of anything else to try. I centralized the rudder, rolled left and pushed, still with full throttle. The wing snapped back into position instantly, with a loud bang which made me even more concerned for the structure. Immediately the negative 'g' started to rise and the nose started coming up, but I was too low: the trees ahead filled the windscreen, the throttle was wide open and I pushed the stick as far forward as I dared. For a split second the leaves and branches seemed to reach out at me, then they were gone and I was clear, climbing fast, inverted. Almost before I could appreciate my escape, the engine spluttered and died. Instinctively I eased back on the stick to glide inverted, while I searched frantically for the cause: then I found it—fuel pressure zero. I checked the fuel cock and found it in the 'off' position. I had been thrown around in the cockpit at the moment the wing failed, and had probably knocked the cock off then. I selected the reserve fuel and immediately realized that this position would take fuel from the bottom of the gravity tank, which was of course now upside down. I quickly reselected main tank, and after a few coughs the engine picked up and ran at full power again.

By now I was quite low and was initially satisfied to climb straight ahead to 1,000 feet and to return to the airfield. The remainder of the team had been very quick off the mark and had alerted the crash vehicles as soon as they saw the wing starting to move. Meanwhile I throttled back to conserve fuel as the Zlin has a maximum endurance of eight minutes in inverted flight. I retrimmed for inverted flight, and steadied the stick between my knees while I used both hands to tighten my shoulder straps. There was no question of baling out—I had no parachute. It was now that I had to fight against giving way to panic. I could not expect to survive this incident, indeed, at any time I expected the left wing to come off completely. There was an overwhelming temptation to stay airborne for the full eight minutes, rather than attempt a landing earlier, thereby cutting my expected life span in half. At a time like this it is surprising how important an extra few minutes can be. I had to force myself to make the decision to try a landing: the question was, how? I considered using undercarriage or flaps, but rejected both. Flaps were no use to me whilst inverted, and I could not fly right way up anyway. Also if only one flap extended it would cause an immediate loss of control. The undercarriage required more thought. If I could make an inverted approach with a last minute rollout, I might be able to put the aircraft down on its wheels. However if the gear fully or partially collapsed the aircraft

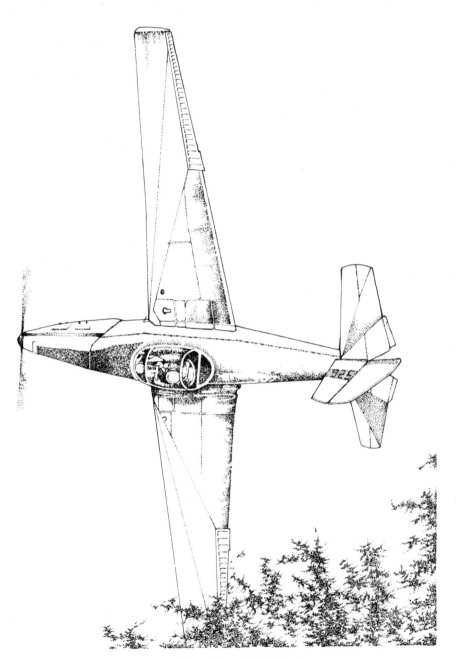

The axis of the roll was the left wing tip.

might turn over. Perhaps the biggest argument against this was that the Zlin undercarriage usually locks down with a solid thump. I did not know exactly what damage had occurred and I was concerned in case the strain of lowering the wheels might remove the wing altogether. It was just as well that I left the wheels up, because the failure was not the wing bolt after all, but a fatigue failure in the centre section lower spar boom, inboard of the undercarriage leg attachment.

I also considered four possibilities for landing, namely inverted ditching, deliberately crashing inverted into trees to take the impact, inverted crash-landing on the airfield or an inverted approach with a last minute rollout for a belly landing.

The last seemed to hold the best chances for survival, but I then decided to experiment to see which way was the best to rollout: if the rate of fold of the wing was sufficiently slow it might have been possible to exercise some control over the proposed landing. A rollout to the left was attempted, whereupon the wing immediately folded again. As gently as possible I eased negative 'g' on again, but the wing still came back into position with a solid bang, and as the speed rose in the ensuing dive I could see the whole wing moving slightly. The wing attachments seemed to be getting weaker, so I decided against further experiments: the next attempt would be the real thing at low altitude. Common sense told me that the whole thing was impossible, but I had to try. At least as long as I kept thinking I was able to control panic. Indeed as one close shave followed another there was less of a tendency to panic: it seemed that the mind could only accept so much in the way of fright, and by the time I had flown a wide inverted circuit and positioned the aircraft on finals, I was concentrating so hard that there was no room for fear. I was aiming for the grass, parallel to the main runway: there was no wind to speak of. The temptation to stay in the air until the fuel was exhausted was still strong, but I determined to stick to my decision. If I got it wrong, I would need that fuel to overshoot and try again. I left the canopy on: I didn't know if the handling would be much affected if I jettisoned it, and also I didn't want my height judgement affected by slipstream: this approach had to be exactly right. I crossed the boundary of the aerodrome slightly high, at 200 feet, at 180 km/hr with the throttle closed. I slowly levelled the aeroplane as low as I dared, at 140 km/hr I rolled hard to the right, opening up to full power at the same time, and holding just enough negative 'g' in a slight outside barrel roll to keep the wing in place. The axis of the roll was the left wing tip, which left a furrow through the grass for 36 feet, without breaking the plastic cover on the navigation light. By a combination of good judgement, and incredible luck, I had got it right!

As the wings started to level, the nose was down due to the barrel roll, and to ease the impact I pulled back hard on the stick and cut the throttle. The good wing eased the fall, against hard aileron, but the left wing folded straight up, though not before the rate of descent had been slightly reduced. With a bang like the end of the world she hit the ground hard. As the controls went slack I released them and tried to curl up into a ball, knees and feet pulled up and in, and head down protected by arms. The aircraft careered across the grass, the left wing bouncing and flapping like a wounded bird, then with a final jolt, everything stopped. I couldn't believe it: I was still alive! Then another thought occurred; the petrol tanks had split! To have survived that experience only to burn spurred me into action. I struggled for long seconds to release the double safety harness only to find the canopy jammed! I gave it a resounding blow and it flew open, and as I scrambled out onto the broken wing I felt quite surprised that I was still mobile—I half expected to discover broken bones, but I was only bruised. I looked back at the Zlin, broken, never to fly again, and marvelled at my escape. I sat on the grass and realized how all my senses had been heightened by the drama of the last few minutes: the colour of the grass and sky, the smell of the earth, the song of birds: never before or since has it been so clear.

We heard from the manufacturer a couple of weeks later; they sent a telegram which summed it all up in three words—'sorry—congratulations—thanks'! They also let us use their factory demonstrator, a Zlin 526F with 180 hp, which I flew into 5th place in the World Championships. But my real victory had been weeks before, in the old 160 hp Zlin Akrobat, where the prize was—life.

BATTLE WITH A MORAY EEL

Hans Hass

Underwater diving expert Hans Hass recalls an adventure which happened off the Dutch Island of Bonaire in the West Indies . . .

After prolonged and unsuccessful filming attempts and a considerably delayed lunch, I felt like going hunting at nightfall. I set out, and in addition to my nose-clip, fins and harpoon I also took the camera. I made for a spot on the north coast of the little island.

I got there after half an hour and found that getting into the water would be exceedingly difficult. There was a large coral reef about twenty or thirty yards offshore, and between it and the shore where I was standing the water was only a little over a foot deep and the bottom covered with countless sea urchins. Only after a long search did I find a spot where a narrow twisting strip of sand ran between these colonies of sea urchins out to the reef.

I carried the camera in one hand and the harpoon in the other, and I had on my fins. Admittedly they were an obstacle to walking in the shallow water, but it was better than having to tiptoe barefoot among the sea urchins. Having reached the reef I had to clamber over a few rounded clumps of coral, covered with slippery coral animals. But at last deeper water lay ahead.

The sea bottom dropped gradually until about seventy-five yards from the shore I came to the steep slope where I wanted to spear some perch. The underwater landscape was by now familiar to me—tall coral mountains, deep gorges and luxuriant 'vegetation'. The first fish I spotted was a small grouper of about four pounds.

I dived, but the camera hanging round my neck and dangling before my nose was a great hindrance. To dive properly with a long harpoon one needs one free arm—so I had no choice but to carry harpoon and camera in the same hand while descending.

The grouper belonged to the species which changes its colour quite strikingly. Sometimes these creatures were such a light grey that from above they looked almost brilliant white, then again they could turn almost black; their normal colouring was brownish with white spots and a narrow dark stripe. My grouper changed colour as soon as it observed me, but the place it had found for itself seemed so attractive to it that it was reluctant to leave it. That was to prove its doom.

A sharp thrust and a moment later I was pulling the wriggling fish to the surface. There I killed it, detached it from the harpoon head and placed it in the net which I carried on my belt.

Shortly afterwards I had killed a second grouper of the same size and was just wondering whether these two fish would be enough for supper when I caught sight of a quite enormous snapper below me. It came swimming up among the coral, its eyes rigid, and although I was not quite sure whether to tackle this powerful creature I dived towards it. I was on my own, there was no one to help me, and underwater the fish was undoubtedly stronger than me. Besides, the camera round my neck and the two fish in the net round my waist made swimming difficult. Undecided, I was approaching the reef from seaward when suddenly the large snapper chased off in a fright and I found myself facing the head of a hideous eery creature.

Without much reflection I arched my body and thrust the harpoon straight through the thick neck of the snake-like moster.

At the same moment the harpoon shaft was snatched from my hand and I could see it bouncing away and disappearing among the coral.

Back on the surface I realized the kind of opponent I had got involved with. Judging by the thickness of its body the moray eel must have been at least as long as myself. Besides, the creature's bite was said to be poisonous. But what I had started I wanted to finish. I peered down to spot my harpoon. It was wedged between clumps of coral at a depth of over thirty feet and the line disappeared in a dark hole.

I dived down, gripped the shaft and tugged as hard as I could. But the moray eel stuck to its hole. I sped to the surface again to fill my lungs with air, hurried down again and tried once more. I dived three, four, eight, twelve, perhaps twenty times, tugging the rope in all directions, wedging myself against the coral, thrusting with the harpoon into the dark where the beast was hiding—I tried everything that was humanly possible but I did not succeed in budging the moray eel by as much as an inch.

I was exhausted and needed a short rest. The sun meanwhile had sunk lower and the blue of the sea seemed darker than before. While I was resting and reflecting I noticed that a small crowd had collected below me—no fewer than five large and seventeen lesser groupers. They had been lured from their holes by the commotion and they had collected to witness our battle. There were also some grey snappers and small barracudas. If my harpoon had not been lodged in the moray eel I could have speared as many fish as I liked.

I was diving again, determined to force a decision. I wedged both my feet against a clump of coral and gave a mighty tug. I reeled back, losing my balance for a moment—the line had broken.

But I was not giving up—I had to kill the monster no matter how long it took. Fortunately I had a spare harpoon head with me; I fastened it to a double length of harpoon cord, to prevent it breaking too easily. I descended once more, swam around the coral and peered into its many caves. In one of them I believed I could see the greenish body of the moray eel. I thrust at once. A sharp jerk proved my suspicion to be correct. But everything else was just as before. My harpoon was once more lying by the clump of coral and the line once more disappeared into a hole, though a different one this time.

To make matters worse, I had run into new trouble. While ascending I had brushed off my nose-clip by a clumsy movement. It had dropped down and was now lying on a round coral, at least thirty-five feet down. Without stopping to think I dived down to get it back, but instantly felt a pain in my sinus which at a depth of about fifteen feet got so bad that I could hardly bear it. I gritted my teeth and forced myself to continue. It simply had to be done.

The pain unfortunately made my eyes water, and when I reached the bottom the nose-clip had become very blurred. Dazed, I clumsily groped for it, trying to pick it up—and pushed it off the coral. It dropped another three feet into a narrow crack. By then I had ceased to care. Although I felt that something was going to give way in my head at any moment I descended the additional three feet and, forcing myself to move with patience, tried to extricate the nose-clip from the crevice. But time and again it slipped back. Then my air gave out and I had to surface.

I was exhausted and had to float on my back, resting. Should I not give up this unequal struggle with a moray eel and my bad luck? But something in me rebelled. It was possibly just pigheaded-ness—but I refused to admit defeat.

I swam into shallower water and removed the camera and the two fish which had been greatly in my way during diving. I realized with some annoyance that in my excitement I had not taken a single photograph and had merely carried the camera with me as needless ballast.

I filled my lungs with an extra large amount of air and dived back

I held the shaft at the eel's head so it could not reach me.

to my nose-clip. This time I was pinching my nose with my left hand and therefore felt no pain. But at the bottom I just could not manage to pull the little thing out of the damned crack. It was so narrow that I could hardly get my fingers in. As the seconds sped away—seeming like eternity—I tried and tried again until, at long last, I had it out far enough for me to reach it with my other hand. But that other hand was pinching my nose and I had to overcome considerable hesitation before I let go of it.

I was holding the clip now but at that instant I felt such a frightful stab of pain that I raced up to the surface like a man demented. The pressure had acted on me too abruptly. My nose was bleeding heavily and I had to wait a while before being able to fit my nose-clip.

I must have been out hunting for a good two hours. I was shivering all over with cold and the sun had sunk so low that only a little time was left to me. My hunting fever together with my stubbornness undoubtedly lent me far greater strength than I normally possessed—otherwise I could not have stood the strain.

I decided to have one last try. The eel, I reflected, would have calmed down in the meantime and it might be possible now to get it out of its hole by an unexpected jerk. I descended as calmly as possible, gripped the harpoon shaft with both my hands, levered my feet against a clump of coral and gave the cord a violent jerk.

The result was staggering. Just as if I had touched off an explosive charge the whole clump of coral, about five feet high and as much across, shattered into countless fragments. At the same moment the moray eel came shooting out of the opaque water. Only then did I realize its huge size. The ugly snake-shaped beast was racing to and fro alongside me and below me, its mouth opened menacingly, trying to reach me. Fortunately the harpoon line—as a result of my having doubled it—was now much shorter and if I held the shaft at its lower end the eel's head could not quite reach me.

With rapid fin movements I made for the surface. I was gripping the shaft with both hands in order to check the furious beast. I knew that if it managed to bite me I would hardly reach the shore alive. This was one thing the natives had told us time and again—once a moray eel had sunk its venomous teeth into something it would not let go again but would bite deeper and deeper into the flesh.

At the surface I quickly gulped for air and continued the struggle. One moment the moray eel was pulling to one side, then it would gyrate furiously, and it took an all-out effort with my finned feet to hold my own. Then again it would shoot up towards me in un-expected snake-like undulations. It would not keep still for a moment.

Only slowly did I manage to drag it towards the shore—but there I faced a new problem. My camera and the two speared fish were lying in the shallow water. How was I to pick them up? If I dived my moray eel might hide among the coral once more. While diving, therefore, I had to hold the harpoon shaft vertically upwards in one hand, so that the eel would chase about above me, and with the other quickly picked up the camera, hang it round my neck, and pick up my creel and fastened it to my belt.

Having accomplished this acrobatic feat I found myself faced with an even greater difficulty. There simply was no clear path through the countless sea urchins in the shallow water. The water, in fact, was quite black with these spiky creatures. But I had no time for reflection: the sun had nearly reached the horizon and I could not risk going ashore with the moray eel in the dark.

I tried therefore to pick my way through the expanse of sea urchins. There were occasional spots where the black creatures were lying less close, and sometimes I could push them aside a little with my fins. I was cautiously advancing while the moray eel still struggled with undiminished energy in the shallow water. Then something happened that might easily have ended tragically for me.

I stepped on a small rounded coral, slipped on the slimy surface, lost my balance and crashed down right among the sea urchins. Instinctively, to protect my face and body, and also to prevent my expensive camera from striking the ground, I put my hands in front of my chest. There was a sharp stab of pain—my hands were pricked by countless spines. But at least I had checked my fall to the extent that only my legs and my left arm touched the sea urchins. But at that moment another horrible danger stared me in the face.

As I instinctively opened my eyes in the water I saw the eel's hideous teeth-studded open mouth close to my face.

By bringing my hands to my chest while falling I had involuntarily brought the harpoon shaft closer to me and very nearly giving the enraged moray eel its chance of attacking me.

During my hunting on Curaçao I had been through a good many adventures and had often displayed a reasonable presence of mind —but I shall never forget this moment. I can still see the small vicious eyes and the greedily opened mouth hard in front of my face and I still wonder how I managed to stretch out my arm with the harpoon quickly enough for the beast to be snatched back at the last moment.

The eel, angrily gyrating, succeeded in getting a hold of the steel shaft on top of the harpoon, and so furiously dug its teeth against it that, as I discovered later, it broke every one of them on the metal.

Once ashore, I tried to kill the creature. I threw a large stone on the back of its neck and repeatedly thrust my knife through its head. Even so the green slimy body continued to lash the ground with undiminished strength for quite a while.

These fish are at least as tough as big snakes and I have repeatedly admired their physical strength. I once speared a somewhat smaller moray eel with a trident spearhead of the best American steel. The trident spun through the water, the eel tore itself free, and when I hauled in my weapon I found that the beast had bent the outer spikes almost through a right angle. It was this huge physical strength that had enabled the eel, in its rage at the sudden pain, to burst the coral clump apart.

With my large trophy on my back I staggered to our tent. I was filled with an indescribable sense of triumph and power. True, my hands and legs were stinging with the pricks of the sea urchins, my head was aching, and my nose was still bleeding—but I was happy enough to embrace the whole world. Thus, victor of a three-hour battle, I struggled across the desert island, my camera and the two groupers in my hand, the huge serpent on my back, while in front of me the sun was plunging into the sea with a glow that flooded the whole sky.

THE MISSING SAILOR

David Rees

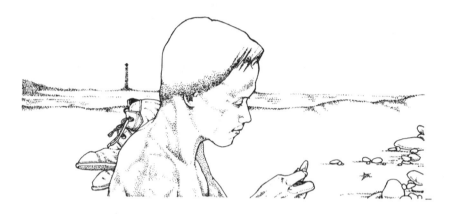

'**G**oodbye, Simon.' Tom Wray took off his glasses and put the newspaper down. 'I'm sorry I can't come to the station. I'm supposed to be fire-watching.'

Simon smiled. 'So long, Dad. Don't get killed.'

'I won't. Don't you worry.'

The underground was twenty minutes' walk away, and soon after they left the house the air-raid warning sounded.

'Hurry,' said his mother. 'We must reach the station before the planes come.'

For a while there was uneasy silence as if London had frozen and cocked its ears to listen, but the click of her heels and the circle of her torch, the only light he could see, were some reassurance.

Then came the familiar distant drone, followed by the gradual
build-up of the searchlights into a stockade, and the first anti-
aircraft guns. The vibrations grew louder and louder, and the roar
that filled the air reminded him of the distorted barrage of a radio
when a valve wears out. He was sure they would be killed. What
would it be like? The muscles in his stomach sprang tight like a
clock wound up; he would disgrace himself by screaming.

A thin high-pitched whine; the clicks stopped.

'Down! Down at once!' He lay flat on the pavement, and she fell
beside him. The explosion seemed to pick him up and shake him
violently; the air was filled with dust and grit, and he was deaf for
some moments.

'Timms Road,' said his mother, laughing. 'The only thing
there's the swimming bath.'

Whistles shrilled in the distance, and they heard the sound of
running feet. More explosions, further off. Thud, thud. Thud.

At Waterloo people on the Northern Line platforms lay sleeping,
row on row. His mother's coat was filthy. In the dawn she looked
lined and sick.

The carriage was full, mostly soldiers. Simon lifted his case onto
the luggage-rack. He had the last seat, but before the train left six
more soldiers squashed in, standing against each other.

'Goodbye, Mum,' he said, trying to lean out of the window.

'Enjoy yourself,' she replied. 'Look a bit more cheerful.'

'I'm tired.'

'You'll like the farm. Better than staying in this hell.'

'Softlygap Farm. It sounds good.'

'And we'll see you in six weeks.' The train began to move. 'Look
after yourself. Look after yourself!'

He waved till she was out of sight, then sank back into his seat.
The dawn showed the drab back-to-backs of Vauxhall and
Clapham, lines and squares of houses; but many holes gaped in the
terraces like toothless sockets. The clouds were low and ashen, and
it began to rain.

The air-raids, the nights without sleep, the strain on the nerves, these were the reasons, his parents said, for his poor work at school. A man his father worked with had sent his son down to Devon, to stay on a farm near the sea, for the whole summer; after the exam results Tom Wray decided that Simon should go too. Simon didn't know Keith Silkin or anything about him, except that they were of the same age, sixteen. He wasn't at all sure what to expect there, but he supposed it might be better than spending the holidays in London.

He slept. The train slowing down woke him; they were crawling into a damaged station, much of it rubble and twisted girders, the glass panels of the roof scattered in splinters on the platform. A church nearby was still smouldering, despite the heavy rain; only its walls and the spire were left. The station was packed with people. Some looked wild and hunted; all were desperate to crush into the train.

'Find me a seat. Please. I'll give you ten shillings.'

'No tips. I won't take tips.'

'We've got to get out. I can't stand another night like that.'

Some did succeed in cramming in, and the soldiers grumbled. The train moved on. Simon dozed, and the rest of the journey for him was a half-awake state like a dream, punctuated with unfamiliar stations, blurs of dirty green and white paint.

At last he was at Bideford. Something new about the air, the sea, he guessed, made him feel sick.

A taxi took him out to the farm. He stood in the warm kitchen, the long low room rocking gently about him as if he were still on the train. Kind faces spoke to him in strange accents. There was a smell, new-made bread perhaps, mixed with the mustiness of an old church. It was quieter than anything he had ever known.

The sun woke him early, splashing a square across the wall opposite his bed and lighting up an old-fashioned dresser on which stood a china bowl and a jug. These puzzled him, then he realized that they were for washing. There was probably no bathroom and no running water here. He looked up and saw that there were no electric light fittings. The wallpaper was patterned, and old, with lines that joined up in diamonds. On the wall to his left was a text, a framed piece of embroidery: 'The Father himself loveth you as ye have loved me,' sewn in pink and black.

He got out of bed and put his hand in the jug: ice-cold water. He could see through the window a thin triangle of the sea between two hills, the dawn sun shining on it so brilliantly he had to turn his eyes away. He was suddenly aware that he could hear the sea; then he knew he had heard it ever since he had woken up but the sound was so soft that he had not heeded it.

A lorry clattered into the yard. A man climbed down from the cab and picked up a milk-churn that had been left on a wooden platform outside the barn. He threw it onto the lorry as easily as if it had been a toy, and drove off.

Simon dressed. Outside his room the stairs led up to an attic; he could see the sloping roof. It looked worth exploring. But instead he went down, and out into the yard, realizing too late that plimsolls were not the right footwear for ground covered with dung. He pushed open the door of the cowshed and wiped his feet on the straw. It was bigger inside than he had imagined, and dark, so he could not see where the voice that shouted 'Hey!' came from.

'Don't look so lost, 'tes only a shippon,' said the voice. 'They cows won't hurt 'e.'

As his eyes grew accustomed to the gloom he could make out the dark shapes of the animals, each chained in its stall. Their mouths were all moving, which explained the strange noise like ropes rasping that he had heard when he came in. A man was milking one of the cows, his head buried against its flank; spurts of milk made a regular psst, psst, psst in the pail.

'The milk lorry be gone, and took only one churn. We haven't even done the milking.' He stood up and thwacked the cow on its side. 'This one's Myrtle. She do give more milk than all they others.'

His head moved into a shaft of light coming from a small window high in one wall. His purplish face was covered with little red veins.

'I'm Mr Cotter, and it's me you're staying with. Last night you

393

seemed to take nothing in. Was you drunk?' He laughed. 'Nay, I
know how things be. This'll be different from London. I daresay.'

The door opened, and a boy came in, eating a pear. He was tall
and thin, but brown with the summer sun.

'Keith, I told you not to eat they pears, didn't I? They be
'fected, they be, can't eat they.'

'Mine's all right.'

'Huh.' And Mr Cotter returned to his cow.

Keith leaned against the door-frame, eyeing Simon. He finished
his pear, and threw away the core.

'Breakfast's ready,' he said, going outside. Simon followed him.
Keith was looking out to sea; there was a ship close to the shore, a
big red cross clearly visible on its side. 'Hospital ship,' he observed.
'Do you swim?'

'Yes.'

'Good. We'll go to the beach after breakfast. It won't be fine
much longer.'

'Won't it?' Simon thought the weather was perfect.

'Rain by evening.' He sounded very confident.

In the kitchen there was a delicious smell of bacon. Mrs Cotter
turned from the stove as they came in. She was a stout red-faced
woman with greying hair; her hands were lined and rough from
scrubbing and cleaning.

'Morning,' she said. 'Are you better?'

'Me?' Simon asked. 'Better?'

'Aye. You was asleep on your feet last night, but it do seem a rest
have done you some good. Keith will show you around when you've
eaten. You'll be company for one another.'

'Whether we like it or not,' Keith muttered.

Mrs Cotter didn't hear this, and went on: 'Not much for two
growing lads like you round here. You'll get on well. Now tuck into
this.' And she put a plate of bacon and eggs in front of each of them.
'Aye, we needn't worry so much about rationing down here,' she
added, seeing Simon's surprise. 'Don't have to bother with that
dried egg stuff you're eating in London. Now. There's tea in the

pot, and make yourselves toast if you want it. I must go and feed they hens.'

When they were alone Simon asked, 'What did she mean there's nothing round here for us?'

Keith shrugged. 'Depends on what you want, doesn't it? It's all right when it's fine. You can swim, go fishing. Or walk on the cliffs. Do you surf?'

'No.'

'Don't you? Oh.'

'What do you do when it's wet?'

'Nothing. Talk to Mr Cotter. Read.'

'How far is it to Bideford?'

'Twenty miles. We could thumb a lift one evening and go to the pictures.'

'I'd like that.'

'Might meet some girls there. There's none here. Do you have a girl-friend?'

'No.'

Keith stood up. 'Come on. We'll wash up, then let's go out.'

'Look, you do it like this.' Keith took a stone and hit the limpet so hard that it slid off the rock as if on grease and dropped into the warm pool they were standing in. Simon picked it up and saw that it had a caricature of a face at one end. He squashed it in the middle, and the face part came out further. The two black blobs were its eyes, he supposed, and there was a pair of things like horns. He dropped it.

'Haven't you ever seen a limpet before?' Keith asked. 'Where were you born?'

Keith was going to get a punch on the nose before long, Simon thought. He seemed to take pleasure in Simon's ignorance of the farm and the sea, showing him up as a fool at every opportunity. Why, Simon couldn't fathom. Maybe it was because he was such a weedy specimen for his age; he looked pitifully emaciated in his swimming trunks, and he was obviously jealous of how well

Simon swam, and how easily he mastered the technique of the surfboard. Simon was good at games, at all physical activities.

'Come on,' said Keith. 'If you can't hurry we won't get there before the tide turns.'

They were scrambling over rocks encrusted with barnacles and vicious to the skin, into Marsland Mouth where they hoped to climb the Gull, the highest and most impressive rock in the bay. They wriggled along passages between giant boulders, and over pools that reflected light in odd dancing patterns onto over-hanging rock-faces, and where a movement in the water suggested something moving to safer depths. Eventually there was shingle above the high-tide-mark, which provided easier going, and patches of almost white sand, the remains of shells crushed to fine crumbs. The high-tide-mark itself was an irregular dark line like the graph of a patient's temperature, made up of oil and dried black seaweed, lumps of cork that smelled of Marmite, sea-plants stiffened and bleached to the colour of pale parchment. Simon was enjoying all these strange smells and sensations, the hard coarse feel of the stones underfoot; the only sea he had known before was Clacton and Margate.

'The coastguard,' said Keith. 'Mr Chart.'

'Why's he carrying a rifle?' Simon asked, immediately wishing he hadn't said anything.

'Not for shooting rabbits.'

'Sorry I spoke.'

The coastguard did not come near them. He was peering under boulders, looking for something. His face was fierce and creased like leather; he had a bristling white moustache.

Keith laughed. 'Silly officious man! Someone told him last week they'd spotted a mine over in Marsland; he's been looking for it ever since.'

'What's silly about that?'

'Just a wild rumour. It was probably a lobster-pot. A mine round this side of the country? Never.'

'It's possible.'

'You don't know what you're talking about.'

A cloud came over the sun. Simon looked up. White clouds were drifting slowly in from the south-west, woolly and vast. The weather was changing as Keith had promised.

'You want to know why he's carrying a rifle?' Keith asked. 'It's for shooting people. If anyone's on the beach after dark he's supposed to shoot them. In case it's the Germans.'

'I don't believe you.'

'You can think what you like.'

Simon ran off down the shingle and onto the sand. Keith could explore the Gull alone; he was too difficult to bother with. There was a long tongue of yellow sand between the rocks, and he raced down it, into the sea. He swam out, well out of his depth, plunging through the oncoming waves instead of riding over them, though this made his head spin. Then he trod water, and looked back at the cliffs, the jumble of rocks and boulders, relics of a huge primeval violence: he could enjoy himself here; this beach, this sea were magnificent. He wondered if his parents would send him the money to buy his own surfboard. It would be better if he could avoid Keith. He didn't mind being alone: he never relied much on other people for his pleasures. He thought of London: so many people he knew had died in the bombing; the air was almost always choked with the acid plaster smell from houses that had been blown to pieces, and every night was full of terrifying sounds: the wail of the air-raid sirens, the thumps of bombs.

He lay on his back, floating, drifting with the rise and fall, the salt water lapping into his mouth; he rolled over and over like a porpoise, then heaved himself onto a rock, scraping a knee on the barnacles. His legs dangled over idly in the water.

From the top of Highcliff he could see that the tide had turned and was beginning to push its way up the shingle. The waves shifting inwards left long trails of white over the surface like the froth that decorated the sides of a beer-glass. There was the Gull, now far below him, its summit green with weed where the sea never reached

There was no sign of Keith. Perhaps he was marooned. He felt guilty now at deserting him; perhaps he really was marooned! A finger of rock sticking upwards at the foot of the Gull pointed like a reproof.

He arrived at the farm just as it was starting to rain. The sea and the edge of one of the hills were lost in heavy cloud, and from where he stood, he could see mist beginning to drift over the distant top into the valley.

That afternoon the wind rose, and by night-fall the windows were constantly jumping against their frames. Keith spent the evening buried in a book, speaking to no-one. Mr Cotter was out at the pub. Simon listened to Mrs Cotter's talk about the problems of farming in wartime, and fiddled about with the radio. He tried several foreign stations, hoping to locate Berlin's service in English, but instead of Lord Haw-Haw he could only hear fragments of unintelligible speech. Then there was the news: gloom on all fronts, the German advance into Russia continuing at frightening speed.

He wrote a letter to his parents, then sat in front of the fire. The Cotters burned a fire in the old inglenook all the year round; a kettle simmered away on it from morning till night. Rain spat continually down the chimney, and draughts raced under all the doors, lifting the rugs and dropping them, phut, which alarmed the cat; the paraffin lamps flickered, causing ghosts of things to leap and point. The dog lay in front of the fire, opening an eye and lifting an ear at every unexplained sound, and growling at shadows.

Simon found curling up in bed that night was comfortable and secure, with the rain lashing the roof, and the gale straining every inch to batter the house, and the sea, which had increased from a distant sonorousness to a roar, sounding as if it would reach the steps of the farm itself.

He was woken up by the sound of someone hammering at the front door. He heard Mr Cotter go downstairs, then Mrs Cotter,

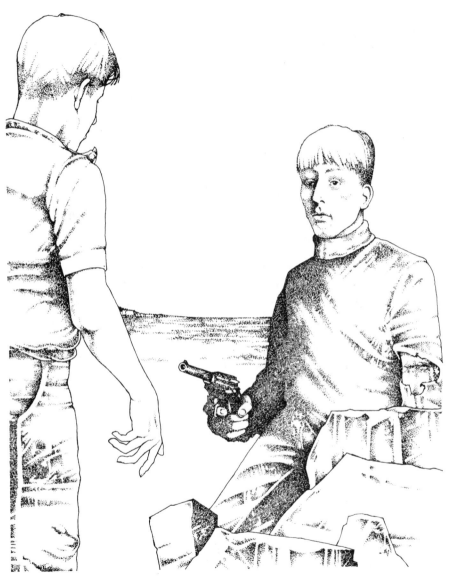

The gun was pointing at Simon.

grumbling and muttering to herself. He crept out of bed, and found Keith on the landing, listening.

'What is it?' Simon asked. Keith did not answer, but went down to the kitchen. Simon followed. Mr Chart was standing in the doorway, all glistening raincoat and sou'wester.

'There's no call for you boys to—' Mrs Cotter began.

'What's happened?' Keith asked.

'A ship in trouble off the Gull,' said the coastguard. 'Can you come, John?'

'Aye, of course. She be wrecked, then?'

'Not yet. She's trying to right herself but she's helpless in that sea; it's boiling. I think it's a submarine.'

'A submarine! What shall us bring?'

'Brandy. There's first aid at the hut.'

'Ropes?'

'She'll use the breeches buoy. Maybe we'll need a stretcher. I've had to walk; my bike's no good in this. I'll just see if Bill Sampson's awake; I couldn't get him on the phone. I've rung Doc Radford and Sam Guyatt, David Owen, and young Dick Townley.'

'Can't we help?' Simon asked.

'Lordy!' Mrs Cotter exclaimed. 'What would your mothers say to me if they knew you was both down on those cliffs in a storm like this?'

The coastguard laughed and hurried out. John Cotter was hunting for something in a cupboard.

'Where's my compass, May?'

'What do you want with a compass?'

'Perhaps not.'

A door slammed; boots trod on flagstones. The other helpers were assembling outside.

'Have you your waterproofs, John?'

'I'm wearing them, my love.'

'Do take care. Promise me you'll take care.'

'Of course.' He sounded brusque. 'Go back to bed now, all of you.' He went out into the night.

Simon was just falling asleep when the door of his room opened quietly. It was Keith, holding a lighted candle.

'It's me, Keith.'

'I know that. What do you want?'

'Soon as we can tomorrow, we'll go down to the Gull and explore the wreck.'

'Sounds like a good idea.'

'Simon. Can we be friends?'

'It's not me who's being unfriendly. It ought to be fun, two of us on holiday in a place like this. You seem to want to ruin it.'

'There are reasons.'

'Oh?' But as Keith did not reply, Simon turned over to the wall, with a sleepy 'Good-night.'

Keith left.

Mrs Cotter was in a state of high excitement next morning. 'My dears, what do 'e think?' She said, in hushed tones, as if she was afraid of being overheard. 'That ship was a *German*!'

'German!' Keith and Simon chorused.

'Aye, German! A U-boat, I think John said, whatever that be. Aye, a submarine. It were in difficulties and surfaced, and the storms have driven it onto the rocks. 'Tis right down there on Marsland beach, an enemy ship, stuck fast! I've never heard the like. A great tooth of a rock has wrenched its bottom open!'

'What's happened to the crew?' Keith asked.

'All rescued, 'cept one. They were all in a terrible state, they say, some with broken legs, and broken arms. Gave up without any fight. Mr Chart, he phoned for the police and he phoned for the army, you know what he's like, and in no time at all they was here, swarming all over the place in the wind and the dark, and took 'em all away.'

'Where to?'

'Lord, I don't know. Prison, I suppose.'

'What happened to the one who wasn't rescued?'

'Well, that's the thing, see, they don't know, my dear. They say he probably drowned, but no-one know for sure. No-one seen a body. He may have escaped, and be running about the countryside, Lord knows where.'

'Come on,' said Keith. 'Let's get down there.'

'What do you think you're going to do?'

'See the ship, of course. The storm's blown itself out. We'll be all right.'

'But—'

But Keith and Simon were already outside in the yard.

It was not possible to reach the wreck. There it lay, embedded on a long line of rocks below the surface, beyond the limit of low tide, a long grey slim thing, much bigger than either of them had imagined. Its conning-tower pointed skywards at a crazy angle. The cable of the breeches buoy ran from the ship through the air to a hastily-erected construction on the cliff-top.

'We could swim out there,' said Simon.

'It's too rough.'

But Simon was already undressing.

'Come back! It's not safe!' Keith shouted.

The waves, restless after last night's gale, were breaking much further out than on a calm day and rolling angrily shoreward, falling and re-forming in long lines of white foam. Simon felt himself sucked under, almost out of control, as each one engulfed him; it was a struggle to come up and breathe. He was more exhilarated than frightened, however, and found it was easier to dive under each crumbling wall of white water than attempt to breast it; the impact was less strong. As he neared the U-boat, he realized how impossible it would be to climb onto it. The sides were too sheer and tall. The cable which linked it with the cliff was being jerked by the waves hitting the ship; it looked as if it was bound to snap. The sea surged over the stern; the water poured back, then the next wave swamped it in sheets of foam. But it was not strong enough to shift the ship at all.

Simon allowed a wave to carry him onto a flat-topped rock, and from there he scrambled back to the beach, gasping and panting. Keith was talking to Mr Chart.

'You're a fool,' said the coastguard. 'Anyone can see it isn't safe to swim today.'

'Told you,' said Keith.

'In any case, the beach is closed,' Mr Chart went on. 'I don't know how you got down here without me seeing you. It's closed. The army want to investigate that sub, and they don't like people snooping around.'

Simon walked off to find his clothes. He wondered for a moment if Mr Chart was telling the truth. There was no sign of any soldiers, and what right, in any case, had a coastguard to close a beach?

'Got to be careful of Mr Chart,' said Keith, following him. 'I told you he was officious. He might report you.'

'Oh . . . get lost!'

Keith, hurt, went over to a rock some yards away, and stared out at the wreck.

Simon, when he was dressed, walked off in the opposite direction. His swim had tired him pleasantly. He felt happy and relaxed, and he whistled a tuneless song between his teeth. He watched a prawn feeding on something in a deep grey pool, and a small dogfish scuttling across the bottom, kicking up clouds of sand. The coastguard was now some way off: like yesterday he was looking for something, the missing body perhaps. Whatever he was doing he seemed more interested in it than in shooing the two boys off the beach. Simon found himself in a deep gully at the foot of the cliff, well above the high-tide-mark. There were orange ribbons of weed smeared with tar, and damp planks of whitened driftwood. He tried to shift the branch of a tree that had unaccountably found its way into the sea and been washed up here. One end of it was buried under a stone and the rest protruded like a deer's antlers. Near it were tiny crushed bones of birds, brown tins coated with rust, fish scales, frayed string from fishing-nets. He turned over the mess with a stick, wondering if there was anything valuable, but there was nothing. Then he did see something that interested him. Blood.

It was fresh blood, still glistening, a trail of it that led across a patch of dried sea-plants that crackled like dead leaves as he trod on them. He followed it, curious. It went through a heap of green seaweed in which there were bootprints. A cloud of flies rose, zigzagging in distraction. Simon walked carefully, his heart beating a little faster. He squeezed between two huge boulders, and found himself on a spit of sand, hidden from the rest of the beach by two tall ridges of rock. He turned. A fair-haired boy not much older than himself was kneeling on the sand. The blood was coming from a nasty cut in his left arm. In his other hand was a gun pointing at Simon.

Simon backed away a couple of steps, but stopped when the boy raised the gun. He was terrified; if his eyes strayed from the muzzle he was sure the boy would press the trigger. His heart was thudding with fear. If only Keith or Mr Chart would come!

'Who are you?' he asked. His tongue and his lips felt dry.

There was no answer. He could hear someone climbing the rocks in the distance, but slowly, taking his time. Then the steps quickened, crunching the shingle. Whoever it was had found the trail of blood.

'Simon! What are you doing?'

But Simon did not dare speak, or turn his head. The muscles of his legs began to tremble.

'Simon! What is it?' Keith struggled between the two great boulders and was standing beside him. The gun shifted slightly and was now pointing at Keith.

'The missing sailor,' said Simon, almost in a whisper.

KING SOLOMON'S TREASURE CHAMBER

H. Rider Haggard

'**N**ow, Gagool,' said I, in a low voice—somehow one did not dare to speak above a whisper in that place—'lead us to the chamber.'

The old witch promptly scrambled down from the table.

'My lords are not afraid?' she said, leering up into my face.

'Lead on.'

'Good, my lords'; she replied. 'Here is the chamber; let my lords light the lamp, and enter,' and she placed the gourd full of oil upon the floor, and leaned herself against the side of the cave. I took out a match, of which we had still a few in a box, and lit the rush wick. Then looked for the doorway, but there was nothing before us except the solid rock. Gagool grinned, and said:

'The way is there, my lords. *Ha! ha! ha!*'

'Do not jest with us,' I answered sternly.

'I jest not, my lords. See!' and she pointed to the rock.

As she did so, on holding up the lamp we perceived that a mass of stone was rising slowly from the floor and vanishing into the roof above, where doubtless there is a cavity prepared to receive it. The mass was of the width of a good-sized door, about ten feet high and not less than five feet thick. It must have weighed at least twenty or thirty tons, and was clearly moved upon some simple balance principle of counter-weights, probably the same as that by which the opening and shutting of an ordinary modern window is arranged. How that principle was set in motion, of course, none of us saw; Gagool was careful to avoid this; but I have little doubt that there was some primitive lever, which was moved ever so little by pressure at a secret spot, thereby throwing additional weight onto the hidden counter-balances, and causing the monolith to be lifted from its bed.

Very slowly and gently the great stone raised itself, till at last it had vanished altogether, and a dark hole presented itself to us in the place which the door had filled.

Our excitement was so intense, as we saw the way to Solomon's treasure chamber thrown open at last, that I for one began to tremble and shake. Would it prove a hoax after all, I wondered, or was old Da Silvestra right? Were there vast hoards of wealth hidden in that dark place, hoards which would make us the richest men in the whole world? We should know in a minute or two.

'Enter, white men from the Stars,' said Gagool, advancing into the doorway; 'but first hear your servant, Gagool the old. The bright stones that ye will see were dug out of the pit over which the Silent Ones are set, and stored here, I know not by whom, for that was done longer ago than even I remember. Only once has this place been entered since the time that those who hid the stones departed in haste, leaving them behind. The report of the treasure went down indeed among the peoples who lived in the country from age to age, but none knew where the chamber was, nor the secret of the door. But it happened that a white man reached this country from over the mountains—perchance he too came from "the Stars"—and was well received by the king of that day. And it came to pass that he and a woman of the country who was with him journeyed to this place, and that by chance, or magic, the woman learnt the secret of the door—a thousand years might ye search, but ye would never find that secret. Then the white man entered with the woman, and found the treasure, and filled with stones the skin of a small goat, which the woman had with her to hold food. Also as he was going from the chamber he took up one more stone, a large one and held it in his hand.'

Here she paused.

'Well,' I asked, breathless with interest as we all were, 'what happened to Da Silvestra?'

The old hag started at the mention of the name.

'How knowest thou the dead man's name?' she asked sharply; and then, without waiting for an answer, went on—

'None can tell what happened; but it came about that the white man was frightened, for he flung down the goat-skin, with the stones, and fled out with only the one stone in his hand.'

'Have none entered here since?' I asked, peering again down the dark passage.

'None, my lords. Only the secret of the door has been kept, and every king has opened it in his day, though he has not entered. There is a saying, that those who enter there will die within a moon, even as the white man died in the cave upon the mountain, where ye found him, Macumazahn, and therefore the kings do not enter. *Ha! ha!* mine are true words.'

Our eyes met as she said it, and I turned sick and cold. How did the old hag know all these things?

'Enter, my lords. If I speak truth, the goat-skin with the stones will lie upon the floor; and if there is truth as to whether it is death to enter here, that ye will learn afterwards. *Ha! ha! ha!*' and she hobbled through the doorway, bearing the light with her; but I confess that once more I hesitated about following.

'Oh, confound it all!' said Good; 'here goes. I am not going to be frightened by that old devil'; and followed by Foulata, who, however, evidently did not at all like the business, for she was shivering with fear, he plunged into the passage after Gagool—an example which we quickly followed.

A few yards down the passage, in the narrow way hewn out of the living rock, Gagool had paused, and was waiting for us.

'See, my lords,' she said, holding the light before her, 'those who stored the treasure here fled in haste, and bethought them to guard against any who should find the secret of the door, but had not the time,' and she pointed to large square blocks of stone, which, to the height of two courses (about two feet three), had been placed across the passage with the object of walling it up. Along the side of the passage were similar blocks ready for use, and, most curious of all, a heap of mortar and a couple of trowels, which tools, so far as we had time to examine them, appeared to be of a similar shape and make to those used by workmen on this day.

Here Foulata, who had been in a state of great fear and agitation throughout, said that she felt faint, and could go no further, but would wait there. Accordingly we set her down on the unfinished wall, placing the basket of provisions by her side, and left her to recover.

Following the passage for about fifteen paces further, we came suddenly to an elaborately painted wooden door. It was standing wide open. Whoever was last there either had not found the time to shut it, or had forgotten to do so.

Across the threshold of this door lay a skin bag, fashioned from a goat-skin, that appeared to be full of pebbles.

'*Hee! Hee!* white men,' sniggered Gagool, as the light from the lamp fell upon it. 'What did I tell you, that the white man who came here fled in haste, and dropped the woman's bag—behold it! Look within also and ye will find a water-gourd amongst the stones.'

Good stooped down and lifted it. It was heavy, and jingled.

'By Jove! I believe it's full of diamonds,' he said in an awed whisper.

'Go on,' said Sir Henry impatiently. 'Here, old lady, give me the lamp,' and taking it from Gagool's hand, he stepped through the doorway and held it high above his head.

We pressed in after him, forgetful for the moment of the bag of diamonds, and found ourselves in King Solomon's treasure chamber.

On the opposite side of the chamber were about a score of wooden boxes, something like Martini-Henry ammunition boxes, only rather larger, and painted red.

'There are the diamonds,' cried I; 'bring the light.'

Sir Henry did so, holding it close to the top box, of which the lid, rendered rotten by time even in that dry place, appeared to have been smashed in, probably by Da Silvestra himself. Pushing my hand through the hole in the lid I drew it out full not of diamonds, but of gold pieces, of a shape that none of us had seen before, and with what looked like Hebrew characters stamped upon them.

'Ah!' I said, replacing the coin, 'we shan't go back empty-handed, anyhow. There must be a couple of thousand pieces in each box, and there are eighteen boxes. I suppose this was the money to pay the workmen and merchants.'

'Well,' put in Good, 'I think that is the lot; I don't see any diamonds, unless the old Portuguese put them all into his bag.'

'Let my lord look yonder where it is darkest, if they would find the stones,' said Gagool, interpreting our looks. 'There my lords will find a nook, and three stone chests in the nook, two sealed and one open.'

Before translating this to Sir Henry, who carried the light, I could not resist asking how she knew these things, if no one had entered the place since the white man, generations ago.

'Ah, Macumazahn, the Watcher by Night,' was the mocking answer, 'ye who dwell in the Stars, do ye not know that some live long, and that some have eyes which can see through rock? *Ha! ha! ha!*'

'Look in that corner, Curtis,' I said, indicating the spot Gagool had pointed out.

'Good heavens! you fellows,' he cried presently, 'see here.'

We hurried up to where he was standing in a nook shaped something like a small bow window. Against the wall of this recess were placed three stone chests, each about two feet square. Two were fitted with stone lids; the lid of the third rested against the side of the chest, which was open.

'*See!*' he repeated hoarsely, holding the lamp over the open chest. We looked, and for a moment could make out nothing, on account of a silvery sheen which dazzled us. When our eyes grew used to it we saw that the chest was three-parts full of uncut diamonds, most of them of considerable size. Stooping, I picked up a handful. Yes, there was no doubt of it, they had the unmistakable soapy feel.

I gasped as I dropped them.

'We are the richest men in the whole world,' I exclaimed. 'Monte Cristo was a fool compared to us!'

'We shall flood the market with diamonds,' said Good.

'Got to get them there first,' suggested Sir Henry.

We stood still with pale faces and stared at each other, the lantern in the middle and the glimmering gems below, as though we were conspirators about to commit a crime, instead of being, as we thought, the most fortunate men on earth.

'*Hee! hee! hee!*' crackled old Gagool as she flitted about like a vampire bat behind us. 'There are the bright stones ye love, white men, as many as ye will; take them, run them through your fingers, *eat* of them, *hee! hee! drink* of them, *ha! ha!*'

At that moment there was something so ridiculous to my mind in the idea of eating and drinking diamonds, that I began to laugh outrageously, an example which the others followed, without knowing why. There we stood and shrieked with laughter over the gems that were *ours*, which had been found for *us* thousands of years ago by the patient delvers in the great hole yonder, and stored for *us* by Solomon's long-dead overseer, whose name, perchance, was written in the characters stamped on the faded wax that yet adhered to the lids of the chests. Solomon never got them, nor

David, nor Da Silvestra, nor anybody else. *We* had got them: there before us were millions of pounds' worth of diamonds, and tens of thousands of pounds' worth of gold and ivory only waiting to be taken away.

Suddenly the fit passed off, and we stopped laughing.

'Open the other chests, white men,' croaked Gagool, 'there are surely more therein. Take your fill! *Ha! ha!* take your fill.'

Thus adjured, we set to work to pull up the stone lids on the other two, first—not without a feeling of sacrilege—breaking the seals that fastened them.

Hurrah! they were full too, full to the brim; at least the second one was; no wretched, burglarious Da Silvestra had been filling goat-skins out of that. As for the third chest, it was only about a fourth full, but the stones were all picked ones; none less than twenty carats, and some of them as large as pigeon-eggs. A good many of these bigger ones, however, we could see by holding them up to the light, were a little yellow, 'off coloured', as they call it at Kimberley. Some, too, were black.

What we did *not* note, however, was the look of fearful malevolence that old Gagool favoured us with as she crept, crept like a snake, out of the treasure chamber and down the passage towards the door of solid rock.

Hark! Cry upon cry comes ringing up the vaulted path. It is Foulata's voice!

'*Oh, Bougwan! help! help! the stone falls!*'

'Leave go, girl! Then——'

'*Help! help! she has stabbed me!*'

By now we are running down the passage, and this is what the light from the lamp shows us. The door of rock is closing down slowly; it is not three feet from the floor. Near it struggle Foulata and Gagool. The red blood of Foulata runs to her knee, but still the brave girl holds the old witch, who fights like a wild cat. Look! she is free! Foulata falls, and Gagool throws herself on the ground, to twist like a snake beneath the lip of the closing stone. She is under—ah! God! too late! too late! The stone nips her, and she yells in agony. Down, down, it comes, all the thirty tons of it, slowly pressing her old body against the rock below. Shriek upon shriek, such as we had never heard, then a long sickening *crunch*, and the door is shut just as, rushing down the passage, we hurl ourselves against its mass.

It was all done in four seconds.

Then we turned to Foulata. The poor girl was stabbed in the body, and I saw that she could not live for long.

'Ah! Bougwan, I die!' gasped the beautiful creature. 'She crept out—Gagool; I did not see her, I was faint—and the door began to fall. Then she came back, and was looking up the path—I saw her come in through the slowly falling door, and caught her and held her, and she stabbed me, and *I die*, Bougwan!'

'Poor girl! poor girl!' Good cried in his distress. Then, as he could do nothing else, he fell to kissing her.

'Bougwan,' she said, after a pause, 'is Macumazahn there? It grows so dark—I cannot see.'

'Here I am, Foulata.'

'Macumazahn, be my tongue for a moment, I pray thee, for Bougwan cannot understand me, and before I go into the night I would speak a word to him.'

'Say on, Foulata, I will render it.'

'Say to my lord, Bougwan, that—I love him, and that I am glad to die because I know that he cannot cumber his life with such as I am, for the sun may not mate with the moon, nor the white with the black.

'Say that, since I saw him, at times I have felt as though there were a bird in my bosom, which would one day fly hence and sing elsewhere. Even now, though I cannot lift my hand, and my brain grows cold, I do not feel as though my heart were dying; it is so full of love that it could live ten thousand years, and yet be young. Say that if I live again, mayhap I shall see him in the Stars, and that—I will search them all, though perchance there I must still be black and he will—still be white. Say—nay, Macumazahn, say no more, save that I love—— Oh, hold me closer, Bougwan, I cannot feel thine arms—*oh! oh!*'

'She is dead—she is dead!' muttered Good presently, as he rose, the tears of grief running down his honest face.

'You need not let that trouble you, old fellow,' said Sir Henry.

'Eh!' exclaimed Good; 'what do you mean?'

'I mean that you will soon be in a position to join her. *Man, don't you see that we are buried alive?*'

Until Sir Henry uttered these words I do not think that the full horror of what had happened came home to us, preoccupied as we were with the sight of poor Foulata's end. But now we understood. The ponderous mass of rock had closed, probably for ever, for the only brain which knew its secret was crushed to powder beneath its weight. The first shock of the knowledge of the slow and miserable end that awaited us was overpowering. We saw it all now; that fiend Gagool had planned this snare for us from the first.

It must have been exactly the jest that her evil mind would have rejoiced in, this idea of the three white men whom, for some reason of her own, she had always hated, slowly perishing of thirst and hunger in the company of the treasure they had coveted. Now I saw the point of that sneer of hers about our eating and drinking the diamonds. Probably somebody had tried to serve the poor old Dom in the same way, when he abandoned the skin full of jewels. And who was that somebody?

'This will never do,' said Sir Henry hoarsely; 'the lamp will soon go out. Let us see if we can't find the spring that works the rock.'

We sprang forward with desperate energy, and, standing in a bloody ooze, began to feel up and down the door and the sides of the passage. But no knob or spring could we discover.

'Depend on it,' I said, 'it does not work from the inside; if it did, Gagool would not have risked trying to crawl underneath the stone. It was this knowledge that made her try to escape at all hazards, curse her.'

'At any rate,' answered Sir Henry with a hard little laugh, 'retribution was swift; hers was almost as awful an end as ours is likely to be. We can do nothing with the door; let us go back to the treasure room.'

We turned and went, and as we passed it I perceived by the unfinished wall across the passage the basket of food which poor Foulata had carried. I took it up, and brought it with me to the accursed treasure chamber that was to be our grave. Then we returned and reverently bore in Foulata's corpse, laying it on the floor by the boxes of coin.

Next we seated ourselves, leaning our backs against the three stone chests which contained the priceless treasure.

'Let us divide the food,' said Sir Henry, 'so as to make it last as long as possible.'

Accordingly we did so. It would, we reckoned, make four infinitesimally small meals for each of us, enough, say, to support life for a couple of days.

'Now,' said Sir Henry grimly, 'let us eat and drink, for tomorrow we die.'

Needless to say, we had but little appetite, though we were sadly in need of food and felt better after swallowing it. Then we got up and made a systematic examination of the walls of our prison-house, in the faint hope of finding some means of exit.

There was none. It was not probable that there would be any to a treasure chamber.

Our lamp began to burn dim. The fat was nearly exhausted.

'Quatermain,' said Sir Henry, 'what is the time—your watch goes?'

I drew it out and looked at it. It was six o'clock; we had entered the cave at eleven.

'Our friend Infadoos will miss us,' I suggested. 'If we do not return tonight he will search for us in the morning, Curtis.'

'He may search in vain. He does not know the secret of the door, not even where it is. No living person knew it yesterday, except Gagool. Today no one knows it. Even if he found the door he could not break it down. All the Kukuana army could not break through five feet of living rock.'

The lamp grew dimmer yet.

Presently it flared up and showed the whole scene in strong relief, the great mass of white tusks, the boxes of gold, the corpse of poor Foulata stretched before them, the goatskin full of treasure, the dim glimmer of the diamonds and the wild, wan faces of us three white men seated there awaiting death by starvation.

Then the flame sank and expired.

I can give no adequate description of the horrors of the night which followed. Mercifully these were to some extent mitigated by sleep, for even in such a position as ours wearied nature will sometimes assert itself.

The irony of the situation forced itself upon me. There around us lay treasures enough to pay off a moderate national debt, or to build a fleet of ironclads, and yet we would have bartered them all gladly for the faintest chance of escape. Soon, doubtless, we should be rejoiced to exchange them for a bit of food or a cup of water, and after that even for the privilege of a speedy close to our sufferings. Truly wealth, which men spend their lives in acquiring, is a valueless thing at the last.

And so the night wore on.

'Good,' said Sir Henry's voice at last, and it sounded awful in the intense stillness, 'how many matches have you in the box?'

'Eight, Curtis.'

'Strike one and let us see the time.'

He did so, and in contrast to the dense darkness the flame nearly blinded us. It was five o'clock by my watch. The beautiful dawn was now blushing on the snow-wreaths far over our heads, and the breeze would be stirring the night mists in the hollows.

'We had better eat something and keep up our strength,' I suggested.

'What is the good of eating?' answered Good; 'the sooner we die and get it over the better.'

'While there is life there is hope,' said Sir Henry.

Accordingly we ate, and sipped some water, and another period of time passed. Then Sir Henry suggested that it might be well to get as near the door as possible and halloa, on the faint chance of somebody catching a sound outside. Accordingly Good, who, from long practice at sea, has a fine piercing note, groped his way down the passage and set to work. I must say that he made a most diabolical noise. I never heard such yells; but it might have been a mosquito buzzing for all the effect they produced.

After a while he gave it up and came back very thirsty and had to drink. Then we stopped yelling, as it encroached on the supply of water.

So we sat down once more against the chests of useless diamonds in that dreadful inaction which was one of the hardest circumstances of our fate; and I am bound to say that, for my part, I gave way to despair. Laying my head against Sir Henry's broad shoulder I burst into tears; and I think that I heard Good gulping away on the other side, and swearing hoarsely at himself for doing so.

Ah, how good and brave that great man was! Had we been two frightened children and he our nurse, he could not have treated us more tenderly. His is a beautiful character, very quiet but very strong.

And so somehow the day went as the night had gone, if, indeed, one can use these terms where all was densest night, and when I lit a match to see the time it was seven o'clock.

Once more we ate and drank, and as we did so an idea occurred to me.

'How is it', said I, 'that the air in this place keeps fresh? It is thick and heavy, but it is perfectly fresh.'

'Great heavens!' said Good, starting up, 'I never thought of that. It can't come through the stone door, for it's air-tight, if ever a door was. It must come from somewhere. If there were no current of air in the place we should have been stifled or poisoned when we first came in. Let us have a look.'

It was wonderful what a change this mere spark of hope wrought in us. In a moment we were all three groping about on our hands and knees, feeling for the slightest indication of a draught. Presently

416

my ardour received a check. I put my hand on something cold. It was dead Foulata's face!

For an hour or more we went on feeling about, till at last Sir Henry and I gave it up in despair, having been considerably hurt by constantly knocking our heads against tusks, chests and the sides of the chamber. But Good still persevered, saying, with an approach to cheerfulness, that it was better than doing nothing.

'I say, you fellows,' he said presently in a constrained sort of voice, 'come here.'

Needless to say we scrambled towards him quickly enough.

'Quatermain, put your hand here, where mine is. Now do you feel anything?'

'I think I feel air coming up.'

'Now listen.' He rose and stamped upon the place, and a flame of hope shot up in our hearts. *It rang hollow.*

With trembling hands I lit a match. I had only three left, and we saw that we were in the angle of the far corner of the chamber, a fact that accounted for our not having noticed the hollow sound of the place during our former exhaustive examination. As the match burnt we scrutinized the spot. There was a join in the solid rock floor and, great Heavens! there, let in level with the rock, was a stone ring. We said no word, we were too excited, and our hearts beat too wildly with hope to allow us to speak. Good had a knife at the back of which was one of those hooks that are made to extract stones from horses' hoofs. He opened it, and with it scratched round the ring. Finally he worked it under, and levered away gently for fear of breaking the hook. The ring began to move. Being of stone it had not rusted fast in all the centuries it had laid there, as would have been the case had it been of iron. Presently the ring was upright. Then he thrust his hands into it and tugged with all his force, but nothing budged.

'Let me try,' I said impatiently, for the situation of the stone, right in the angle of the corner, was such that it was impossible for two to pull at once. I took hold and strained away, but no results.

Next Sir Henry tried and failed.

Taking the hook again, Good scratched all round the crack where we felt the air coming up.

'Now, Curtis,' he said, 'tackle on and put your back into it; you are as strong as two. Stop,' and he took off a stout, black silk handkerchief, which, true to his habits of neatness, he still wore, and ran it through the ring. 'Quatermain, get Curtis round the middle and pull for dear life when I give the word. *Now!*'

Sir Henry put out all his enormous strength, and Good and I did the same, with such power as nature had given us.

'Heave! heave! it's giving, gasped Sir Henry, and I heard the muscles of his great back cracking. Suddenly there was a grating sound, then a rush of air, and we were all on our backs on the floor with a heavy flagstone lying upon the top of us. Sir Henry's strength had done it, and never did muscular power stand a man in better stead.

'Light a match, Quatermain,' he said as soon as we had picked ourselves up and got our breath; 'carefully, now.'

I did so, and there before us, Heaven be praised! was the first step of a stone stair.

'Now what is to be done?' asked Good.

'Follow the stair, of course, and trust to Providence.'

'Stop!' said Sir Henry; 'Quatermain, get the bit of biltong and the water that are left; we may want them.'

I went, creeping back to our place by the chests for that purpose, and as I was coming away an idea struck me. We had not thought much of the diamonds for the last twenty-four hours or so; indeed, the very idea of diamonds was nauseous, seeing what that had entailed upon us; but, reflected I, I may as well pocket some in case we ever should get out of this ghastly hole. So I just put my fist into the first chest and filled all the available pockets of my old shooting-coat and trousers, topping up—this was a happy notion—with a few handfuls of big ones out of the third chest. Also, by an afterthought, I stuffed Foulata's basket, which, except for one water-gourd and a little biltong, was empty now, with great quantities of the stones.

The old hag started when Dr Silvestra's name was mentioned.

'I say, you fellows,' I sang out, 'won't you take some diamonds with you? I've filled my pockets and the basket.'

'Oh, come on, Quatermain! and hang the diamonds!' said Sir Henry. 'I hope that I may never see another.'

As for Good, he made no answer. He was, I think, taking his last farewell of all that was left of the girl who had loved him so well.

'Come on, Quatermain,' repeated Sir Henry, who was already standing on the first step of the stone stair. 'Steady, I will go first.'

'Mind where you put your feet, there may be some awful hole underneath,' I answered.

'Much more likely to be another room,' said Sir Henry, while he descended slowly counting the steps as he went.

When he got to 'fifteen' he stopped. 'Here's the bottom,' he said. 'Thank goodness! I think it's a passage. Follow me down.'

Good went next, and I came last, carrying the basket, and by reaching the bottom lit one of the two remaining matches. By its light we could just see that we were standing in a narrow tunnel, which ran right and left at right angles to the staircase we had descended. Before we could make out any more, the match burnt my fingers and went out. Then arose the delicate question of which way to go. Of course, it was impossible to know what the tunnel was, or where it led to, and yet to turn one way might lead us to safety, and to turn the other, to destruction. We were utterly perplexed, till suddenly it struck Good that when I had lit the match the draught of the passage blew the flame to the left.

'Let us go against the draught,' he said: 'air draws inwards, not outwards.'

We took this suggestion, and feeling along the wall with our hands, whilst trying the ground before us at every step, we departed from that accursed treasure chamber on our terrible quest for life.

We seemed to be in a stone labyrinth which led nowhere. What all these passages are, of course, I cannot say, but we thought that they must be the ancient workings of a mine. This is the only way in which we could account for such a multitude of galleries.

At length we halted, thoroughly worn out with fatigue and with that hope deferred which maketh the heart sick, and ate up our poor remaining piece of biltong and drank our last sip of water, for our throats were like limekilns. It seemed to us that we had escaped death in the darkness of the treasure chamber only to meet it in the darkness of the tunnels.

As we stood, once more utterly depressed, I thought that I caught a sound, to which I called the attention of the others. It was very faint and very far off, but it *was* a sound, a faint murmuring sound, for the others heard it too, and no words can describe the blessedness of it after all those hours of utter, awful stillness.

'By Heaven! it's running water,' said Good. 'Come on.'

Off we started again in the direction from which the faint murmur seemed to come, groping our way as before along the rocky walls. I remember that I laid down the basket full of diamonds, wishing to be rid of its weight, but on second thoughts took it up again. One might as well die rich as poor, I reflected. As we went the sound became more and more audible, till at last it seemed quite loud in the quiet. On, yet on; now we could distinctly make out the unmistakable swirl of rushing water. And yet how could there be running water in the bowels of the earth? Now we were quite near it, and Good, who was leading, swore that he could smell it.

'Go gently, Good,' said Sir Henry, 'we must be close,' Splash! and a cry from Good.

He had fallen in.

'Good! Good! where are you?' we shouted, in terrified distress. To our intense relief an answer came back in a choky voice:

'All right; I've got hold of a rock. Strike a light to show me where you are.'

Hastily I lit the last remaining match. Its faint gleam discovered to us a dark mass of water running at our feet. How wide it was we could not see, but there, some way out, was the dark form of our companion hanging on to a projecting rock.

'Stand clear to catch me,' sang out Good. 'I must swim for it.'

Then we heard a splash and a great struggle. Another minute and he had grabbed at and caught Sir Henry's outstretched hand and we had pulled him up high and dry into the tunnel.

'My word!' he said, between his gasps, 'that was touch and go. If I hadn't managed to catch that rock and known how to swim, I should have been done. It runs like a mill-race, and I could feel no bottom.'

We dared not follow the banks of the subterreanean river for fear lest we should fall into it again in the darkness. So after Good had rested a while, and we had drunk our fill of the water, which was sweet and fresh, and washed our faces, that needed it sadly, as well as we could, we started from the banks of this African Styx, and began to retrace our steps along the tunnel, Good dripping unpleasantly in front of us. At length we came to another gallery leading to our right.

'We may as well take it,' said Sir Henry wearily; 'all roads are alike here; we can only go on till we drop.'

Slowly, for a long, long while, we stumbled, utterly exhausted, along this new tunnel, Sir Henry now leading the way. Again I thought of abandoning that basket, but did not.

Suddenly he stopped, and we bumped up against him.

'Look!' he whispered, 'is my brain going, or is that light?'

We stared with all our eyes, and there—yes there, far ahead of us, was a faint, glimmering spot, no larger than a cottage window pane. It was so faint that I doubt if any eyes, except those which, like ours, had for days seen nothing but blackness, could have perceived it at all.

With a gasp of hope we pushed on. In five minutes there was no longer any doubt; it *was* a patch of faint light. A minute more and a breath of real life air was fanning us. On we struggled. All at once the tunnel narrowed. Sir Henry went on his knees. Smaller yet it grew, till it was only the size of a large fox's earth—it was earth now, mind you; the rock had ceased.

A squeeze, a struggle, and Sir Henry was out and so was Good, and so was I, dragging Foulata's basket after me; and there above us were the blessed stars and in our nostrils was the sweet air. Then suddenly something gave, and we were all rolling over and over through grass and bushes and soft, wet soil.

The basket caught in something and I stopped. Sitting up I halloaed lustily. An answering shout came from just below, where Sir Henry's wild career had been checked by some level ground. I scrambled to him, and found him unhurt, though breathless. Then we looked for Good. A little way off we discovered him also, jammed in a forked root. He was a good deal knocked about, but soon came to himself.

We sat down together, there on the grass, and the revulsion of feeling was so great that really I think we cried with joy. We had escaped from that awful dungeon, which was so near to becoming our grave. Surely some merciful power guided our footsteps to the jackal hole, for that is what it must have been, at the termination of the tunnel. And see, yonder on the mountains the dawn we had never thought to look upon again was blushing rosy red.

MY FIGHT WITH THE NATIVES

William Thornley

William Thornley, a British corn-merchant, emigrated to Tasmania (Van Diemen's Land) in 1817.

Leaving his family in Hobart Town he set off with Hector, his kangaroo dog, into the unexplored bushland where he hoped to claim farmland for himself.

The day was clear and bright, and though the early time of June is the real beginning of winter in Van Diemen's Land, the beams of the sun which shone splendidly at midday still had power to spread a feeling of summer warmth over the park-like plains. I shall never forget that memorable day of my fight with the natives. Alone, buried in the wilderness of the vast woods, wearied by six days of travel in the bush in which I had been lost, worn down by fatigue from loss of sleep and by scanty fare, I was now exposed to a deadly struggle with a body of furious natives, led on by the fierce and malignant Musquito. I am amazed, when I look back on the events of that fearful day, to find that I am still alive to relate the story.

I hastened on my way towards the east, hoping to come across some track of man or beast on which I could rely to lead me to human habitations. The natives ceased to molest me for some miles, nor could I detect any signs of their vicinity. My leg gave me some trouble at first, but as I got warmed up, the pain left me, and I ceased for a time to feel much inconvenience from the wound.

In this manner I proceeded some miles when my sight was gladdened by the appearance of a stock-keeper's hut, to which I eagerly hastened. When I got to the door, I called out, 'Hulloa! Anybody home?'

No answer.

'Is anybody inside? I have been lost in the bush, and the natives have been attacking me. Don't be afraid of me. I am William Thornley, of the Clyde.'

Still no answer.

I then knocked loudly at the door, thinking that someone might be asleep inside and not liking to burst in suddenly, lest I should be mistaken for a bushranger and fired at. The equivocal appearance which my person had presented a week since to the soldiers had not improved, I felt aware, by six days of scramble in the bush. But as no reply was made to my repeated knocking, I concluded that the hut was empty.

I tried the latch, therefore, of the upper half of the door. It was not fastened. I opened it easily, and a view of the interior satisfied me that the hut had not been occupied for a long time. I examined its capabilities of defence and found that it consisted, as usual, of two rooms or divisions. Without losing any time, I set to work to render the hut as secure as possible against the natives, should they have a mind to follow up their first attack.

I pulled down the split logs which formed the partition between the two rooms, and with them I barricaded the window, and jambed one log against the lower half of the door. These preparations took me about one hour to complete and, having concluded them, I felt that I was very hungry and, what was worse, that I was suffering from thirst. It occurred to me that the spot chosen to

425

build a hut would not be far from water. As the extremity was pressing, I thought I might venture to get a drink, so I clambered over the lower half of the door, followed by Hector who was panting for water. I left Hector to his instinct and, after sniffing about for a few minutes, he went straight to a little spring not twenty yards from the hut.

I first took a good drink, which refreshed me greatly, and then I cast about how to get a supply of water inside the hut. While I was considering this, I was terribly startled by Hector suddenly darting off into the bush. I thought, to be sure, that the natives were on me. But it was a false alarm, for a few seconds after Hector came to the door wagging his tail and holding in his mouth a small kangaroo-like animal which he had killed and which was the cause of his run into the bush.

I was not a little rejoiced at this unexpected supply, for I was sadly at loss for food. I was not long in kindling a fire and skinning the animal which, although smaller than the usual kangaroo, was about twice the size of an English rabbit and excellent eating. I made a broil of it which afforded Hector and me a delicious repast.

My spirits revived after this refection, and I began to consider that I was perhaps only losing time by remaining in the hut. I prepared, therefore, to leave, and put myself in order accordingly. I was in the very act of throwing my leg over the half-door when I was stopped in exit by a growl from Hector who immediately galloped towards a thicket of trees about a hundred yeards from the hut. He quickly returned and, by his crouching attitude and peculiar whine, I at once knew he had scented the presence of some natives.

It was too true. In less than a minute afterwards, a body of about twenty men and women, headed by Musquito, moved rapidly towards the hut. I was confident in the security of my little fortress and, for a moment, I felt a sort of reluctance to fire into the mob of naked savages, but the natives were fast approaching, and the feeling of self-preservation regained its predominant influence.

My left-hand barrel contained a single ball. I fired. A native fell, but the others continued to advance and sent a shower of spears through the open top half of the door. One of the spears went through the lower part of the back of my left hand and tore the skin, while some went past me into the hut. I fired off my second barrel loaded with shot and, slamming the door close, I bolted it.

They now commenced a furious yelling around the hut, and some of them tried the window, but they found it secure. In the meantime I reloaded my fowling-piece, putting a couple of bullets in each barrel, for I felt that the natives were in earnest and that it would require my utmost efforts to save my life from their furious assault. I was standing by the door uncertain about what to do next when suddenly a spear was thrust between the crevice of the lower and upper parts of the door. Fortunately it encountered my shot belt, which it perforated, and gave me time to jump back. I retaliated by pushing the muzzle of my fowling-piece through the crevice and letting fly with both barrels. A horrid yell, that made the woods re-echo, proclaimed that my fire was successful, and I could hear the tramping of their feet as they retreated to a distance.

There was now a pause for some time and a dead silence. I reloaded my gun and stood on my guard. I wondered what they were about, but I was afraid to put my eye to the crevice, lest some devil thrust a spear into it. While I thus stood, my ears were again assailed with horrid shouts and yells of the natives whose rage seemed to have redoubled at the sight of their dead companions. Expecting another rush at the door, I began to pile some more logs from the partition against it.

The precaution was unnecessary, because the devils had hit on a surer and safer means of accomplishing my destruction. To my terrible dismay I smelt smoke. They had set fire to the thatch of the hut! The smoke increased, and presently the light of the flame was visible. As the smoke and flames increased, the rejoicing natives yelled and screamed with frantic delight!

My presence of mind almost forsook me at this crisis. Escape seemed impossible, and I felt I was doomed to die the most horrible of deaths: that of being roasted alive!

The light of the flames increased, and the smoke inside the hut became almost insufferable. Feeling that death was certain, if I remained where I was, I determined to make a desperate effort to escape. The natives, as I knew by their cries, were assembled at the front of the hut, so I thought my best chance of escape would be by the back window. I hastily tore down my barricade of logs and jumped through the opening into a dense pall of smoke. I was nearly suffocated, but with my gun in my hand I dashed through the haze.

For the moment I was not perceived, but the natives soon got sight of me, and a volley of spears around me, one of which struck me in the back but dropped out again, proclaimed that they were in chase. I kept running as fast as I could towards a tree which I intended to make my fighting-place, by setting my back against it and so protecting myself in the rear.

The spears flew around and near me, but I reached the tree and, instantly turning round, I fired among the advancing natives. This checked them, and they retreated to some distance. But they continued to throw some spears, most of which fell short, and kept shouting and yelling in a frightful manner.

Taking advantage of the temporary inaction of the natives, I felt for my powder-horn to reload the barrel which I had discharged. To my unspeakable horror and disappointment, it was missing! I searched every pocket in vain. I had laid it on the table in the hut, and there I had left it! To recover it was impossible, as the hut was all in flames, and while I gazed on the burning mass a dull report and a burst of sparks from the building made known to me that the powder had become ignited and was lost for ever!

In my agony of mind at this discovery, my hair seemed to bristle up. I now felt that nothing but a miracle could save me. I had but three shots left, one in my fowling-piece, and two in my pistols. Casting my eyes upwards to the branches of the tree under which I was standing, I observed that it was easy to climb, and there appeared to be a hollow between the principal branches which might serve me for a place of shelter till the night should enable me,

The natives were assembled in front of the hut.

under cover of darkness, to escape from my pursuers. I knew that the natives were afraid of moving about in darkness, under the impression that evil spirits were abroad.

I scrambled as fast as I could to the fork of the tree and found, to my infinite relief, that my anticipation was right. There was a hollow large enough to admit my whole body and effectually to shield me from the spears. As my foot reached the bottom, it encountered some soft body, which I quickly learned was an opossum which asserted its right of habitation by a severe attack on my legs with its teeth and claws. I was in no humour to argue the matter with my new assailant, so with a quick jerk of my arm I pulled the animal out, and it scampered higher up the tree.

As I crouched myself down, I thought I heard a breathing above me. I looked up and beheld the hideous visage of one of the savages glaring on me with his white eyeballs which exhibited a ferocious sort of exultation. He had a waddy in his hand which he slowly raised to give me a pat on the napper, thinking that he had me quite safe, like an opossum in its hole. 'You're mistaken, my beauty,' thought I. 'I'm not done for yet.' Drawing one of my pistols from my pocket, which was rather a matter of difficulty in my confined position, I fired. The ball crashed through his face and skull, and I heard his dead body fall heavily to the ground.

As I lay in my retreat, I heard a sound as if heavy materials were being dragged towards the tree. I ventured to peep out and beheld the savages busy in piling dead wood around the drunk, with the intention, as I immediately surmized, of setting fire to it and of burning me in my hole. I looked on these preparations as a neglected but not indifferent spectator, the natives disregarding my appearance above the opening and waiting with a sort of savage patience for the sure destruction which they were preparing for me.

Led by that devilish savage, Musquito, the natives began a death-dance around the tree, and at a sign from Musquito, a native woman with fire-sticks in her hand stepped forward and set light to the faggots. As the blaze increased, the savages danced and yelled round the tree in a complete delirium of range and exultation.

The fire burned up! The smoke ascended! I already felt the horrid sensation of being stifled by the thick atmosphere of smoke before the flames encompassed me. In this extremity I determined at least to inflict some vengeance on my savage persecutors. I scrambled from my hiding-place and crawled as far as I could on one of the branches, and I fired the remaining barrel of my fowling-piece at the yelling wretches; then I hurled the empty gun at their heads. I did the same with my remaining pistol when, to my amazement, I thought I heard the reports of other guns. The smoke and flames now mastered me, and I remember vaguely falling from the tree. Then my senses left me.

I was roused from my trance of death by copious deluges of water, and I heard a voice, which was familiar to me, exclaiming, 'Well, if this is not enough to disgust a man with this horrid country, I don't know what more he would have. For years and years I have been preaching to him that nothing good could come out of this wretched den of bushrangers and natives, and now the evil has come at last.'

I opened my eyes at the words. It was the voice of my friend Crab, whom Heaven had directed with a party to this spot to deliver me! Overcome with the intensity of my emotions, racked with pain, and sick with the very fullness of joy at my escape from death, I fainted.

WRECKED IN THE
RAIN FOREST

Hector Holthouse

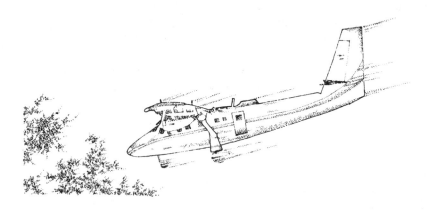

It was a slow-moving cyclone that dawdled its way down the Queensland coast in February 1937, claiming the first Australian airliner to be a victim of a cyclone, and setting the scene, in the rain-drenched jungles of the McPherson Ranges on the Queensland–New South Wales border, for one of the greatest dramas of survival and rescue in aviation history.

The Meteorological Bureau issued a warning on 13 February 1937 that the cyclone was centred east of Willis Island and was moving south-west. By Wednesday, 17 February, it was 300 miles north-east of Rockhampton, whipping up rough seas, and delaying shipping. The master of the AUSN motor vessel *Bingera* said he had never known a cyclone to hang fire for so long.

Another of the company's vessels, the *Babinda*, was caught in it off Double Island Point on Friday. Her intermediate propeller shaft broke, and in response to her SOS she was towed to Brisbane. Her crew said it was the worst weather they had ever encountered.

Conditions at Archerfield (then Brisbane's main air terminal) that Friday were wet and unpleasant, but not bad enough to prevent the Airlines of Australia Stinson monoplane, City of Brisbane, leaving on its regular run to Sydney at 1 p.m. Like many planes at that time, it carried no radio.

In those days it was for the pilot to decide whether he took off or not, and on this run there were two possible routes. The safer, bad weather route, was along the coast. The other, and normal route, lay inland through Lismore and entailed crossing the McPherson Ranges in the region of the Lamington Plateau, a 2,000 foot high maze of ridges and mountain gorges, with isolated peaks rising to more than 3,700 feet. This was rough country covered with thick rain forest in which progress on foot was made slow and dangerous by precipitous gorges, wet, moss-covered boulders and thick undergrowth matted with vicious, hook-thorned vines, stinging trees and rotting, fungus-covered tree trunks. Lonely farm houses and patches of cultivation patterned some of the lower valleys, but on the upper slopes a man could wander until his strength gave out and see no more than the high wall of jungle and a hint of sky through the interlocking branches overhead.

The day the Stinson took off the plateau was being lashed by heavy gales coming from cyclonic disturbances of the upper air, but there was no weather station in the area to advise Archerfield of this.

By 5.30 p.m. the Stinson had not arrived at Sydney. As the news spread reports began to come in. It had been seen passing over Currumbin on the Gold Coast. It had been seen circling over Boambee, just south of Coffs Harbour about 3 p.m. This report said heavy rain was falling at the time but the red and blue plane could be seen plainly through the clouds as it headed away south.

At 3.30 p.m. it was heard over the Macleay River. A few minutes after 4 p.m. three different people saw it near Taree. The post-master at Davistown and the postmistress at Avaca Beach, just north of Broken Bay, saw the plane pass about 5 p.m. Three residents of Patonga, on the northern shore of Broken Bay, said they saw the plane flying over at 5 p.m., heading for Cowan on the southern side of the bay. A man reported having heard cries and cooees coming from the direction of Coal and Candle Creek, a tributary of the Hawkesbury. A large oil slick was reported on the Hawkesbury River. Wreckage was seen off Palm Beach.

Aboard the missing plane were the pilot, Rex Boyden, the co-pilot, Beverley Shepherd and five passengers: Roland Graham and William Fountain on the starboard side, and on the port, J. K. Westray, J. S. Proud, and J. R. Binstead who, in order not to worry his wife who was nervous of air travel, had given his name as J. Barnett. He had nearly missed the plane by being late, but it had waited for him.

The organizers of the search, not unnaturally, decided that Stinson had got as far as the Hawkesbury River and had come down somewhere within fifteen minutes of its destination.

Four hundred miles to the north a woman in the foothills of the McPherson Ranges, in the face of such evidence, saw no reason to report that she had seen the Stinson pass overhead on the inland route within forty minutes of its having left Brisbane. The natural conclusion was that the pilot had later headed back for the coast.

He had, in fact, done no such thing, and as search planes prepared on Saturday morning to comb the country between Newcastle and Sydney the wreckage of the lost Stinson lay smouldering on a jungle-clad mountainside of the Lamington Plateau four hundred miles away. At dawn there had been three survivors beside the wreckage; now there were two.

After the Stinson left Archerfield that wet, windy Friday afternoon, nobody aboard felt they had anything to worry about. The pilots were taking it cheerfully and the passengers were laughing and joking among themselves.

Binstead, the passenger whose wife worried about his flying, recalled that about forty minutes after leaving Archerfield they 'struck a patch of bad weather over the ranges'. The pilot was trying to bank and climb, but there were down currents of the gale coming over the top of a gorge and these were forcing the plane down. Binstead glanced out of the window and noticed the trees. They seemed to be quite close. The plane banked to starboard and then, suddenly, came the crash. The plane chopped through the top of a tall tree, ploughed into a second about thirty feet up, and crashed down through the branches onto the ground. One wing was torn off and fell about a chain away, one propeller was smashed off, and in the fall through the trees the rudder was carried away.

Inside there was turmoil. A broken branch speared through the metal fuselage on the starboard side, killed Graham instantly, and slammed Binstead across the knees.

As the plane hit the ground everyone was hurled into a heap. Binstead was nearly knocked out by a blow on the head. He stumbled to his feet to see Proud, who had been sitting two seats away from him, smash a port window and begin to scramble through. With his head and shoulders out, he seemed to get stuck. The cabin was filling with black smoke.

Binstead began to push from behind. Proud let out a yell. 'My leg! I think it must be broken.'

Somehow he got clear, turned round, grabbed Binstead by the hand and dragged him out through the window. It was a tight squeeze and by the time he was out there were flames everywhere.

Binstead, with most of his clothes ripped off in his escape, looked back into the blazing cabin. There was another man moving there. 'Here,' yelled Binstead. 'Over here.'

Above the crackle of the fire the man heard and, between the two of them, Binstead and Proud dragged him out through the window. By then the whole plane was in flames and the last man— Westray—was badly burned on the back and hands.

Seared by the red, petrol-fed flames, the three men crawled

away into the rain-sodden jungle and from a safe distance crouched to watch the plane reduced to a heap of twisted, charred metal. So great was the heat that several green trees caught fire and a thick column of smoke billowed up through the rain.

None of the men had any idea how wild and isolated was the terrain in which they had come down, and all the rest of that day they were expecting someone to arrive to see what had happened. When darkness came with no sign of other human life, they settled themselves as well as they could for the night. There was still enough left of the fire to provide some warmth, but all were badly shaked and Proud was in great pain with his broken right leg from which the bone was protruding.

In the morning the rain seemed to be clearing and Westray announced his intention of trying to get through to the nearest farmhouse. He was an Englishman in Australia on a business trip, and had little knowledge of local conditions. The others tried to dissuade him, but Westray was determined. He had done some mountain climbing in the Highlands of Scotland and thought he had a chance of getting help. The last they saw of him was as he disappeared behind a thick bush about sixty yards away.

Westray, in fact, did not get further than about a mile from the plane. His tracks, when they were found, told their own tale. At the bottom of the steep, jungle-clad slope he came to a fast-running mountain stream—it was Christmas Creek and, unknown to Westray, it led down to a settlement.

Westray, as any experienced Australian bushman would have done, turned to follow the stream down, but before long his progress was barred by a thirty-foot waterfall and a steep cliff. He tried to climb down the cliff and fell. Shaken and apparently injured, he dragged himself on a little further downstream and then stopped and propped himself against a large boulder to rest. There he died.

The two who remained behind had neither food nor water from the plane, but Binstead had found a coffee flask in the wreckage. It was still usable and held half a gallon. He climbed with it down the slope of the ravine to the creek and brought it back full—enough water to last the two of them for one day.

Proud, unable to move because of his broken leg, filled in the time by scratching a diary with a penknife on a loose piece of metal from the plane.

'Friday 19th. Plane crashed on hillside at 1.50 p.m. Trees could plainly be seen before the crash about 50 feet from the starboard window. The plane had a heavy list to starboard and immediately crashed, got to the ground somehow or other and burst into flames. Cabin filled with black smoke. Proud was the first to gain exit by removing the port window. Lying on the wing, he pulled Binstead out and assisted him in pulling the young Englishman Westray out. When Westray got out he was suffering from burns to the back. The heat was so great we had to get clear of the plane. Raining like hell. We left fire up all night and rain petered out next morning.'

'Saturday 20th. Morning. Weather clear. Englishman left seeking assistance. He sang out he could see a farmhouse but did not return.'

Though the rain seemed to be returning, they had a fire going that day and Binstead was straining his ears for the sound of the search planes he was still sure would be overhead at any moment.

The search was, in fact, well under way, but most of it was concentrated 400 miles to the south.

That Saturday ten planes, including three from the RAAF buffeted through rain and winds in an unsuccessful search for the missing plane. It was assumed that the Stinson, hugging the coastline all the way, got as far as the northern side of Broken Bay and then came down. Leading pilots, basing their opinions on the apparently reliable reports, said that if the plane was found it would probably be in the Broken Bay area. The main search was concentrated between Newcastle and Sydney. Not surprisingly it disclosed nothing.

One of the search planes from Brisbane covered the inland route, but over the McPherson Ranges ran into fierce south-westerly head winds which tossed the machine about like a leaf, cut visibility almost to zero and forced the pilot to climb to about 5,000 feet to get some relief. He circled as long as he could, waiting for the storm to clear, but it did not and he had to fly on.

On Saturday night two spiritualist mediums made their own contribution to the confusion by holding a long seance and stating that they had seen the missing Stinson crashing near Branxton, about thirty miles west of Newcastle.

By Monday it was thought the plane had gone down in the sea off the coast near Broken Bay, into the waters of the Bay or into one of the surrounding deep, densely wooded gorges. Of the twenty-five planes that searched that day twenty-three concentrated on the area south of Newcastle.

On Wednesday the search was abandoned. Proud's mother offered £500 to keep it going but found no takers.

As the days went by the hopes of the two men beside the plane wreck faded. Once they heard a plane circling somewhere nearly overhead, but after a while it went away. The Sydney–Brisbane mail plane passed over every day but saw nothing.

There was no longer a single fire because it was raining nearly all the time and everything was soaking wet. Even the matches were sodden. Not knowing how isolated they were, the men still had hopes of rescue by land and they took it in turns to 'cooee' every half hour to guide possible searchers to them.

Binstead, on his way down for water, had found some small red berries growing on ferns along the steep, jungle-clad sides of the gorge. They were sweet but not very nourishing. Both men became weaker daily. Binstead's hands, scraped on rocks and scratched on thorny vines, became infected and so numb and powerless that he could hardly use them. He brought the berries back to Proud in his mouth. As he became weaker and his hands and feet more painful, he had to abandon his scrambles for the berries and conserve his strength for carrying the water supply.

Many times Proud urged Binstead to leave him and do the best he could for himself. Binstead refused. They were in this together and they would stick together whatever way things came out.

Proud was so weak that Binstead feared for his life.

Proud made an undated entry in his diary which read: 'Long time. Nothing done. Do not know why search is not made.'

Proud's broken leg got worse every day. Binstead had torn what was left of his shirt into strips and bandaged the leg as well as he could. But the rain was almost continuous. The bandages were always wet and soon they were flyblown. In an attempt to keep off the flies Binstead ripped away a piece of the charred fuselage of the plane and bent it into the form of a shield which he placed over the injured leg. This was fairly effective.

Neither of the men slept much. Though Proud never complained, he was in intense pain all the time and occasionally became delirious and called for Binstead who could do no more than make him as comfortable as possible.

On the Thursday—seven days after the crash—Binstead was so doubtful of his strength to get down to the creek and back to the plane that he scratched a message on a piece of the fuselage to let any searchers who might arrive know where he was. It said: '25/2/37 Binstead at creek, water. Proud lying at plane with broken leg. Rapidly tiring.'

He did manage to get down and back that day, and again on the Friday, though it took him five hours to make the trip—about 200 yards each way.

On Saturday he tried to do it again but could not. His strength was finished. He and Proud lay there, talking fitfully, feeling there was little chance now that rescue would come in time, but hoping against hope. They still kept up the cooees for help, taking it in turn to call every half hour.

Most of the day drifted away in a haze of exhaustion. From the look of the sun it was late afternoon. The night that was coming could be their last. Then, from somewhere on the slope above them, so close that they jumped at the sudden sound of it, came the long, clear call of a bushman's cooee.

While the search planes were combing the country south of Newcastle for the wreck of a plane that was not there, there were, in the valleys of the McPherson Ranges, farmers who had seen the Stinson pass overhead on that Friday of the gale, apparently heading for Lismore. But bad weather and heavy work limited communication between them and evidence of the southern sightings seemed so overwhelming that few gave a thought to the possibility that the plane could have come down in the McPherson Ranges.

It was only a week later that Bernard O'Reilly, one of the district's pioneers and an expert bushman, had an opportunity to compare local reports with published accounts of the plane's disappearance. To him the answer to the puzzle was immediately obvious. Men he knew had seen the Stinson heading for the ranges in the direction of Lismor. It had not arrived there. It must have crashed in the ranges.

Next day, Saturday, 27 February, he set out on foot to work his way along the range to the New South Wales border. The country was rocky and rough and progress was slow. He camped that night in the bush, was moving again by daylight on Sunday, and by 8 a.m. had reached the crest of a spur which, as the cloud broke momentarily, gave him a view of the surrounding country. Six miles or so to the south, on the next spur of the range but one, he saw the top of a tree that looked as if it had lately been burnt.

Scrambling painfully through scrub and tangled vines down to the bottom of the gorge, up the opposite side, pausing only for a quick meal from the provisions he carried. O'Reilly stood at last on the crest of the next range. There he waited, hoping for a break in the clouds that would let him get his bearings. All around him the jungle was still. Then, from somewhere ahead came the last thing he had expected to hear—the distant but clear sound of a cooee.

O'Reilly headed towards it but the country was rough and he could not see ahead because of the trees. It was about 4 p.m. before he stood on high ground which he felt must be somewhere near the burnt tree he had seen that morning. Waiting only to get back his breath he sent his own cooee echoing down the gorge. Almost at once came an answer, loud and clear.

Ignoring thick scrub and tearing thorns, O'Reilly plunged down the slope. Then he saw it—a burnt clearing and a wrecked plane. As he came to the edge of the clearing he saw two men, one lying on the ground, the other sitting up. The men saw him. They all stared at each other as though struck dumb. At last O'Reilly found his voice. 'Oh, you poor bastard,' was all he could say.

He clambered down to the clearing. They were all too stunned to talk coherently. Binstead grinned across at Proud. 'We'll be able to have that drink at the Australia after all,' he said.

Binstead told the story as O'Reilly lit a fire, made tea and gave them some bread and butter, which was the only food he had. Proud was so weak that O'Reilly doubted if he would live another day. There was no time to be lost.

With only a few hours of daylight left, O'Reilly gave them the last of the bread and butter, and with no more than a brief 'I'm clearing out now,' headed off down the slope in the direction taken a week earlier by Westray.

He found the Englishman's body and pushed on in the fading light down Christmas Creek. Darkness caught up with him and he still plodded on, telling himself all the time that he had to be quick or Proud would die. Then he saw the light of a hurricane lantern. He staggered up to it and found a farmer who was out shooting flying foxes.

The rescue party made up of local farmers set out on the return trip at 11.30 that night carrying hurricane lanterns. By daylight they were in the heart of the ranges, clambering over boulders as big as haystacks, struggling up steep banks to avoid waterfalls, and often wading waist deep through mountain streams running strongly with the rain which was still falling.

The leaders cleared a track with axes and brush hooks, while bearers followed with ropes, tents, bedding and medical supplies. Dr N. A. Lawlor of Beaudesert had come equipped to amputate Proud's leg if necessary.

They found the body of Westray and, about a mile further on, located the wreck of the plane about 11 a.m.

The two survivors were made as comfortable as possible with food and cigarettes. Proud's leg, though in bad shape, had actually been saved by the flies. Maggots had destroyed gangrenous flesh which otherwise would have killed him, and the leg eventually healed.

As the almost exhausted doctor squatted to examine him, Proud managed a grin. 'Don't bother about an anaesthetic, doc; just inject something into the old leg; you've had a hard enough trip.'

Bush splints were cut for the leg and both men were carefully moved to higher ground where a tent was put up so they could be treated properly.

Reinforcements arrived to carry them out. Stretchers were made of bush timber and bearers took turns forcing their way through the thick jungle and doing their best to avoid jarring the sick men. Every time they stopped for a rest Binstead, cracking jokes between times, told the story of their nine days in the rain forest.

He was still cracking jokes thirty years later when, at the age of eighty-four, he and Proud flew from Sydney to join Bernard O'Reilly and others who had taken part in the rescue for a commemorative dinner on 1 March 1967 at O'Reilly's home, Green Mountains, Lamington National Park.

ATTEMPT ON

THE ATLANTIC

John Frayn Turner

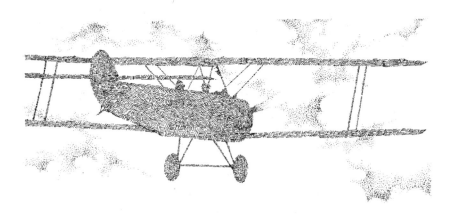

It was just after three o'clock on the afternoon of Sunday, 18
May 1919. Two Englishmen clambered into the cockpits of
their Sopwith biplane at Mount Pearl airfield, St Johns, Newfoundland, hoping to be the first to fly the Atlantic non-stop. Aptly
enough their speck of a plane was christened *Atlantic*.

The pilot was Harry Hawker and his navigator Commander
Mackenzie Grieve. Hawker had flown throughout the four years of
the Great War. For weeks they had been waiting for the weather to
improve. Now it seemed perfect.

Hawker had made several last-minute changes in his aeroplane,
including replacing the original four-bladed propeller by a more
conventional two-bladed one, and planning to take the highly

unconventional step of jettisoning the undercarriage on take-off to give the machine maximum lift. To lessen the risk of a crash on landing Hawker fitted small steel skids which he hoped would enable the machine to glide along the ground to a stop.

But the landing was far in the future. Now it was 3.15 p.m. as the two men shook hands and waved the usual farewells to the crowd on the airfield. The sky was blue and the wind blew from the north-west as the little aeroplane jolted off on its long take-off run. It was carrying a huge load of fuel, and the spectators wondered whether it could ever take to the air.

But it did, though to get it up at all, Hawker had to taxi it diagonally across the field for extra length. Finally he managed to coax it into a laborious climb clear of the fence at the edge of the airfield—and they were away.

The sun glinted on the biplane, with its tail waggling slightly as if in pleasure at being airborne. And on that tail was the name Sopwith Aviation Company, Kingston on Thames.

Hawker and Grieve were really on their way, the first men ever to try and fly the Atlantic in a powered aeroplane.

The aircraft ascended steadily to some 2,000 feet and set its nose eastward for Ireland—nearly 2,000 miles off. And they knew that if they couldn't keep airborne all that way, it was a million to one that they would drown.

Wearing a check cap back to front, Hawker flew straight over the city of St Johns and the Quidi Vidi airfield, where rival airmen were actually preparing to take off on this fantastic race to be the first across the Atlantic and win the *Daily Mail* prize of £10,000.

Hawker signalled 'Farewell' to the crowds gathered below, and then just before leaving the land altogether, he jettisoned his undercarriage, and with it the landing wheels. Many people thought him unwise, but he knew that every extra pound must make the flight more difficult and more dangerous.

The signalman at the marine lookout on Newfoundland reported: 'Atlantic plane flying south-easterly out of sight at 8,000 feet and a speed of 80 mph.'

After only ten minutes in the air, though, Hawker and Grieve lost the strong sunshine as the aeroplane faded into the infamous fog banks off Newfoundland. Hawker decided to try and rise above them, and soon succeeded in raising *Atlantic* well over the swirling sea-mists.

This was better in one way, but worse in another—for the fog blanketed all sight of the sea from them. For over an hour they flew blindly on eastward, though a brief break in the mixture of mist and cloud did give Grieve a chance to take bearings.

For four hours they droned on, then they suddenly ran into blusters of cloudbanks, building up with every eastward mile. Their black outlines looked ominous against the oncoming night.

Four or five hundred miles out, the storm started.

Rain raged against the poor little aeroplane, shaking it from propeller to tail, making every yard more of a struggle both for the men and the machine. The squalls seemed to be coming at them almost horizontally.

The silver wings fluttered, quivered, but remained more or less level. This was the weather they had waited to avoid all those endless days. As night fell they met more great gusts of wind and rain, which roared through the thin struts of the biplane.

It seemed impossible that with everything else coming *down*, the aeroplane could stay *up*.

Grieve tried to take sights with frostbitten hands, as Hawker veered, banked, dived, dodged, to get round those black blots of clouds. Their course became erratic, but they flew on.

Harry Hawker said later:

'The trouble did not start until we were five and a half hours out from St Johns.

'*Then the temperature of the water in the radiator began to rise.*

'It did not mean a great deal at that moment, but we could see that something was the matter with the water circulation.'

They couldn't just stop and cool it off, like a car on a road. They were at 10,000 feet now—two miles over the angry Atlantic. Not many people would be where they were for ten million pounds—let alone ten thousand.

Grieve continued trying to take sights, though they had not seen the water since that moment ten minutes out from St Johns.

Hawker, too, peered outside at the dark facade of sky. He saw cloud peaks towering up to 15,000 feet, making a very bad horizon. The moon had not yet risen, so the whole scene seemed appallingly dark. Yet he said, 'We were very comfortable'!

After the first shock of that rise of the radiator temperature, Hawker glanced down regularly at the dial registering the thermometer level of the cooling system in the engine. At first the water temperature in the radiator read 168 degrees Fahrenheit. Two or three minutes later it showed 176 degrees Fahrenheit—an eight-degree jump. Things were hotting up.

'Only 36 degrees to boiling point,' he thought aloud.

But luckily there it stayed for the next couple of hours.

Then it started to creep up again.

Hawker wiggled the lever controlling the shutters on the radiator. These were supposed to vary the temperature—but they didn't. The needle showed another two-degree rise.

Hawker had thought it was as much as he could do to fly the plane through the dark drifts of clouds. Now he had the problem of heat to cope with as well. For the first time he felt slightly worried.

If the water reached boiling point and evaporated, their Rolls-Royce engine would overheat and seize up, and they would fall into the hidden storm-ridden waters below.

He started searching for the cause and came to the conclusion that something must have got into the water filter in the feed pipe from the radiator to the water cock and blocked it. Most probably solder or the like shaken loose in the radiator. Then he tried to remedy the fault.

He throttled down the motor, stopped it altogether, and pointed the nose of the *Atlantic* down towards the ocean. He hoped this would give the system a chance to cool, and also clear anything blocking the filter.

The aeroplane drove down through the rain, with the wind twanging the taut wire struts. Hawker screwed up his eyes to try and see something, but couldn't really, so went by his instruments.

Between 6,000 and 7,000 feet he flattened out in a graceful arc and opened the throttle again. He had done the trick. The filter was clear and the thermometer needle flickered back to a lower level.

'Thank God,' he breathed.

After another hour of ploughing through the fleeting films of cloud, they were about 800 miles out from St Johns. The weather was still stormy, with a northerly gale coming up fast.

Then it happened all over again.

The filter choked, the water got hotter; the needle on the dial moved steadily upwards. The moment of truth was approaching, and so was the point of no return.

Hawker did the only thing he could. He dived again to try and clear it, but it was no use this time. And the climb up afterwards heated the water more rapidly still.

The dial now read 200 degrees Fahrenheit: twelve degrees off boiling point.

The aeroplane staggered up through the stormy clouds, the engine getting hotter all the time. The two men were in a tight corner and they knew it. Midnight had come and gone, but for the fliers it was still the middle of a wild night over the Atlantic—in an aircraft that must soon seize up. They were now 900 miles from St Johns, and nearing the point of no return. No men had ever flown here before.

Hawker tried again to clear the filter by diving, but failed. And after the third attempt the water was boiling fiercely.

The dial read 212 degrees.

If he went on like this, they would waste all their precious water for cooling the engine, so he climbed to 12,000 feet and they decided to stay at that height for the rest of the way.

They hadn't yet seriously doubted the aeroplane's ability to get across. At two and a half miles up, they were above most of the

The aeroplane staggered up through the clouds.

clouds. Moonlight broke the blackness, and they managed to keep a better course. They discovered that the gale had been blowing them southward, miles out of their course.

By throttling down to a slower speed, Hawker got the water off the boil and back to 200 degrees again. Nursing the controls with all the tenderness he could muster, he kept them flying for the rest of that endless night.

Dawn edged alight ahead of them.

Then, twelve hours out from Newfoundland, they came to clouds again, too dense to fly through and too tall to climb over. And anyway, each time Hawker ascended, the water boiled.

'Nothing for it,' he shouted. 'Have to go below them.'

But the cloud base seemed to be non-existent. Hawker took the aeroplane lower and lower. At 6,000 feet the clouds were thicker than ever. Down and down they manoeuvred, praying for a break. At 1,000 feet they suddenly saw the sullen swirling sea. Hawker reacted instantly and opened the throttle.

There was no response.

As the last few hundred feet slipped away, Grieve desperately fiddled with the fuel pump to get the engine going. It looked as if all was lost, when literally yards from the waves, the engine coughed, convulsed, and came back to life.

Up at 1,000 feet again, they were on course as a stormy sunrise loomed red and grey ahead. But even without climbing any higher they could not keep the temperature below boiling. Now they knew the worst—they had passed the point of no return—and they could not hope to reach their goal. It was a grim moment. They could go neither forward nor back.

The water began to boil steadily away, and with it went their hopes. Hawker reckoned he could keep the aeroplane flying for another two or three hours: their expectation of life, for as the Irish coast was still nearly 900 miles off, he knew they could not hope to reach it.

'There's only one chance,' he called to Grieve, 'and that's seeing a ship. We're near the main routes.'

But both of them knew that the chances of spotting a vessel in the vast watery wastes of the Atlantic were extremely small, and to do so before they burned up were virtually nil.

Hawker swung the nose and began to zig-zag across the line of their original route. The minutes, the miles, the fuel and—worst of all—the water, were all being consumed.

Both men craned out of their cramped cockpits, desperately scanning the sea through the scudding clouds. But no ship came in sight. It seemed silly even to hope for one.

This went on for an hour. They had really burned their boats now, and the water went on boiling away. They knew, too, that the chances of setting an aeroplane down on this churning ocean were as slim as sighting a ship.

The *Atlantic* chugged on, back and forth. They had no radio to call for help. The whole world was waiting to hear news of them, but wouldn't begin worrying till they became overdue in Ireland.

Only these two men in the entire world knew of their plight. All they could do now was to keep their aeroplane airborne for as long as they possibly could. For the throb of the motor was virtually their own heartbeat. When one stopped, the other would soon follow.

It was now two hours since Hawker had decided to adopt their zig-zag course. There was still not a sign of a ship. The temperature needle stayed permanently above boiling point as they flew to and fro.

Hawker still had his hands full controlling the plane, for half a gale was whipping the sea and buffeting the frail fuselage. It was as if they were being softened up for a final knockout. The rollers rose and fell to the gusts of the gale.

Another half-hour passed, and Hawker wondered how much longer they could last. In his heart he knew it was only a matter of minutes.

Through it all the Rolls-Royce engine purred on, but by now all the water had boiled away. The engine was red-hot and growing hotter.

They were at latitude 50°20′N and longitude 29°30′W. St Johns was now 1,100 miles away, and Ireland 800 miles away.

This was when they should have died—but they didn't.

The miracle happened.

'It's a ship! A ship!' Hawker shouted, pointing down for Grieve to see. They nodded to each other, overcome.

She was quite close on the port bow, and came looming out of the low morning mist.

Hawker swooped down to 400 feet, fired three Very distress signals, and then flew across her until he saw some men on deck. The next problem was *landing* on the sea. At any rate he wouldn't miss his wheels.

He went a couple of miles ahead of the little vessel, veered round, and then came down towards the storm-ruffled surface.

Now Harry Hawker had to call on all his reserves of calmness and skill. He saw the sea spread out beneath him like a rippling landscape. At last came the touchdown. With infinite care he set the machine down on top of the waves—and it actually floated on an even keel.

The next step was for the two of them to take to their little emergency boat. Useful as this was, it would not have supported them very long in the restless rollers of the mid-Atlantic.

The waves were running up to twelve feet and breaking right over them and the aeroplane, which slowly started to settle and sink. Soon only its tail remained above the water.

An hour or so later the ship's boat reached them. The rescuers turned out to be the *Mary*, a small Danish steamer bound for the Scottish coast.

The ironic thing was that this 1,824-ton vessel had no wireless, so the world went on waiting for news of the famous fliers. In fact it was a week after their take-off that the *Mary* passed Lloyd's signal station at Butt of Lewis and broke the breathtaking fact that the aviators were safe, long after they had been given up for lost.

They were both awarded the Air Force Cross, and the *Daily Mail* gave them a consolation prize of £5,000 for their gallant attempt which took them nearly two-thirds across the Atlantic. So the names of Harry Hawker and Commander Mackenzie Grieve went down in aviation annals as the men who were nearly the first to fly the Atlantic.

And the strange postscript: their plane did *not* sink. The US steamer *Lake Charlotteville* spotted it bobbing up and down and salvaged it.

TRACKING DOWN
THE SMUGGLERS

Dennis Wheatley

Gregory Sallust wants to smash a smuggling ring masterminded by the evil Lord Gavin Fortesque, but finds himself in love with the beautiful Sabine, who is involved in the racket.

One night he and Inspector Gerry Wells track down the smugglers airfield, and Wells asks Gregory to parachute down and investigate . . .

'**Y**ou'll make the landing,' Wells bawled. 'What's your parachute for, man! Out you go.'

'Not likely,' Gregory bawled. 'Never made a parachute jump in my life—not going to start now. Think I'm going to risk my neck?'

'Dammit, you must,' yelled the Inspector as he banked, circling still higher, over the secret landing ground. 'We'll never find this place in daylight. It's our one chance to register their base. You've got to do it: don't let me down.'

Gregory stared over the side of the plane at the little cluster of lights seeming now so infinitely far below. He was no coward in a fight. All his life he had taken a grim delight in facing odds and winning through where battle with other human beings was concerned—but this was different. To jump from the safety of the plane into thin air with the horrible uncertainty as to whether the parachute would open, or if he would be dashed, a bleeding mass of pulp, on to the distant ground. Was the risk worth it? Why the hell should he? And then the heart-shaped face of Sabine came clear before his eyes.

'If I do, will you let Sabine out?' he cried.

'I can't. You know I can't.' Well's voice just reached him above the roar of the engine, angry at this frustration when he was so near securing evidence of real importance.

'You must.' Gregory's voice pierced the wind and thunder of the engine; 'otherwise I won't play.'

'Will you—if I agree?' Wells shouted.

'Yes, damn you!' Gregory screamed back.

'I can't speak for my superiors,' bawled Wells.

Gregory was already fumbling at his back, seeing that the parachute was in position. He stood up uncertainly swaying as the plane soared through the air at 150 miles an hour. 'You've got to let her off,' he thundered, leaning over Wells's shoulder, his mouth close to the Inspector's ear.

'Go on, I'll do my best,' Wells turned his face up, shouting, 'won't arrest her myself anyhow.'

Gregory peered over the side again. The thought of leaping into that black immensity of space made his heart contract but he climbed out onto the fuselage. The wind rushed past him tearing at every corner of his garments as though it would strip him naked. For a second there was an awful pain which stabbed him in the pit of the stomach. He felt sick and giddy as he clung on with all his might to prevent the force of the blast ripping his clutching fingers from their precarious hold. Then he took a breath—screwed his face up into a rueful grin—and jumped.

As Gregory leapt the body of the plane seemed to shoot up like an express lift behind him. He felt himself gripped and twisted as though he was a straw in a tempest; then hurled violently downward. The plane roared away into the darkness above him.

His last thought before going overboard had been 'mustn't pull the rip cord until I'm clear of the plane.' He knew little enough about parachute diving, but he'd heard somewhere, back in the war days, before it became a sport and when it was only undertaken as a dire necessity, that many a stout fellow had come to grief because he'd opened his parachute at the moment of jumping and it had caught in the fuselage of the machine, tearing the fabric and so making it useless or hanging the miserable parachutist.

He had not realized that in such cases the machine, crippled and often burning from anti-aircraft shell or the enemy's inflammatory bullets, was falling too and that the wretched pilot might be a moment or more before, dropping with greater speed, he could get any distance from the wreckage; whereas in a normal jump, such as he had just made, he had been torn away from the fast-moving plane in a fraction of a second.

His fear, that if he had his hand on the rip cord the shock of the jump might open it immediately, had caused him to stretch his arms out sideways so that he could not possibly pull it inadvertently. Now, as he was flung face downwards by the rushing air current, his arms were forced back behind his shoulders and he was hurtling earthwards like a diver who has taken a fancy jump from a spring-board, head foremost into the sea. The wind had ceased to turn him but seemed instead to be rushing upwards as he plunged down into the awful void.

Nearly a mile below him lay the earth; pitch black and terrifying; the friendly trees and inequalities of surface which formed its landscape blotted out by the midnight gloom. Not a light was to be seen in any direction, except the little 'T' of flares which now appeared to be some way towards his right as he shot earthwards.

With horrifying rapidity the 'T' grew larger. By a stupendous effort he forced his right arm inwards to grab the rip cord. The wind, tearing at his left as at some fin, instantly flung him over on to his back, and then, to his utter horror, he began to spin like a top.

His fingers were numb from the icy blast of the rushing air. He had an awful moment when he feared that they would no longer have sufficient feeling left in them for him to use them. Cursing himself for a panicky fool he tried to snatch comfort from the thought that plenty of people who did this thing for fun took extra pleasure in waiting until the very last moment before opening their parachute and that he must have a long way yet to drop.

It seemed an age since he had sprung off the plane; an eternity since he had begun his fight against the up-rushing air to force his hand in to the rip cord. At last he found it and, half-choking from relief, jerked it with all his might.

Nothing happened. He pulled again but the cord was hanging loose now in his hand. Still nothing happened. He made a desperate effort to force his head round so that he could look over his shoulder. The movement flung him out of his spin and he was facing the earth head downwards again. The 'T' of flares was much bigger now. It seemed like some fiery group of stars rushing up out of the darkness which would roar past him over his right shoulder with the speed of an express train at any second. But it wouldn't—he knew that. When his right shoulder came level with the flares he would hit the earth. It would be as though some giant, greater than any fabled hero, had flung the whole world at him. He would be broken, burst, shattered into a thousand fragments by that appalling impact.

Almost sick with horror, he pulled and pulled at the useless rip cord, while he alternately cursed his utter folly in flinging himself to his death and gasped breathless prayers to God to save him.

Time ceases to exist at such awful moments. He was still plunging downwards at a fantastic speed and had virtually given himself up as finished when, without a second's warning, his arms were nearly torn from their sockets and a violent jerk at the belt round his middle drove the breath out of his body.

He had forgotten that a short interval must elapse between releasing the parachute and its opening to its full spread when it would arrest his headlong descent. Now, as that thought flashed into his agonized mind, he could still hardly believe that the safety device had begun to function efficiently the second he had pulled the cord.

His feet sank down lower than his head and before he knew quite what had happened he was standing upright, swaying a little from side to side, his long legs dangling.

Almost collapsing with relief he found he could look upwards and saw the dome of the fully opened parachute like a great dark mushroom against the starlit sky above.

For the first time since leaving the plane he was able to gasp in a full breath and look about him consciously. The 'T' of flares towards his right was still larger now but only the blackness of the land below had caused him to think he was so near it. His terror had been engendered by his complete inexperience; for he had made a good take off, although he had lost some seconds before being able to pull the rip cord, but when he had done so the parachute had opened perfectly normally.

The swaying motion increased, until he was covering an arc of about thirty degrees; as if he were the pendulum of some huge clock. He knew he should try to check the movement, otherwise he might make a bad landing, but he did not know how to, not realizing that a pair of ropes now dangling one at each side of him were for that purpose. Apart from the fear that he might suddenly be swung into a tree he found the motion rather enjoyable. The lights were now rising gently towards his right, but he did not seem to be coming any nearer to them, and he judged that he would make his landing quite a long way from the smugglers' secret base.

As they came low on the horizon it warned him that he was nearing earth and he gathered his muscles taut together, so that as his feet touched he might spring into the air again, in order to reduce the force of the impact. A faint shimmer showed to his left and he realized that it was the reflection of the starlight upon a winding creek of water. Next moment the flares disappeared from view; blotted out by an unseen crest. Then his right foot hit something with a thud and instantly he was sprawling on the ground with every ounce of breath knocked out of his body.

Gregory could see the smugglers in the distance.

He clutched wildly at the grass as he felt himself moving still, but sideways now, dragged by the parachute. Bumping over a ditch he was pulled into some low bushes. There was a sharp crackling as the dry twigs snapped and he thrust up his arms to protect his face, then the dragging ceased, for the parachute had sunk to earth.

For a moment he remained there, bruised and breathless, then he struggled into a sitting position and wriggled out of his harness. Only a dull glow, coming from over a crest of rising ground to the north, now indicated the smugglers' landing place. He stood up and pulled his big torch from his pocket then cursed aloud as he found that his fall had broken the bulb. He had meant to bundle up the expensive parachute and hide it somewhere but time was precious and he dared not waste it fumbling round for something that he could not see. Except for the lighter patch of sky low on the horizon to the northward, caused by the flares, and the faint starlight, the whole countryside was shrouded in darkness. Abandoning the parachute he set off towards the north. Only the deeper patches of blackness indicated the taller grass and low bushes when he was almost upon them while there was nothing at all to show the frequent ditches which intersected the marshes.

Pressing forward warily, he stumbled at almost every step, and was compelled by some obstacle to alter his course every ten yards or so. He thanked his gods at least that it was August. Most of the smaller water courses now had dry beds and the marshland squelched under foot only in the lower places. To have attempted to cross this wild country in winter would have been impossible; he would have been bogged for a certainty.

As it was, he had to cross two creeks; stagnant, scummy bands of water with muddy bottoms which dragged and sucked at his boots when he floundered through them and thrust his way among the tall knife-like reeds that fringed their banks.

It was a nightmare journey. Wet to the waist, tired, bruised and angry, he struggled onward; yet the glow from the flares seemed little nearer and the going so difficult he doubted if he had traversed more than half a mile in twenty minutes. Then he came to a wire fence, climbed over, and found a steep grassy bank, up which he crawled on all fours. The top was level; next moment he tripped over a sleeper and came down heavily between two railway lines.

Picking himself up with renewed curses, he found he could now see the flares some distance away on the far side of the embankment, and turned northwest along it.

Knowing how quickly smugglers completed their operations, he began to hurry; fearing that with all the time he had lost plunging into ditches and over tussocks of coarse grass he would be too late to find out what was going on.

He had barely covered another two hundred yards when he caught the sound of a train puffing up behind him from Dungeness and, jumping off the permanent way, slid down the bank to conceal himself while it passed.

A short goods train of no more than half a dozen closed wagons rumbled by shaking the embankment. The sparks from its engine and glare of the furnace temporarily lit up a small section of the surrounding country.

When the train had gone past, Gregory stumbled onto the permanent way again and set off after it. To his surprise he saw it pull up ahead of him, opposite the flares, so he broke into a jog trot, spurred on by the thought that his gruelling experiences of the last hour might, after all, have been well worth while.

Five minutes later he was within fifty yards of the train's rear wagon and, slipping down the far side of the embankment, he crawled along under its cover still nearer, until he could see by the bright light of the landing flares the business which was proceeding. Beyond the flares were a couple of big planes and big stacks of boxes at intervals on a level stretch of ground showed where they had unloaded their cargoes. One of the large planes took the air as he watched and he was able to see enough of it to recognize it as a 240 hp twin-engine de Havilland Dragon, which would normally carry eight passengers, but in their place was capable of transporting about half a ton of cargo.

From the sound of the engine, as the plane circled in the air, he knew that something of its cruising speed, which should have been 140 mph, had been sacrified by the appliance of the latest silencing devices, so that the noise of even a fleet of these machines, crossing the coastline at six thousand feet, would barely be noticeable and certainly not sufficient to attract undue attention.

At the bottom of the embankment he wriggled through the fence and found a dry gully which offered such excellent cover that he determined to risk crawling even nearer; soon he was crouching in it no more than twenty yards from the landing ground.

About forty men were working with frantic speed unloading the goods train; pitching dozens of wooden boxes from it down the embankment. They had already cleared the first three wagons and, while a number of them attacked the rest, the others went off to the dumps which had been unloaded from the planes, then began to carry the boxes towards the empty wagons.

For ten minutes Gregory remained a silent spectator of their intense activity. By the end of that time the contraband cargo had all been loaded onto the train, the wagons relocked, the last big plane was gone, and all the flares except one had been put out.

The train moved off and, rapidly gathering speed, disappeared in the direction of London. The men then flung themselves upon the great higgeldy-piggeldy pile of boxes which had been thrown out of it, and started to hump them across the landing ground, disappearing into the belt of shadows beyond the flare's range.

'What now?' thought Gregory. 'My luck's been in so far and I'm not chucking up till I find out what they do with the stuff.' Crawling back by way of the ditch, he began to make a detour outside the lighted patch of ground and, after going a hundred yards, he stumbled through some low bushes, up a small bank and onto a road. Having crossed it, he slid down the slope on the other side and proceeded to follow the line of the lane, which curved slightly. The flare was now some distance away, but he could hear muffled voices carried on the night wind to the front of him and, a moment later, came upon a thick hedge which barred his passage.

. Scrambling up the bank again he got round the corner of the hedge and saw that it hid the kitchen garden of a solitary house, which loomed up before him, abutting on the road. A faint square of light filtering through a heavy curtain marked one of its downstair windows.

He got down on his hands and knees and crawled forward under cover of the hedge which here fringed the roadside. The voices of the men grew louder as he advanced and then he saw the dark outline of a lorry. There were others behind it and on these the men were busily loading the boxes that had come off the train.

From this new position he could see some of the smugglers in the distance, silhouetted against the light of the flare, as with the boxes on their shoulders they trudged in Indian file across the grassland. Suddenly the last flare was put out and two minutes later the loading of the lorries was completed. The men climbed into them and the lightless convoy set off in the direction of New Romney.

One by one they crawled passed Gregory, where he crouched in the shadows, and shortly after the last one had disappeared a sudden vibrant hum, which grew lower and then receded, told him that the Limper had departed unseen in his plane. The rumble of the lorries faded in the distance and an utter silence closed down upon the deserted stretch of country.

Gregory came out into the lane and tiptoed along it towards the front of the silent house. The light in the ground floor room had gone out but there was now one showing in a front window upstairs. The heavy curtains had been carelessly drawn and a bright ray filtered through between them. The window was too high for Gregory to see into the room, but a wooden sign above the doorway of the place showed that it was a wayside inn and, by the light which came from the crack between the curtains he was just able to make out the lettering upon it. Thankful that he would be able to find the place again in this desolate stretch of country he read the faded lettering on the weather-beaten board. It was the Brown Owl Inn and he knew that it must lie within a few hundred yards of the railway line south of Romney.

463

IN THE HANDS OF GOD

Captain Marryat

Peter Simple describes how as a young man aboard the sailing ship *Diomede* the vessel and the lives of all on board are put in jeopardy by a storm which threatens to drive the ship onto a rocky lee shore. . .

We cruised along the coast, until we had run down into the Bay of Arcason, where we captured two or three vessels, and obliged many more to run on shore. And here we had an instance showing how very important it is that a captain of a man-of-war should be a good sailor, and have his ship in such discipline as to be strictly obeyed by his ship's company. I heard the officers unanimously assert, after the danger was over, that nothing but the presence of mind which was shown by Captain Savage could have saved the ship and her crew. We had chased a convoy of vessels to the bottom of the bay: the wind was very fresh when we hauled off, after running them on shore; and the surf on the beach even at that time was so great, that they were certain to go to pieces before they could be got afloat again. We were obliged to double-reef the topsails as soon as we hauled to the wind, and the weather looked very threatening. In an hour afterwards, the whole sky was covered with one black cloud, which sank so low as nearly to touch our mast-heads, and a tremendous sea, which appeared to have risen up almost by magic, rolled in upon us, setting the vessel on a dead lee shore. As the night closed in, it blew a dreadful gale, and the ship was nearly buried with the press of canvas which she was obliged to carry: for had we sea-room, we should have been lying-to under storm staysails; but we were forced to carry on at all risks, that we might claw off shore. The sea broke over as we lay in the trough, deluging us with water from the forecastle, aft, to the binnacles; and very often, as the ship descended with a plunge, it was with such force that I really thought she would divide in half with the violence of the shock. Double breechings were rove on the guns, and they were further secured with tackles; and strong cleats nailed behind the trunnions; for we heeled over so much when we lurched, that the guns were wholly supported by the breechings and tackles, and had one of them broken loose, it must have burst right through the lee side of the ship, and she must have foundered. The captain, first lieutenant, and most of the officers remained on deck during the whole of the night; and really, what with the howling of the wind, the violence of the rain, the washing of the water about the decks, the working of the chain-pumps, and the creaking and groaning of the timbers, I thought that we must inevitably have been lost; and I said my prayers at least a dozen times during the night, for I felt it impossible to go to bed. I had often wished, out of curiosity, that I might be in a gale of wind; but I little thought it was to have been a scene of this description, or anything half so dreadful. What made it more appalling was, that we were on a lee shore, and the consultations of the captain and officers, and the eagerness with which they looked out for daylight, told us that we had other dangers to encounter besides the storm. At last the morning broke, and the look-out man upon the gangway called out, 'Land on the lee beam!' I perceived the master dash his fist against the hammrock-rails, as if with vexation, and walk away without saying a word, and looking very grave.

'Up there, Mr Wilson,' said the captain to the second lieutenant, 'and see how far the land trends forward, and whether you can distinguish the point.' The second lieutenant went up the main-rigging, and pointed with his hand to about two points before the beam.

'Do you see two hillocks inland?'

'Yes, sir,' replied the second lieutenant.

'Then it is so,' observed the captain to the master, 'and if we weather it we shall have more sea-room. Keep her full, and let her go through the water; do you hear, quarter-master?'

'Ay, ay, sir.'

'Thus, and no nearer, my man. Ease her with a spoke or two when she sends; but be careful, or she'll take the wheel out of your hands.'

It really was a very awful sight. When the ship was in the trough of the sea, you could distinguish nothing but a waste of tumultuous water; but when she was borne up on the summit of the enormous waves, you then looked down, as it were, upon a low, sandy coast, close to you, and covered with foam and breakers. 'She behaves nobly,' observed the captain, stepping aft to the binnacle, and looking at the compass; 'if the wind does not baffle us, we shall weather.' The captain had scarcely time to make the observation, when the sails shivered and flapped like thunder. 'Up with the helm; what are you about, quarter-master?'

'The wind has headed us, sir,' replied the quarter-master, coolly.

The captain and master remained at the binnacle watching the compass; and when the sails were again full, she had broken off two points, and the point of land was only a little on the lee bow.

'We must wear her round, Mr Falcon. Hands, wear ship—ready, oh, ready.'

'She has come up again,' cried the master, who was at the binnacle.

'Hold fast there a minute. How's her head now?'

'N.N.E., as she was before she broke off, sir.'

'Pipe belay,' said the captain. 'Falcon,' continued he, 'if she beaks off again we may have no room to wear; indeed there is so little room now, that I must run the risk. Which cable was ranged last night—the best bower?'

'Yes, sir.'

'Jump down, then, and see it double-bitted and stoppered at thirty fathoms. See it well done—our lives may depend upon it.'

The ship continued to hold her course good; and we were within half a mile of the point, and fully expected to weather it, when again the wet and heavy sails flapped in the wind, and the ship broke off two points as before. The officers and seamen were aghast, for the ship's head was right onto the breakers. '*Luff* [1] now, all you can, quarter-master,' cried the captain. 'Send the men aft directly. My lads, there is no time for words—I am going to *club-haul* [2] the ship, for there is no room to wear. The only chance you have of safety is to be cool, watch my eye, and execute my orders with precision. Away to your stations for tacking ship. Hands by the best bower anchor. Mr Wilson, attend below with the carpenter and his mates, ready to cut away the cable at the moment that I give the order. Silence, there, fore and aft. Quarter-master, keep her full again for stays. Mind you ease the helm down when I tell you.' About a minute passed before the captain gave any further orders. The ship had closed-to within a quarter-mile of the beach, and the waves curled and topped around us, bearing us down upon the shore, which presented one continued surface of foam, extending to within half a cable's length of our position. The captain waved his hand in silence to the quarter-master at the wheel, and the helm was put down. The ship turned slowly to the wind, pitching and chopping as the sails were spilling. When she had lost her way, the captain gave the order, 'Let go the anchor. We will haul all at once, Mr Falcon,' said the captain. Not a word

[1] Turn the head of the ship to face the wind.

[2] To tack a ship by letting the lee-anchor down as soon as the wind is out of the sails, by which her head is brought to the wind. A last resort (in a very dangerous situation) to change the ship's direction.

was spoken. The men went to the fore brace, which had not been manned; most of them knew, although I did not, that if the ship's head did not go round the other way, we should be on shore, and among the breakers, in half a minute. I thought at the time that the captain had said that he would haul all the yards at once. There appeared to be doubt or dissent on the countenance of Mr Falcon; and I was afterwards told that he had not agreed with the captain; but he was too good an officer, and knew that there was no time for discussion, to make any remark; and the event proved that the captain was right. At last the ship was head to wind, and the captain gave the signal. The yards flew round with such a creaking noise, that I thought the masts had gone over the side, and the next moment the wind had caught the sails; and the ship, which for a moment or two had been on an even keel, *careened* [1] over to her gunnel with its force. The captain, who stood upon the weather-hammock rails, holding by the main-rigging, ordered the helm amidships, looked full at the sails, and then at the cable, which grew broad upon the weather bow, and held the ship from nearing the shore. At last he cried, 'Cut away the cable!' A few strokes of the axes were heard, and then the cable flew out of the hawse-hole in a blaze of fire, from the violence of the friction, and disappeared under a huge wave, which struck us and deluged us with water fore and aft. But we were now on the other tack, and the ship regained her way, and we had evidently increased our distance from the land.

'My lads,' said the captain, to the ship's company, 'you have behaved well, and I thank you; but I must tell you honestly that we have more difficulties to get through. We have to weather a point of the bay on this tack. Mr Falcon, splice the main-brace, and call the watch. How's her head, quarter-master?'

'S.W. by S. Southerly, sir.'

'Very well; let her go through the water'; and the captain, beckoning to the master to follow him, went down into the cabin. As our immediate danger was over, I went down into the berth to

---

[1] To heave over to one side.

The ship forced her way through whole seas, dividing the waves.

see if I could get anything for breakfast, where I found O'Brien and two or three more.

'By the powers, it was as nate a thing as ever I saw done,' observed O'Brien: 'the slightest mistake as to time or management, and at this moment the flatfish would have been dubbing at our ugly carcases. Peter, you're not fond of flatfish are you, my boy? We may thank Heaven and the captain, I can tell you that, my lads: but now, where's the chart, Robinson? Hand me down the parallel rules and compasses, Peter; they are in the corner of the shelf. Here we are now, a devilish sight too near this infernal point. Who knows how her head is?'

'I do, O'Brien: I heard the quarter-master tell the captain S.W. by S. Southerly.'

'Let me see,' continued O'Brien, 'variation $2\frac{1}{4}$—lee way—rather too large an allowance of that, I'm afraid; but, however, we'll give her $2\frac{1}{2}$ points; the *Diomede* would blush to make any more, under any circumstances. Here—the compass—now we'll see'; and O'Brien advanced the parallel rule from the compass to the spot where the ship was placed on the chart. 'Bother! you see it's as much as she'll do to weather the other point now, on this tack, and that's what the captain meant when he told us we had more difficulty. I could have taken by Bible oath that we were clear of everything, if the wind held.'

'See what the distance is, O'Brien,' said Robinson. It was measured, and proved to be thirteen miles. 'Only thirteen miles; and if we do weather, we shall do very well, for the bay is deep beyond. It's a rocky point, you see, just by way of variety. Well, my lads, I've a piece of còmfort for you, anyhow. It's not long that you'll be kept in suspense, for by one o'clock this day, you'll either be congratulating each other upon your good luck, or you'll be past praying for. Come, put up the chart, for I hate to look at melancholy prospects; and, steward, see what you can find in the way of comfort.' Some bread and cheese, with the remains of yesterday's boiled pork, were put on the table, with a bottle of rum, procured at the time they 'spliced the mainbrace'; but we were all too anxious to eat much, and one by one returned on deck to see how the weather was, and if the wind at all favoured us. On deck the superior officers were in conversation with the captain, who had expressed the same fear that O'Brien had in our berth. The men, who knew what they had to expect, were assembled in knots, looking very grave, but at the same time not wanting in confidence. They knew that they could trust to the captain, as far as skill or courage could avail them; and sailors are too sanguine to despair, even at the last moment. As for myself, I felt such admiration for the captain, after what I had witnessed that morning, that, whenever the idea came over me, that in all probability I should be lost in a few hours, I could not help acknowledging how much more serious it was that such a man should be lost to his country. I do not intend to say that it consoled me; but it certainly made me still more regret the chances with which we were threatened.

Before twelve o'clock the rocky point which we so much dreaded was in sight, broad on the lee-bow; and if the low sandy coast appeared terrible, how much more did this, even at a distance. The captain eyed it for some minutes in silence, as if in calculation.

'Mr Falcon,' said he, at last, 'we must put the main-sail on her.'

'She never can bear it, sir.'

'She *must* bear it,' was the reply. 'Send the men aft to the main-sheet. See that careful men attend the buntlines.'

The mainsail was set, and the effect of it upon the ship was tremendous. She careened over so that her lee channels were under the water; and when pressed by a sea, the lee-side of the quarter-deck and gangway were afloat. She now reminded me of a goaded and fiery horse, mad with the stimulus applied, not rising as before, but forcing herself through whole seas, and dividing the waves, which poured in one continual torrent from the forecastle down upon the decks below. Four men were secured to the wheel—the sailors were obliged to cling, to prevent being washed away—the ropes were thrown in confusion to leeward, the shot rolled out of the lockers, and every eye was fixed aloft, watching the masts which were expected every moment to go over the side. A heavy sea struck us on the broadside, and it was some moments before the ship appeared to recover herself; she reeled, trembled, and stopped her way, as if it had stupified her. The first lieutenant looked at the captain, as if to say, 'This will not do.' 'It is our only chance,' answered the captain to the appeal. That the ship went faster through the water, and held a better wind, was certain; but just before we arrived at the point, the gale increased in force. 'If anything starts, we are lost, sir,' observed the first lieutenant again.

'I am perfectly aware of it,' replied the captain, in a calm tone; 'but, as I said before, and you must now be aware, it is our only chance. The consequence of any carelessness or neglect in the fitting and securing of the rigging will be felt now; and this danger, if we escape it, ought to remind us how much we have to answer for, if we neglect our duty. The lives of a whole ship's company may be sacrificed by the neglect or incompetence of an officer when in harbour. I will pay you the compliment, Falcon, to say, that I feel convinced that the masts of the ship are as secure as knowledge and attention can make them.'

The first lieutenant thanked the captain for his good opinion, and hoped it would not be the last compliment which he paid him.

'I hope not, too; but a few minutes will decide the point.'

The ship was now within two cables' lengths of the rocky point. Some few of the men I observed to clasp their hands, but most of them were silently taking off their jackets and kicking off their shoes, that they might not lose a chance of escape, provided the ship struck.

' 'Twill be touch and go, indeed, Falcon,' observed the captain (for I had clung to the belaying-pins, close to them, for the last half-hour that the mainsail had been set). 'Come aft; you and I must take the helm. We shall want *nerve* there, and only there, now.'

The captain and first lieutenant went aft, and took the fore-spokes of the wheel, and O'Brien, at a sign made by the captain, laid hold of the spokes behind him. An old quarter-master kept his station at the fourth. The roaring of the seas on the rocks, with the howling of the wind, were dreadful; but the sight was more dreadful than the noise. For a few moments I shut my eyes but anxiety forced me to open them again. As near as I could judge, we were not twenty yards from the rocks at the time that the ship passed abreast of them. We were in the midst of the foam, which boiled around us; and as the ship was driven nearer to them, and careened with the wave, I thought that our main yard-arm would have touched the rock; and at this moment a gust of wind came on, which laid the ship on her beam-ends, and checked her progress through the water, while the accumulated noise was deafening. A few moments more the ship dragged on, another wave dashed over her and spent itself upon the rocks, while the spray was dashed back from them, and returned upon the decks. The main rock was within ten yards of her counter, when another gust of wind laid us on our beam-ends, the foresail and mainsail split and were blown clean out of the bolt-ropes—the ship righted, trembling fore and aft. I looked astern: the rocks were to windward on our quarter, and we were safe. I thought at the time that the ship, relieved of her courses, and again lifting over the waves, was not a bad simili- tude of the relief felt by us all at that moment; and, like her, we trembled as we panted with the sudden reaction, and felt the removal of the intense anxiety which oppressed our breasts.

The captain resigned the helm, and walked aft to look at the point, which was now broad on the weather quarter. In a minute or two he desired Mr Falcon to get new sails up and bend them, and then went below to his cabin. I am sure it was to thank God for our deliverance: I did most fervently, not only then, but when I went to my hammock at night. We were now comparatively safe— in a few hours completely so; for strange to say, immediately after we had weathered the rocks, the gale abated, and before morning we had a reef out of the top-sails. It was my forenoon watch, and perceiving Mr Chucks on the forecastle, I went forward to him, and asked him what he thought of it.

'Thought of it, sir!' replied he; 'why, I always think bad of it when the elements won't allow my whistle to be heard; and I consider it hardly fair play. I never care if we are left to our own exceptions; but how is it possible for a ship's company to do their best when they cannot hear the boatswain's pipe? However, God be thanked, nevertheless, and make better Christians of us all! As for the carpenter, he is mad. Just before we weathered the point, he told me that it was just the same 27,600 and odd years ago. I do believe that on his death-bed (and he was not far from a very hard one yesterday), he will tell us how he died so many thousand years ago, of the same complaint. And that gunner of ours is a fool. Would you believe it, Mr Simple, he went crying about the decks, "Oh my poor guns, what will become of them if they break loose?" He appeared to consider it of no consequence if the ship and ship's company were all lost, provided that his guns were safely landed on the beach.'

Acknowledgments

The publishers would like to extend their grateful thanks to the following authors, publishers and others for kindly granting them permission to reproduce the extracts and stories in copyright included in this anthology.

ANNAPURNA from *Annapurna South Face* by Chris Bonington (this extract by Dougal Haston), by kind permission of John Farquharson Ltd and Cassell Ltd.

CAR WITH NO BRAKES from *It Shouldn't Happen to a Vet* by James Herriot, by kind permission of Michael Joseph.

TWO VC's FOR SUBMARINE THRASHER from *Discharged Dead* by Sidney Hart, by kind permission of Rupert Crew Ltd.

TREASURE IN LORD KITCHENER'S TOMB from *The Treasure Seekers* by Hans Roden, by kind permission of George G. Harrap & Company Ltd.

RALLY DRIVE from *Marathon in the Dust* by Innes Ireland, by kind permission of John Farquharson Ltd.

FIRST FLIGHT from *The First Flight* by John Evangelist Walsh, by kind permission of George Allen & Unwin Ltd.

CROSSING THE FRONT LINES from *Greenmantle* by John Buchan, by kind permission of Lord Tweedsmuir and Hodder & Stoughton Ltd. © 1944 by Lady Susan Caroline Tweedsmuir. Reprinted in USA by permission of Houghton Mifflin Co. Boston.

DÉDÉE – RESISTANCE FIGHTER from *Little Cyclone* by Airey Neave, by kind permission of Hodder & Stoughton Ltd.

THE DEATH OF A SHIP, an extract originally entitled Valediction from *Lower Deck* by John Davies, by kind permission of Rupert Crew Ltd.

HUNTING THE HAMMERHEAD SHARK from *Shark Hunter* by Trevor Housby, by kind permission of Wayland Publishers Ltd.

A CAPE HORN SNORTER from *The Cape Horn Breed* by Capt. W. H. S. Jones, by kind permission of Hutchinson Publishing Group Ltd.

STRANGE EVENTS AT ZINDERNEUF from *Beau Geste* by P. C. Wren, by kind permission of John Murray (Publishers) Ltd.

EXPLORING AN UNTAMED WILDERNESS from *The Magnificent Adventures of Alexander MacKenzie* by Samuel Edwards, published by Alvin Redman.

FIRST ASCENT OF MONTE INACCESSIBLE from *Cockleshell Journey* by John Ridgway. Reprinted by permission of A. D. Peters & Co. Ltd and Hodder & Stoughton Ltd. © 1974 John Ridgway.

THE RANNOCH MOOR RESCUE from *Call-Out* by Hamish MacInnes, by kind permission of Hodder & Stoughton Ltd and John Farquharson Ltd. © 1974 John Ridgway.

ESCAPE FROM COLDITZ from *Colditz Recaptured* by Rheinhold Eggers, by kind permission of Robert Hale Ltd.

THE MYSTERY OF THE DRIFTING DERELICT, from *What Happened on the Mary Celeste* by Rupert Furneaux. Originally published by Max Parrish & Co. Ltd.

Designed by Astrid Publishing Consultants

Illustrations by Malcolm Barter